When God
Was A Little Boy

When God
Was A Little Boy

A Novel

Les Woodson

For My Wife Betty

Other Books by Les Woodson

> *A View from the Cornerstone*
> *Divorce and the Gospel of Grace*
> *Eight Days of Glory*
> *Evangelism for Today's Church*
> *Getting Ready to Live Forever*
> *Hell and Salvation*
> *How to Get to Heaven without Being Good*
> *Make My Day*
> *Population, Pollution, and Prophecy*
> *Signs in the Son*
> *The Beginning*
> *The Church: United or Untied*
> *The Swinging Church*
> *Seminar on the Entire Bible*
> *What You Believe and Why*

INTRODUCTION

A biography of Jesus is impossible to write. The life of Jesus before his baptism is a silent epoch with no voice save that of the apocryphal narratives written in the second and third centuries, all of which are considered spurious, and Luke's story of the twelve year old boy's experience at the Temple in Jerusalem.

The apocryphal writings portray the infant as being pursued by dragons during the flight into Egypt with his parents. At last, in complete control of the vicious beasts, he crawls from Mary's lap to stand before their captive and adoring eyes.

While still a boy, Jesus is said to have resurrected dried fish and made clay birds which flew away at his command.

On one occasion, the Holy Child is seen carrying water home to the family in the lap of his robe after having broken the vessel intended for the purpose. In the workshop of Joseph, he uses his powers of touch to change the size and shape of the lumber. And, so as not to be outdone by Moses, he divides the waters of the Jordan and walks across on dry land.

None of these stories is worthy of our Lord. Each tale results only in rendering him less human. We may be thankful that the Early Church fathers were wise and inspired of God to reject them.

Even the later life of Jesus, which is recorded in the New Testament, is of piece-meal nature since only a few of the incidents in his three year public ministry are entered by the biblical narrators on the written page. But, at the end of John's Gospel are the thought-provoking words, "There are also many other things that Jesus did, which if they were written one by one, I suppose that even the world itself could not contain the books that would be written" (John 21:25).

What else He did, whom else He healed, what else He said is left to the imagination. By such speculation, one can create a completely distorted portrait of the Master.

Yet, risky as the pursuit may be, the Church has no choice other than to assume, on general principles established by what we know of Jesus, what our Lord must have been like during the silent years.

The missing pieces of the puzzle may be forever misplaced, but from the available parts which surround the holes in the picture, one can at least be fairly certain about the shape and contour of the lost segments.

Or to use another analogy, when a link is gone from a chain, the links which remain, though they give no insight into the original length of the whole, provide the smith with a pattern for restoring the chain to something more in keeping with what it was before.

What kind of lad was Jesus? Some real help is given by Luke in his account of Jesus' pilgrimage to Jerusalem at Passover time (Luke 2:42) and by Mark's clear reference to the boy's learning of Joseph's carpenter trade (Mark 6:3). Other than this, there is no clear record of what the boy Jesus was doing during that thirty year period of his life.

Some insight may be found as one studies the events which transpired across the Roman Empire, especially in Jewry, within the interval mentioned. Further suggestions are offered by the kind of community life known to Jewish children of his day. He was most certainly a part of the common life of his people.

The Christian world would like to know much more about the people who figured in the life of the Son of God. What happened to Joseph that he should so abruptly disappear from the scene after the journey of the holy family to Jerusalem? Jesus was only twelve years old, yet we hear no more of Joseph following that incident.

Were the brothers and sisters of our Lord the children of Joseph by a previous marriage and thus not related by blood to Jesus? Or were they children born later to Jesus' own mother? What kind of father did Joseph make for his growing household and what was the relationship between him and the son of Mary?

Who were the parents of Mary? What may have been their reaction when they found out about her pregnancy?

How much contact did Jesus have with James and John, his cousins and later disciples from the north, during those days of adolescence?

What happened to the wives and families of the Twelve who, with the exception of Simon Peter's wife and mother-in-law, are never mentioned? Did they actually find themselves forsaken by their husbands and fathers? Would Christ have condoned such irresponsibility to one's family when He so emphatically insisted on the binding contract of marriage?

Could they all have been bachelors except Simon Peter?

And what may have happened to Jesus' own immediate family? While James, the older brother, eventually became a believer and bishop of the mother church in Jerusalem, none of the other siblings appear to have any significance in the biblical account. Did they marry and have children? Was Jesus an uncle?

All these questions are intriguing and exciting to the mind of an inquiring student. Many related mysteries might be solved if answers could be found to these puzzling queries. But the most exciting find of the Christian era would be information on the activities and relationships of Jesus as a growing boy, information which could be established as reliable and authoritative.

It is not likely that such a discovery will ever occur. Since the family of Jesus was only one of thousands of poor, unnoticed households, no records would have been kept and no memoirs written. In addition, during the two thousand years since the birth of Christ, the villages of his time have been ravished, burned, and leveled by wars. Towns and cities have been built atop those ruins only to be toppled again and have the same procedure start over. No one knows how much valuable material was burned during those raids, vital information about the life of people like Jesus and his family, never to see the light of day again.

How helpful it would be if we knew something about the formal education of Jesus; the attitude of the townspeople toward him and his mother; the relationships which He had with other children of his own age; his feelings about Rome and his attitudes toward the local priests and religious leaders; his reaction to dishonesty and thievery on the part of those who took advantage of the poor in the markets; the temptations which He confronted and how He handled them; what the young girls of the village thought of him and what He may have felt in his heart for them; whether He ever shared the infatuations common to all growing boys and girls; and whether He ever fell in love!

Did Jesus get angry as other boys when fellows cheated in the neighborhood games? Was there ever a time when He defended himself against some bully who tried to impress the girls by picking on him?

Is it possible that He may have raised his voice when tempers flared and accusations were carelessly flung against another in a fight on the back lot playground? And could it be thinkable that He might have gotten into the fray itself? Would He have joined sides with a boy whom He believed to be unjustly abused? Can we be sure that the incident in the Temple, when He used the whip, was the first time He had gotten involved in the use of force to correct a wrong?

Just questions. No answers.

All boys and girls disobey their parents at some time. In fact, most of them require continuous discipline. No child is considered normal by his father if he never rebels against the rules of the house. Was Jesus a normal boy?

Did He ever fail to dispose of the kitchen garbage when told to do so? When a teenager, did He ever come in after curfew? Would He have asked any special privileges which were in conflict with what Mary and Joseph expected of him? Were his manners always above reproach?

By causing the traveling party grief in the discovery that He had stayed behind when Passover ended, had He disobeyed the explicit rules made clear to him by Joseph as the family left for Jerusalem? And when the Pharisees questioned his neglect of tradition in not washing his hands before eating, was he revealing only the bad manners which He had developed as a boy?

As a member of a devout Jewish family and a strongly nationalistic people, were there times when Jesus had mixed emotions as some of his friends joined the underground Zealots? Was he tempted to help them purge Israel of her forces of occupation and restore the theocracy of David?

As this lad grew older, how must He have felt about the galling taxation of the pagan Roman Empire? What did He think of the bleeding of the common people by the priests who demanded their share for the Temple? How those folks suffered from this abuse which only added immeasurably to their impoverished misery. And how was He affected by the efforts of the Jewish publicans who tried to be both Roman and Jewish, padding their pockets with excessive assessments on hard-working peasants who barely eked out a living for their households? It was enough to disturb any sensitive boy.

What may have been the reaction of Jesus to the political maneuverings of the Sadducees? Everyone knew that they sought to keep control of the priestly class while collaborating with Rome and living in the lap of luxury, a compensation from the Imperial Court for their cooperation. Did the Lord ever grow inwardly impatient with such corruption before beginning to preach at the age of thirty?

How must Jesus have been affected by the gory sight of bloody sacrifices, the nauseous smell of death, when frequenting the Temple on Mount Zion? Did it sicken him, displease him, or leave him unmoved.

We can project the attitudes of his public ministry back into earlier years, but no one can be certain that the responses of Christ after thirty years of age were the same as those while still a young man at home musing on the complex issues of the day. Was Jesus aware of his identity as the Son of God from the moment when He opened his eyes in the manger at Bethlehem? Did that consciousness come to him gradually as the Father revealed more and more of His will through the advancing years? We are clearly informed in the scriptures that He grew in stature and wisdom with God which would suggest that the divine disclosure was given to him incrementally from his infancy to his baptism.

The thoughtful student of Christianity is concerned about all these questions as well as a maze of others related to the hidden years in the life of our Lord. Most, if not all of them, will remain unanswered until the final day of truth when all mysteries will be revealed and every enigma explained. None of us wants to miss that exciting time when the answers will be given to us. In this interval between two eternities, however, one is quite justified in at least attempting to create a provocative atmosphere for discussion.

The contents of this book are largely fictional and intended only for the cultivation of the mind and heart. What we have here is a reverent effort to make some approach to the life of our Lord as it may have been developed between circumcision and baptism. Every supposition is deeply rooted in the author's firm conviction that Jesus was wholly divine and completely human – fully God and fully man.

After two thousand years, it is still hard for some of us to accept the complete humanity of Jesus. For some sentimental reason, which has been disguised as reverence, we just cannot bring ourselves to see the Lord in flesh and blood situations.

This is probably because of our built-in awareness of the scandal of the Incarnation, the story of God's becoming man. No one can ever understand fully how God could really become man and still be God. Some things are for his mind alone. But this is the glory of the faith. While we may find it difficult to grasp with our finite minds, it is to be recognized that the nature of God is infinite.

To think of Jesus as being confronted with the same kind of life situations as those which we encounter is not a grave problem until we see him caught up in pure, fleshly conflicts. Of course, we know that a Jesus who was an infant and much later a full grown man had to be an adolescent and a teenager in between. But we are piously afraid to look at that real interval in his life lest we find him more human than we are willing to concede. From the beginnings of Christianity until this very day, sincere students of Christology have wrestled with the two-fold nature of our Lord. He is portrayed as either more divine than human or more human than divine. Both extremes are wrong. Jesus, if He is to be our Savior, must be one hundred percent God and one hundred percent man.

When God was a little boy, living on the earth, He was young in years and attitudes exactly like all boys around him.

It is one thing to think of God as an old man with long, white whiskers living up in heaven. It is another thing entirely to think of him as a young man with youthful dreams living on the earth.

Scholars should not read this book since it has not been pursued with them in mind. There is nothing scholarly about a work of fiction, even historical fiction. Scholarship seeks to reduce the revealed truth of the biblical record to what can be proved. Often the endeavor results in the very scientific method of voting on what is acceptable to the human intellect!

What we have done in this book takes nothing away from the inspired word of God concerning His Son, Jesus Christ. Rather, it has been our intent to reason deductively, to infer from general biblical revelations, what the silence is saying. While there are no new revelations in these pages, the author has walked with the Lord since the tender age of thirteen. During those passing years, insights into the person of our wonderful Lord have been too insistent to be ignored.

In no way is this book to be viewed as history. Nowhere does it intend to say "This is the way it was," nor does it claim that "Now you know the rest of the story." What it does say is "This is the way it might have been."

PROLOGUE

With the taste of supper still in their mouths, eleven confused men descended the limestone stairs on the outside wall of a friend's house in Jerusalem. The day had been one of unfolding bewilderment and the time spent about the table at eventide evoked a sense of impending dread which not even the scholarly Nathaniel could explain.

An eerie quietness filled the minds of the disciples as, with an uneasy gait, they trudged west across the Kidron Valley in the direction of the Mount of Olives. The melancholy singing of the Hallel Psalms, which rent the night as they had filed down the crude steps, had faded into the crisp air. The night – normally being one of joy for a nation recalling a miraculous deliverance from the angel of death – was laden with a sadness which had fallen over the city like a heavy shroud. The silent darkness spoke loudly of an approaching disaster.

In the distance loomed the hillside where their teacher often went to pray. There was little question but that Jesus was headed for the sacred rock in Gethsemane where Isaac, two thousand years earlier, had been taken by his father for sacrifice.

There their teacher, who had grown up among the hills of Galilee, would enter into his final tryst with destiny. There He would confront the age old human struggle for survival, an encounter with death which would test every fiber of his being. And there He would determine what exactly was to be the will of God for the boy from Nazareth.

As the temple police, with torches blazing, approached the garden from the city, the eleven were sleeping fitfully near its entrance while their beloved teacher prayed at the sacred rock. Rising from his aching knees, Jesus could see the flaming torches which were, in themselves, an ominous declaration from the nation's determined rulers that He should die. For months, He had felt the hot breath of the authorities on his neck, an unrelenting animus which pursued him like a crazed animal, but now the die was cast and his hour had come.

He thought of his mother, who had harbored such great dreams for him, and it broke his heart. He remembered the good times which He had spent with the children in Nazareth, the hard times which He and Joseph had gone through in the carpenter's shop. He recalled the pain in his gut when Joses died, and the loneliness which had haunted him every day since Joseph was laid to rest in the village cemetery. That was long ago, but it all came flooding back now.

Philip, who had been sleeping with the others at the entrance to the garden, had been roused from his slumbers by the smell of the approaching torches. Always a little dense and slow to understand, at this moment he was filled with an unholy dread which struck terror in his heart. "Here they come," he cried. We're gonna catch it now. Wake up, Peter! They are right on top of us. Somebody do something!" Peter reached for his sword, ready for any impending fight. Panic seized the hearts of the other nine men.

"We are looking for Jesus of Nazareth," announced a gruff, harsh looking captain of the Temple guard, squinting in the darkness which was only partly dispelled by the flaming torches carried by his men.

"I am He," replied Jesus, showing no emotion other than willing compliance with the law. Shocked by his response, the soldiers staggered back in disarray, sprawled on the ground. Bewildered and embarrassed, they struggled slowly to their feet, each man staring at his comrades in bewilderment and disbelief.

Being first to regain his composure, the captain stood with feet apart and his hand on the sheath which housed his sword. "You are under arrest," he said. "If you do not resist, you will not be harmed. But if you give us trouble, we will restrain you by whatever means needed."

Forming a circle around the prisoner, the armed police, ready for any resistance, marched him out of Gethsemane to the house of Annas and, from there, to the court of the ruling high priest, Caiaphas. Out of the corner of his eye, Jesus could see young John Mark running naked from the garden, having left his linen garment in the hands of a guard who had ripped it from him. His heart ached for the adventurous youth for whom it would have been impossible to understand what was happening.

Prior to the arrest, arrangements had been made

17

with rabble from the streets who, for the payment of an agreed upon price, would provide false witness against the accused. In addition to the presence of hired witnesses, at least a quorum of the Sanhedrin – the highest court of the land – awaited the arrival of the Temple police with their charge.

The Sanhedrin, being already assembled for a night session, which was contrary to their own law, were embroiled in heated debate long before the prisoner appeared. While the meeting of this body was regularly scheduled at a place near the so-called Xystos, on the east side toward the Temple mount, the urgency of the matter now before it allowed an exception to the rule.

Caiaphas struck his fist on the table, gritting his teeth in anger, his dark eyes spitting fire. "We must act quickly," he shouted, "we've no time to lose! It is now or never!"

Less than half the high court members was present as they assembled in a semi-circle facing the high priest and two solemn-looking clerks who recorded their votes. When the full body was present there were seventy plus the supreme priest himself. It was within their legal jurisdiction to acquit or condemn, but not to execute without the sentence being ratified by the Roman procurator who, at this time, was one Pontius Pilate, an appointee of Caesar himself.

"We have one of his followers on our side," said Caiaphas as he leaned forward across the table with an air of pompous authority. "I have placed in his greedy hands thirty pieces of silver for which the little weasel has promised to deliver his teacher to us." The high priest was ecstatic with the prospects of apprehending this trouble-maker at last. "Even as of this moment the police are meeting the traitor at a pre-determined spot where the rebel from Galilee will be trapped."

A roar of relief rose from the assembled elders, their heads filled with delight at the thought of cornering the mad teacher who had skirted their efforts for nearly three years.

"Soon He will be here," continued the priest, hands raised and waving, signaling for order. "I want no outburst when He comes through the door. This is a session called to deal with an emergency and we must handle it with decorum and wise deliberation. Not since the day that I became high priest has there been such a crisis in Israel as we face here tonight."

"Are we within the law?" one of the younger clerics dared to ask. "This is the first time we have met at night and, unless I have misread the law, we are not within our rights to meet during a holy festival. There can certainly be no justice if we operate outside the law."

The bearded men, who had been staring in disbelief at the youthful-looking speaker, snapped back to attention as Caiaphas, greatly agitated, began to respond. "Hermon, you have been in the Sanhedrin a very short time and there is yet much for you to learn. You are right regarding the guidelines of this body, but this *is* an emergency as has already been explained. And there are exceptions to every law as we all know. I alone can make those decisions."

"Hear! Hear!" shouted a number of the older men in unison. With slow and cautious movement, an older man, whose body was racked with arthritic joints, finally

19

managed to get to his feet. His was an imposing figure and he spoke with a clear and resonant voice. A hush fell over the room.

"What are we going to charge this peasant with having done?" It was a reasonable question posed by one of the court's more seasoned members. Joseph of Arimathea was a long-standing member of the Sanhedrin and highly respected by all, with the possible exception of the high priest himself. While the wealthy rabbi from Benjamin was older than Caiaphas, the devious leader of the body had always disliked Joseph because of the numerous times he had challenged his decisions.

"More than one charge," replied the chair, irritated with his judgment's being questioned. After all, Caiaphas was in charge and invariably felt a deep down disdain for anyone who chose to interrupt his plans. Power and ultimate control were the benchmarks of his rule.

"First, He is a pain in the neck! Everywhere He goes, He causes trouble for us. If He continues, which He will certainly do unless we stop him, we are going to be in serious trouble with Pilate. The governor will not tolerate unrest among our people, certainly not now in the midst of Passover."

"Exactly what kind of trouble is this man guilty of causing?"

"Joseph, you are a wise man. You know what is happening in Israel. Crowds follow this fellow around. He does all kinds of magic tricks to impress the ignorant and they are beginning to think He is God! You can see what will happen to our traditions if this lunatic is permitted to challenge our authority. And it is plain that

20

this is going on from Judea to Galilee. Not just occasionally, but every day."

"Have you ever talked to this young man about your misgivings?" By this time, Joseph was beginning to grate on the nerves of Caiaphas who was beginning to show his impatience. "Joseph!" Clearly irritated to the point of disgust, the high priest could not believe that anyone should think there was any question as to the guilt of the teacher from Nazareth.

"Several of our members have countered his attacks made on the faith of our fathers, but the people hold him in such esteem that we are rebuffed and often embarrassed. The fellow is sharp, that I do not deny, but that makes him all the more dangerous. Time is running out and we must defend our long-established traditions."

There was a pause in the proceedings as the men, brows knitted with uncertainty, sorted out what they had been hearing. Uneasy with the quietness, Caiaphas went on, as if he had rehearsed his speech again and again.

"Second, it is one thing to be a popular religious figure; another thing entirely to leave the impression that one is God. And this is what is taking place. Why, suppose I should tell the people that I am God? While this trouble-maker should be insisting that He is *not* God, He is allowing the people to believe that He is. That's blasphemy!"

"Has He said that He is God?" asked Joseph quietly.

Having been among the elders, who had been charged with hearing Jesus teach and finding something to charge him with, an angry member sprang to his feet, calling for the floor. "This joker has an uncanny way of avoiding direct questions," he cried, swinging his white-knuckled fist in the air. "He will never come right out and say it, but it is clear to us that He wants people to *think* He is God. And we cannot permit this to continue! Our task is to protect the nation from heresy, especially blasphemy. We must put this arrogant guy away. He is a bigger threat than Rome!"

"Hear! Hear!" roared the elders. This time the response was louder and angrier. The highest court in the land was in total disarray and in danger of coming to blows.

Banging both his fists on the table, the high priest once more brought the unruly assembly back to the point of order. "But, I haven't yet got to the real problem, the nasty one. You see, we have witnesses just outside these walls who will swear that they heard this wild man threaten to destroy the Temple! He even bragged that He would rebuild it ! The Temple which took forty-six years to build. He intends to destroy and rebuild it . . . in three days!" Sneering in disgust, Caiaphas spat at the floor and ground the spittle beneath his foot.

The Sanhedrin rose to its feet as one, the angry men pulling their beards in anguish and slapping their own heads in horror. Their faces were flushed with hate as together they shrieked with the uncontrolled frenzy of a bunch of wild beasts.

"Away with this heathen!" shouted some. Others cried, "Stone him!" even though they knew there was no way such a thing could be done lest the people themselves rise up in revolt. "Let him be publicly whipped," another, clamoring for attention, was heard to say. "Lay the scourge to his filthy back!"

This time the high priest stamped his sandaled feet on the hard pavement, pounding his fists on the table. Even the clerks attempted to shout down the unruly mob of clerics, a judicial assembly ready to kill in the name of religion, but with little success.

Not until the senior member of the Sanhedrin waved his arm for quiet did the ranting men return to their seats. Some were wiping foam from their mouths with the sleeves of their tunics, so fierce had been their madness. A few clutched handfuls of hair which they had torn from their own heads while venting their emotions of hatred.

"Dare we judge a man without first hearing him?" asked the little man with the close-cropped beard. If there were any one member of this ruling body beloved more than anyone else, it was this little old man. While disputes within the court often got out of hand and left some with hostile feelings toward their peers, there was yet to be a single person who failed to respect the opinions of Nicodemus. He had been around a long time.

"Any person accused by this judicial body of having committed a crime, against our nation and its God, must be heard. And He deserves to have at least two witnesses. It sounds to me as if, without a fair hearing, we have condemned this young rabbi."

Whispered sounds were heard across the room. One of the men, who was so deaf that he did not know his whispers were audible to those around him, was saying, "Alibi? What alibi? This young fool has no alibi!"

"How can you be so sure that Jesus is a bad man?"

Nicodemus waited for an answer. None came. Slowly scanning the faces in the room, the old rabbi looked into the eyes of some who were bored by the whole thing, some who were filled with disgust, and others who were obviously bewildered. No one save Joseph appeared to show any sign of compassion.

"How many of you have taken the time to talk to him? How well do you know him? What about the good things He has done? Do none of them count? There are people out there whom we know who were blind. Now they can see. Some were crippled, but now they walk. I have heard from the priests that they have seen lepers who were made clean by him. Maybe He is a wolf in sheep's clothes, but unless we hear him ourselves, we cannot possibly know. I have taken the time to talk with him. It was a while ago, but He doesn't seem to me to be a threat to Israel. I am much alarmed that we are so ready to condemn him."

With that, Ibrahim, the elder from Hebron, muttering to himself to muster his courage, stood to his feet. Extending his open palm to Nicodemus, in a gesture of respect, he began to speak. "As much as we all admire your wisdom, my friend, we do not agree. No authority has been given this peasant to teach. This pretender has no training. His background is without distinction. He certainly is not leading the people to Jehovah, but has rounded up a cadre of the dregs of society who know no better than to call him Lord. He may not be a bad man, Nicodemus, but He is doing bad things and that in itself makes him bad. He does not deserve a hearing although we are about to grant him one. And the witnesses? They wait in the hall!"

At that moment, the doors swung open and there appeared, between two armed Temple police, a striking young man, hands tied together in front of him. "Well," said the high priest, turning toward the prisoner and signaling the guards to leave, "We were just talking about God and here He is!"

The men in the hall, which had been rife with anger, threw back their heads and guffawed as they slapped their knees in glee. For a moment, the courtroom was filled with raucous howls of mocking laughter.

"Good one!" shouted Ibrahim. "Good one, indeed!"

The auburn-haired youth from Nazareth stood quietly, his brown, penetrating eyes focused on Caiaphas' face. The white, though soiled, tunic accented the sun-tanned but vibrant skin of his face and hands. His hair was clean and well-groomed and his beard was neatly trimmed. There was nothing about his appearance which would suggest a demented, self-crazed, religious fanatic. Caiaphas, however, who had already made up his mind, was not impressed.

"Welcome to judgment day," said the priest, bowing in mockery, with his left palm extended toward Jesus. "This is your day; this is the day when the court of Israel will acclaim your divinity." The smile on his face was more a snarl than anything else.

Calling for the guards, who had stepped outside the door, the presiding priest commanded them, "Drape this lavish robe around him." Then, handing them what looked like a crown of some sort, he hissed, "And give the king his crown. Now bow your knees before the Messiah."

Leaning over and looking up into the face of Jesus, he asked, dripping with contempt, "How does it feel to be the king of Israel? How does it feel to be God? Tell us! We would like to know. None of us has yet achieved this high and holy honor."

By this time, the assembly hall was filled with shrill curses and loud demands for justice, the kind of justice which puts a man to death without proof of his crime. Springing to his feet, one of the Sadducees struck the prisoner across the face, Caiaphas having blind-folded Jesus' eyes lest he be forced to look at them. "If you are God, tell us who struck you," he demanded, lips curled in disdain. There was no reply.

Jerking off the blinders and turning the prisoner to face the elders, Caiaphas shouted to the top of his lungs, "Do you really think you are God? Do you really believe that you are the Messiah? Tell this court! We are not your ignorant masses. We have the power to put a stop to your demented antics. You are nobody here! Tell us who you think you are!"

Stepping closer to the anxious members of the court, the high priest defiantly exclaimed, "Not only is this clown a blasphemer; He is a fool! Now is the time to save our nation. Let us agree to put this fool to death! It would be a crime against reason to permit him to live, continuing day after day to deceive the people."

"Kill him! Kill him!" shouted the rulers of the Jews, all of them save two. Joseph and Nicodemus were trying desperately to be heard above the cries of the hysterical mob of robed justices.

"No! This is an act of shame which will stain our image forever," shouted Joseph. "No! No! This is infamy! We cannot do this! This man has done us no wrong and we have no right to remove him from the living. He is still one of our own!"

As Jesus was pushed through the door, Nicodemus was cupping his hands around his mouth and crying, "Put him in the Tower of Antonia. We must look into this more thoroughly. We must know the truth. This young man has done nothing for which He should die. Do not kill him!" But he was old and his voice was weak. No one heard him.

The streets were nearly vacant in the Holy City. Most of the unwitting residents were still sleeping as the faint hint of an ashen dawn filled the eastern sky. They would be rising soon, however, as this Friday was the holiest day of the year. It was Passover and the now quiet streets would soon be filled with crowds, a sea of bodies from all over the world, who had come to participate in the long-awaited festival of faith. A light rain had fallen during the night and the brown cobblestones were wet and a bit slippery. Somewhere a farmer's rooster announced the coming of a new day.

Only a few hours had passed since the young teacher from Galilee had been shoved by the guards into a secure enclosure in the holding quarters of the high priest. There, hands tied and chained to one of the temple police, He would wait until morning when they would take him to the Roman hall of justice for a civil trial. Like the

27

gaggling of geese, several of the Hebrew jurists could be heard still discussing the fate of the prisoner in the adjoining room.

At the gate stood a nervous and frightened man gripping a pouch in his hand. "Open the gate!" he yelled, kicking at the iron grating which barred his entrance into the courtyard of the supreme justice of the nation. "Open the gate! I must see the priest. Hello! Hello!" Rattling the gate vigorously, the anxious stranger cried. "Anyone hear me? Open the gate or I will break it down!"

"Coming," called a voice from inside as the intruder, kicking until his feet bled, tried to tear the iron gate from its hinges.

"I must see the priest. Where is he? Is he here? Quick. I cannot wait!"

"What do you want?"

"The silver! I must give him the silver."

"Wait here," said the keeper of the gate, turning back into the courtyard, his sandaled feet leaving hollow sounds as they crossed the pavement.

It seemed like hours to the man at the entrance, but it was really only a few minutes until the guard returned with Caiaphas.

As the high priest neared the gate, the pouch with the thirty pieces of silver struck the cobblestone pavement, the bag bursting and the coins rolling across the floor. "It's cursed!" cried Judas. "The silver is cursed. It is blood money. I have sinned. Our teacher is innocent. Where can I find forgiveness? Help me. Please, help me!"

"You're too late, weasel," answered Caiaphas, laughing fiendishly. "You should have thought of this

28

earlier, you fool. Go cry somewhere else. We won't take your dirty money."

The guard, unmoved by what he had seen, watched as Judas turned and ran sobbing into the darkness. "What I have done will never be forgiven! There is no hope for a traitor! I must kill myself . . . I must kill myself . . . I must . . ." The screams echoed across the sleeping city, finally dying out in the night air, as the priest returned to his plush quarters within the walls.

"What's all the devilish racket?" asked the pampered governor as he bolted upright in his lavish bed, rubbing the sleep from his eyes.

The quietness of Passover morning had been suddenly broken by loud and angry shouts coming from a small group of disheveled men who appeared outside the shuttered window of Pontius Pilate. Many of them were clergy as was easy to see if only by their clerical garb. They had worked themselves up into a lather following the events which had transpired in the house of Caiaphas.

Already they were demanding the execution of their prisoner whom they surrounded like an armed garrison. Some carried rocks in their hands while others armed themselves with sticks from the roadside.

"What do they want? What are they saying?" said Pilate to his wife, squinting his eyes as he strained to separate the words from the noise.

"They are demanding that you crucify Jesus."

"What! I am sick and tired of these trouble-making, religious fanatics. Those bearded freaks have been out to get this fellow for months. What's the big deal? What are they afraid of? How can one insignificant peasant from Galilee threaten an entire gang of religious thugs? The whole thing is a thorn in my side and I might just crucify all of them!"

"Take care, my husband, that you not get mixed up in this thing," warned Procula. "We women talk you know, and most of the ones who have mentioned him to me believe He is a prophet. My friend, Joanna, is one of his followers. She says that Jesus healed her of a grievous and long-standing disease. True, she is not one of us, but she moves in the highest political circles of Herod's family. And, in addition, several of my closest friends listen to him every time they have the chance."

"Even our own people?"

"Oh yes, especially our Roman women. They are much taken with him. True, He is not handsome as you, my love, but He has the stature and composure of a Greek god. I even dream about him sometime. And, in my dreams, anyone who crosses him gets into serious trouble."

"Just last night," continued Pilate's wife, "as I dreamed, you were standing down there on the veranda and Jesus was up here. You were in chains and Caesar's crown was on the head of the Galilean. The crowds were crying for your crucifixion and you were sobbing. You were begging him for mercy. The dream was so real. I'm afraid for us, Ponti dear. You must not touch this."

"Nonsense, Procula. He is just another Hebrew milking the cause for whatever He can get out of it. There's nothing about him to be afraid of, my dear. After all, I am the governor and I can stop this folly anytime I wish."

"Don't be too sure, Ponti," replied Procula, looking at the smug governor out of the corner of her eye, shaking her finger in his face. "You will regret the day when you allowed yourself to get cornered by these barbarians. They only want to get rid of a young nuisance who threatens their power. Send them away."

The growing tumult outside the veranda had attracted passers-by who, craning their necks, stopped to see what was happening. Some had even gotten into the spirit of things and begun to shout and jeer though they had no idea what it was all about. Protests and demonstrations against the government were commonplace and an early morning riot at Pilate's house was made to order for young nationalists. In fact, as they joined in the cry, "Crucify him," they thought they were calling for the death of the much hated governor himself.

Aware that Passovers were always ripe times for rebellion, Pontius Pilate knew that he must nip this little flurry in the bud at once lest it get out of hand. Throwing a purple towel around himself – carefully arranging it so that the gold embroidered crown could be seen from the street below – he rushed toward the window, threw back the shutters, and looked down on the scene below. What he saw slightly unnerved him. Upturned faces of scores of inflamed men, wild men whose clenched fists were raised in growing impatience.

Lest he appear powerless to control the hysterical mob before him, the governor laid aside the purple towel and replaced it with his judicial robes. A servant arranged his curly hair while another strapped on his royal sandals. At last, looking every bit a Caesar in his own right, Pontius Pilate strode out onto the balcony over-looking the paved veranda where the crowd waited. As a gesture of authority, the governor raised his arm, short sword in his hand, chin raised in defiance, and cried above the din, "Caesar is Lord!"

One by one the elders lowered their arms, turning to the spectators with a call for calm. When the tumult had subsided, the governor's deputy declared in a mighty voice, "This is a court of law. The court is now opened. The honorable Pontius Pilate." Deferring to the fragile-looking, chisel-faced man who was in charge, the deputy stepped aside into the shadows of the marble columns which surrounded the balcony.

"And what is today's problem?" asked Pilate, weary with disgust at the petty quarrels of a nation he despised. "Why are you here? You act like you are all drunk! Had a bad night, did you? You have no right to come here unannounced. You know that."

In route to the hall of justice, the elders had cast lots to determine who would speak on their behalf to Pilate.

"I am Ephram," declared a stocky figure at the front of the crowd, "duly selected by the Sanhedrin to address your excellency. We have brought an arch-enemy of the people and a seditious threat to Rome with the demand that He be properly punished for his crimes."

"And what are those crimes?" The governor laughed sarcastically as he spoke, recalling the many times he had been expected to solve their silly disputes. "You are all a bunch of criminals. How can one of you be worse than the rest?"

"Blasphemy!" shouted Ephram. "He claims to be God! He is telling the people that He is the Messiah, God's Son. Our law says He should die. We ask that you find him guilty and put him to death."

"How dare you bring your religious scruples to me. Rome has granted you, of all people in the empire, religious freedom and all you do is fight among yourselves. This is your problem, not mine. Jesus is from Galilee anyway. Why didn't you take him to Herod? He is right here in the city for your Passover."

"Herod cannot sentence the prisoner to death," replied Ephram. "Only you have that power, your excellency."

"You are right about that," replied the governor, noticeably inflated with pride. "But this is a religious matter, not a civil one. Take him away. Do not bother me again with these trifles."

When Herod Antipas saw Jesus, having never taken time to hear him before, he was elated. A little excitement was a welcome relief in the dull life to which he was accustomed. The sight of the acclaimed magician from Nazareth would be the best entertainment of the week. It would be more hilarious than the Passover.

"Dazzle me with one of your tricks," the half-breed puppet from Idumea said, palms together and smirking behind his wide smile. "I hear you mesmerize the people. You must be pretty good. Now is your chance. Try it out on me. Who knows? I might make you my court jester."

When it was evident that Jesus was not going to entertain the ruler of Galilee, the soldiers were instructed to dress him in Herod's own robe and mock him, treating him with callous contempt. While Herod was disappointed, he was not surprised.

"Why need we be enemies any longer," wrote Herod in the message carried by the guard who returned Jesus unto Pilate. "You have my blessing. Do what you think is right." The loathing, which the governor of Judea felt for the tetrarch of Galilee, quickly turned to admiration as he read the word from Herod. There are no better friends than those who have a common enemy. That day the old political rivalry ended.

"I warned you not to return," threatened the governor. "You are testing my patience. I will not be party to your ignorant scruples. Keep on and I will arrest the whole bunch of you."

Ceremonially seating himself on his throne and turning his gaze upon the prisoner, Pilate asked, "Are you really a king? Who do you represent? Who crowned you? Where are you from?" Not waiting for a reply, he cocked his head to the side and continued, "Do you not realize that these men actually want to kill you and that I am the only one who can save your life? Do you know who I am? Your life is in my hands. I have power to execute you or power to set you free."

"You have no power other than what is given you by my Father," answered the prisoner, looking intently at the astonished ruler of Judea.

"Your father? Your father has been dead for

34

years. Your father was a village carpenter. What power did he ever have? Is he going to punish me from the grave? Will he beat me with his hammer or maim me with his saw?" Amused by the governor's witty remarks, the soldiers laughed with merriment. Even the solemn-faced elders took a chance on a faint smile.

Pilate turned as if to walk away, only to stop in his tracks and return to face the prisoner before him. "If your father is so all-powerful, maybe he'll do something about this weather. Looks like a bad storm coming in. We don't need that to mess up Passover, now do we? Think you can get him to do something about that?" The governor was adept at sarcasm and on this morning he was in rare form.

"If this fellow is persuading people that He is a king," whispered one of his advisors, "you will have to put him away. If word of this gets to Caesar and you permit this to grow, your seat of power will be in question. There has been enough trouble with these people. You cannot afford anything else. Your safest solution to this problem is to give these people what they want."

Meanwhile, working the crowd, the elders took note of the indecisiveness of Pilate and used the moment to threaten him. They were leading the frenzied mob in a kind of chant, "We have no king but Caesar! We have no king but Caesar! Vox populi! The voice of the people! We have no king but Caesar!"

Sensing the precariousness of the situation, the governor quickly called for order and nervously insisted, "I find no crime to have been committed by this man. Therefore, I cannot sentence him to die. But, if you will keep the peace and cause me no further trouble, on this your most holy day, I will grant you the right to do with him what you will." The crowd went wild with excitement, the priests and elders dancing in approval.

"Strip the prisoner and apply the whip," commanded the governor. "Do it at once." Then, whispering to his senior officer, Pilate explained, "Possibly this will create some pity and we can avoid the complications that a crucifixion could cause."

Stripped to the waist and beaten into semi-consciousness, Jesus collapsed prostrate on the ground, his hands still tied to the whipping post and his bare back covered with blood. But there was no pity in the hearts of the accusers. They watched with smug satisfaction, literally cheering at each lash of the whip. The young blasphemer had been given just what He deserved.

From the adjoining room, at Pilate's request, a basin of water was brought, in which he dramatically washed his hands, insisting that he shared no responsibility for the fate of the prisoner. His heart was beating wildly and his mouth was dry as dust. None of what had just happened made any sense at all. How had he allowed himself to be forced into letting a decent man be killed solely because of some words He had spoken? Great beads of steamy perspiration ran down his pallid face as, with wildly shaking hands, he tried to wash away his guilt.

The guards dragged the half-conscious, bleeding victim out of the hall of justice to a work area where soldiers prepared a cross. Meanwhile, the governor's wife sat silently in her chambers. Filled with her own thoughts, she watched her husband pacing the palace floor, quietly muttering to himself. His rambling words came like a torrent of incoherent profanity. With all the power given to him by Caesar himself, Pilate was being held captive by his own stupid subjects. She could only imagine how confused and angry he must have been.

Procula thought of her own son, Anthony. He was a good boy, eleven years old at the time and already planning to get into Roman politics like his father. It was not hard to see that he was a born leader. Had this Jesus been anything like her Tony while growing up in the distant hills of Galilee? She wondered. What must have been the dreams his mother had for him? How had He come to this tragic end? Could it happen to Tony? And, in her heart, she felt sorry for Jesus' mother, imagining what might be going through her mind at that moment. The tears rolled easily down her painted face. Procula did not remember ever crying before over her husband's hard decisions. But this was different.

Outside the morning sky was turning gray. Procula could not begin to explain why she felt like the wheels of destiny were turning at that moment, but she knew that nothing would ever be the same again. Not for her. Not for Israel. Not for Rome. And not for Ponti who returned to the basin of water at least a dozen times that afternoon just to wash his trembling hands.

The sun had hidden itself somewhere in the mid-morning sky. But the city was astir and the streets were filled with people in celebration of Passover. A strange sense of dread filled the morning air, an ominous dread of an unknown and unexpected visit from God on this holy day. The light rain, which had come during the night, had cleared, but across the mountains and above the noise of the multitudes, there was the faint rumble of distant thunder. Heavy clouds were rolling in and the wind was kicking up debris from the city streets.

"Sounds like the gods are angry, Ponti dear," said Procula, as she gazed from their lofty balcony into the streets of the crowded city. The bright colors of the garments of multitudes of pilgrims from other lands were subdued by the threat of a downpour of rain.

From behind the lavish curtains which surrounded the private quarters of the royal family, a servant entered the room with morning wine for the procurator of Judea. Pouring the sparkling wine into the silver goblet reserved only for Pilate, the servant bowed low and prepared to remove the basin of soiled water in which the procurator had been washing his hands.

"Don't touch that basin!" cried the nervous governor. "I may yet need it."

CHAPTER ONE

"How could this have happened? We hear about these horrible things happening all the time, but when it hits home, it is different!"

His eyes were swollen from crying as Ben and his wife left Jerusalem early on the morning following the Sabbath. The trip back to Nazareth would be long and tiring and Ben, the father in the Haggi family, had to get back to work in the village stone cutter's shop. Being devout Jews, the family went to Passover as often as they could. However, being poor as well as devout meant that there were times when they could not manage it. But this year they were able to get away from the business. And it was a Passover they would never forget.

They were hardly out of hearing distance, of the Roman sentry near the city gate, when Ben broke down. His mind was in a whirl and the hollow pain in his chest was like an ache he had never known before. The sense of loss when his father died had hurt, but nothing compared to this.

Hannah, Ben's wife, had been crying all night until she had hardly enough strength to begin the arduous journey home. The children had been left in Nazareth with grandma Haggi and their parents were anxious to see them. They never liked being away from the rest of the family, but they were relieved that they had not brought them along. No child should have to witness anything like they had just seen.

"God of Abraham, Isaac, and Jacob," Ben was saying, as he ran his fingers through his graying and unruly hair. "Why would You let this happen?"

The black grief which engulfed her was so great that Hannah flung herself into the open arms of her husband and they both collapsed beside the dusty road. Their pent-up emotion gave way to loud wailing like that of Job when told of his children's death. No, they had not lost their children, but what had happened felt like a loss a thousand times as great.

"Oh, Ben," sobbed Hannah, "why would anyone do such a terrible thing to him?"

"I cannot begin to imagine what they were thinking," said Ben, wiping his tear-stained face on the folds of his tunic. "They murdered him, Hannah . . . killed him in cold blood! And it was our priests who did it, not cut-throats from the hills."

Regaining their composure, the couple pulled one another back on their wobbly feet and continued their sad journey. The air seemed too thick and heavy to breathe. Their feet weighed a ton as they dragged themselves in the direction of Nazareth.

Only a few hours earlier, they had watched, from a safe distance, as a long-time friend of the family died. They saw the calloused soldiers drive nails into his hands and heard him scream as the men dropped the cross into the hole. Hannah caught her breath and turned away as the centurion thrust his sharp sword into the side of their dying friend. She could see Mary at the foot of the cross and wanted desperately to get to her, but the guard held her back.

When the storm broke across the hill of execution, Ben and Hannah had run for cover and, unable to bear the sight of what was happening and feeling helpless to do anything, they walked slowly back into the city. Neither of them spoke a word, swallowing hard, as they choked back a flood of tears. Almost embarrassed to face one another, they reminisced about how guilty they felt at that moment as if they were responsible for not rescuing the dying man.

There was no way to reach sweet Mary since they had no idea where she might have gone. Everybody in town was talking about what had just happened. The Haggis were fearful, however, of expressing themselves to anyone else for fear they could get into trouble with the authorities. So when they finally did speak, it was only to each other.

Ben could not understand the political fervor which seemed to saturate the air as if the young man on the cross were a serious threat to the nation and, unbelievable as it seemed, the empire of Rome. It was true that life in Israel had been going from bad to worse for as long as he could remember, but to think that their friend had anything to do with it was totally ridiculous.

There was precious little sleep that night in Jerusalem. In fact, the entire city had been unusually noisy and Herod's police, brought in from Galilee, were kept busy controlling the confused crowds.

"Why did they do this?" asked Hannah, throwing her hands into the air, as if she were at a total loss to comprehend the mystery of it all.

"It's not easy to understand," answered Ben. "Our priests accused him of claiming to be God, so I hear. They accused him of lying . . . in the name of God!"

"That's nonsense. He was just one of us. I never heard him say anything like that. All the time He lived just up the road He was just like the rest of us."

"Well, that's what the elders have been saying anyway."

"I don't care. They are wrong!"

"Of course, I guess the big threat to the Romans was the report that He was some kind of king in waiting. Once that kind of rumor gets out there is no way of knowing what may come of it. Kings don't cotton well to such threats."

"A king?" said Hannah, wiping the tears from her eyes, her brow knitted in confusion.

"That's what they put on the sign. It was hanging around his neck as He carried his cross. Plain as day, it read, JESUS OF NAZARETH, KING OF THE JEWS."

Hannah shrugged her shoulders. "Ben, we have known him and his family all our lives. Where do they get this crazy stuff? Kings are born in palaces, not in Nazareth!"

"You don't need to prove anything to me, dear. I remember dad's talking so many times about how much he admired the boy and Old Joe. Jesus was always so polite and well mannered. And He was a hard working boy just like his dad. Other than being extra smart and very alert, He was about like the rest of the youngsters in town."

"My heart breaks tonight for Mary."

"She was sure proud of that boy," replied Ben, nodding his head in disbelief. "You could see it in her eyes when she talked about him. And she talked about him a lot!"

As they sat staring at the ground, lost in their thoughts, they were suddenly interrupted by a stranger who, unnoticed in the shadows, had been standing nearby.

"You must have known the man on the cross," observed the stranger. His voice was pleasant and, as he moved closer, his face displayed a look of kindness. It was easy to see that Hannah was startled and suspicious. Had this stranger been listening? Was he an enemy of Jesus? And, if he were, might she and her husband be in trouble?

Cautiously, Ben replied, "We know the family, yes. Why do you ask?"

"There's a lot of unrest in town about this incident. The whole thing seemed to happen on the spur of the moment without anybody being aware of what was taking place. The priests appeared intent on his execution, but I had never heard any of the people say anything bad about him. A few of the people around here had never seen him, but those who remembered him had nothing but words of praise. I take it that you are as puzzled as the rest of us."

"As a matter of fact, we are," said Hannah, shaking her head in agreement. "We have not seen him for the last three years, but we see his mother quite often. Mary lives only a few paces from our place. Jesus was back in Nazareth once and we heard that some of the locals were angry with him about something, but we did not see him. There's just no way He could have done something deserving of such gross injustice."

As Ben finished, the stranger reached out his hand and said, "I am Enos, from right here in Jerusalem. And you are . . . ?"

Introductions having been made, Enos quickly returned to the conversation.

"It was my good fortune to hear Jesus *one* time. I was in Galilee, on business, when I chanced to see this big crowd seated on the hillside a distance from the footpath. A tall, sun-tanned figure was standing stark against the afternoon sky as He spoke to the crowd. The people were deathly quiet. When I had ventured close enough to hear him, his eyes seemed to be looking straight at me. I was hypnotized. There was no shouting or brandishing of arms, as we have seen so often with revolutionaries. No, He was quietly saying something about loving one's enemies and taking no revenge when we are abused by others."

"That sounds like him. Even when still a growing boy, Jesus liked to talk about things like that. It seemed a little strange for so young a child, but it never turned us off. And He never gave the impression that He thought he

44

was smart. Personally," said Ben, "I was impressed."

"Did you ever hear him talk politics? Did you ever see him act aggressively toward someone else? I guess what I'm wondering is whether He seemed like a boy who would one day get into trouble."

"Heavens no," answered Hannah, suggesting by her tone of voice that such an idea was ludicrous. "There are a lot of trouble-makers in Galilee, as you know, but Jesus was not one of them. Everybody liked him."

"You know what I think?" continued Enos. "I think this has been a political thing from the beginning. Jesus had become so popular with the common folks that the elders were threatened. For a long time now, there has been a lot of unrest among the people. Some blame Rome, of course, but many others blame our own leaders. Everything has just gotten out of hand and there seems to be no way to appease the people. Ultimately, I believe, Jesus became a scapegoat."

"If that is true," replied Ben, "this has been a terrible mistake, an awful crime."

"Well, that's how it appears to me," insisted Enos as all three wiped at their eyes and blew their noses.

By this time, the police were clearing the streets and Enos suggested that they further their conversation at his house. Several people were already in the private courtyard, having pre-arranged with the owner for a place to stay during Passover. At once it was obvious that Enos and his family were far from being as poor as Ben. The house was spacious with several rooms opening into the courtyard. Through one of the doors, which stood ajar, Ben could see that the interior was well furnished.

"Sit here, Hannah," said Enos, pointing to a rock ledge over which burned an oil torch giving off a pungent smell in the night air.

There they talked until the wee hours of the morning, all of it about Jesus and the tragic events of the day, while Enos' wife, Ruth, kept them supplied with flat bread and wine.

"The awful thing we saw today we will never forget," Hannah said to Ruth. "You should be glad you were not there." Enos had earlier explained that his wife stayed with the house to see after the guests.

Ruth was a quiet, withdrawn woman, who listened more than she spoke. Hannah observed at once that Enos had instructed her that a wife, unless spoken to, should leave the talking to her husband. But Ruth seemed so timid. Reaching out to her, Hannah sought to force some little bit of conversation.

"Jesus is gone now. They have probably put his body to rest somewhere and Jehovah only knows what his mother is going through." Tears gushed like a fountain as Hannah buried her face in her hands.

"Mary is my friend," she went on. "We are like sisters. Just a few days ago, she told me how worried she was about Jesus. She just had a sixth sense that something bad was going to happen to him. You know how mothers are."

Ruth still said nothing.

"Put yourself in Mary's place tonight. How would you feel if your first-born son, for whom you had such strong hopes, was suddenly arrested, beaten, and put to death for crimes he did not commit? Think of the many precious memories which would be breaking your heart. All Mary's memories were wonderful. She never had any trouble with Jesus. He was a joy to be around, so understanding of everybody. I remember how devoted He was to his mother, how kind and considerate He was when around her. In fact, He treated everyone that way."

"Jesus was such a gentle boy," explained Hannah, as she recalled the day, nearly twenty years earlier, when her baby girl was born. Mary had come at once and Jesus, a teenager at that time, had made it a point to come by the next morning. Men were not very affectionate. It wasn't the manly thing to do. But Jesus picked up the tiny girl and, looking into her innocent face, said, 'You look just like God'! Then he kissed her soft cheek, gently laying her back in her bed."

Finally, Ruth spoke. "Who knows what God looks like? Our rabbis say that no one has ever seen God. What did He mean by that?"

"I never knew, but it just seemed like the right thing for him to say. Jesus was such a warm, sensitive child. Every time I look at my daughter, I think of what He said."

"Sounds like Jesus was the kind of son who would make any mother proud. I wish I had known him when He was a boy, too."

47

"It would have made all the difference in the world," answered Hannah.

With that, Enos extinguished the torch. Billows of black smoke rose from the extinguished wick. The courtyard was finally quiet. Within hours, Ben and Hannah would be leaving for home. Sleep was hard to come by. Wide-eyed, mesmerized by the stars, they remembered happier times. There were just too many memories of the wonderful things they knew about him as a boy.

CHAPTER TWO

For nine long months before his birth, the virgin watched her girlish waistline expand. She would have suspected that she was ill with some dread disease had it not been for that memorable day when the angel of the Lord explained what was happening. Never, not even one time, did Mary doubt her God. Never did she question what He had done or why. Yet, it was so mystifying. To her limited knowledge, such a thing had never happened before in the history of the world. Having never known a man, it was not only incredible for her mind to accept – it was absolutely impossible.

Although there was no way to prove it, Mary was sure that no woman on earth had ever loved a man as much as she loved Joseph. When they first met, the one thing she noticed most was his devotion to Jehovah. Not that he said anything much about it, but there was a kind of holy aura which surrounded him. As she looked at him, there was something different, something very special about him.

It could not be said that it was love at first sight. At the beginning, it was warm respect, nothing more. Joseph was almost a score of years older than she, but Mary never thought much about that. Why should she? There was nothing between them but friendship. But the relationship developed and one day it dawned on her that there was something she felt for Joseph that had not been there before. It must have been a mutual thing because this older man had been looking for a wife for several years. He had finally come to see that young Mary was the end of his search.

When Joseph admitted to Mary that he was in love, she blushed, tucking her head and smiling. He knew then that his hopes were not going to be rejected. The betrothal, which was a kind of engagement except considerably more binding, was properly agreed to and witnessed by the parents. Soon, however, Mary was confronted with a frightening realization. Shortly after the betrothal, Mary knew she had to tell her husband-to-be what had happened to her. If she didn't do so, he was bound to notice soon for she was already beginning to show. But how would she do it? And would he believe her?

As long as she lived, Mary would never forget the hot afternoon when she tremulously broke the news. She had walked haltingly to the carpenter's shop where she waited in the yard until no customers were inside. Then she pulled the wooden latch and quietly entered to the surprise of Joseph for she had never been in the shop before. He was glad to see her and smiled widely as he untied his leather work apron and took her in his strong arms.

Mary thought it best not to waste time so, as she snuggled in his embrace, she blurted out, "Joseph, I am with child." In a flash, his arms grew limp and fell to his side. He did not move. Nor did he speak. Mary's heart was filled with panic and she feared the worst.

"It isn't what you are thinking," said Mary as she pulled away and looked up into his wondering face. The light had gone out in Joseph's eyes. His lips trembled and his face had lost its color.

"Mary, we have never slept together! I have never even asked you. You know me better than that. We had an understanding. Why have you done this?" Joseph never raised his voice, but spoke with his customary deliberate calmness.

"No, no! Please Joseph, I must tell you something that you will find hard to believe," pleaded young Mary. "You must help me, believe me, because I have done nothing wrong."

Turning away slowly, the man she loved answered gently, but firmly, "I want you to go now. Don't say anything else. We will have to talk, but our emotions are too edgy right now to even think. Go! Say nothing to anyone. We will meet in the morning."

Twin rows of tears ran down her cheeks, but Mary had been taught by her conservative parents to respect her husband and be subject to his wishes. So, with the awful pain of being misunderstood, she ran out the door. Giving vent to her locked-in emotions, she muffled the sound of her sobbing in her hands. Thinking for sure that her heart would burst, her body shook uncontrollably under what felt like a hundred pound weight   squeezing the hope out of her soul.

Closing the shutter and latching the door, the village carpenter, who had never gone home early, moved with haste in the direction of his house. As he walked, his mind had trouble taking in what he had just heard from the lips of his beloved. Mary was not that kind of girl. He was sure of that. And yet . . . there was nothing else to think.

He had searched so long for a wife. No doubts had ever entered his head about this beautiful young woman. It was not that such doubts were never allowed to arise. Rather, there had been no shadow of a reason to suspect her. "It just cannot be," muttered Joseph to himself. "Why would she tell me such a thing? There is no way the child could be mine. I never touched her. Had I tried, she would have refused. How could my Mary sleep with another man when she promised her faithfulness to me?"

Whatever the answers to those questions might have been, of one thing he was certain. He was sure that he could not go through with the planned marriage. And it tore at his aching heart like a dull knife.

The night was long, unbearably long. And it was unusually dark. Though he was bone-weary from the grueling day, there was no chance that he would sleep. Several times during the night, a night which seemed never to end, he got off his hard mat and walked out into the chilled air. The struggle going on in his mind was so great that he wondered if Jacob had felt similar pain as he wrestled with the angel at Peniel. Like every other man, Joseph had encountered hard times more than once. But nothing that he could remember had ever knocked the wind out of him like this.

It was just before daybreak that he made his decision to call off the wedding. He would do what he could to save Mary all the embarrassment. A shudder went through his mind as he envisioned the moral police of the community demanding her execution. After all, this was adultery and she would have to pay unless he married her. Although deeply hurt, Joseph was not so much angry as he was fearful for the life of his betrothed. At last, mentally and physically exhausted, he fitfully dozed into slumber.

Suddenly, the room was filled with an unearthly light. Sitting straight up, he saw at his feet what he had never before even faintly imagined. There stood a man in brilliant white who began to speak.

"Joseph," he said, "You are a son of David. Fear not to take unto thee Mary as thy wife: for that which is conceived in her is of the Holy Ghost. And she shall bring forth a son, and you shall call his name Jesus: for he shall save his people from their sins."

No sooner had the light appeared than it was gone and the man in white with it. Joseph swallowed hard. Beads of perspiration covered his forehead. His eyes were open so wide that it felt like they were going to pop right our of their sockets. Even his breathing was labored. He could not move.

By the time the morning dawned, Joseph had settled his nerves and regained some degree of composure. Quickly, he made his way through the quiet village to the house of Mary's parents. The bride-to-be had spent a restless night, too, and her parents had stayed awake with her. As Joseph reached the door, both parents met him, opening the door before he had knocked, distraught to the point of sobs.

"We really do not know what is wrong with her," said the father. "She has cried all night, but we don't know why. Our Mary refuses to talk to us. Says we would never believe her. She has been sitting there all night staring at the floor. Maybe you can help. We have never seen her this way before."

Joseph's eyes looked into Mary's swollen face, wet with a night of crying, as he told her what had just happened to him, the appearance of the man in white and the great light.

"The same angel," she cried out, "the same one who explained to me what was happening inside my body? "Oh, Joseph, what is happening to us?"

"Shhh . . ." said Joseph, putting his finger to his lips. Then he recited word for word what the angel had said to him.

"I will never forget those words. They burn in my heart like a fire. I do not understand, but I know what I saw and heard. We must keep this to ourselves, not breathe a word about it to anybody. Nobody would believe it if we told them. I couldn't expect them to."

"Joseph," remarked Mary's mother, "We are in the dark about all this. But we know how you must feel. We are so sorry that our Mary has put you through this. And we cannot blame you if . . ."

"Never! Never in a thousand years," interrupted Joseph with loud bursts of holy laughter. What has been done here is of God. And none of us can question it. My love for your daughter is a million times stronger now than it was yesterday. And we will see this through together."

If she had thought she loved Joseph before, Mary discovered that her feeling for him had been as nothing compared to the love in her heart at that moment. Throwing her arms about his neck, she kissed his lips passionately, while her parents looked on in wonder. How she loved this man! What incredible faith he had in God . . . and in her as well! It couldn't be easy for Joseph. She knew that. If she herself were mystified, how much more must be Joseph.

The years had passed so quickly. It was now nearly nine years since that morning when her sweetheart pledged his faith in the midst of what still remained a mystery. As soon as Joseph got home from work they were going to have a party. It was the ninth anniversary of the birth of their miracle son. To say the least, Jesus was as excited as any nine year old boy could be. Joseph had been saving all year out of his meager income so that there could be a little extra on the table for this special occasion. Other than the family and two of Jesus' friends, there would be no one else there. Such celebrations were kept simple for poor folks in the village, but there was always a lot of singing and much laughter.

Not every year did the children in such families get birthday gifts. Money was scarce. This year, however, Joseph had arranged, with the help of his very talented wife, to purchase enough colorful material to make a special coat for Jesus. It was far more than could be justified, but it seemed like the thing to do.

Of all the stories in the Torah, Jesus' favorite was the one about Joseph, beloved son of Jacob and Rachel. Even as a grown-up man, this one boy stood tallest as Jesus' hero. He could not remember when He heard the story the first time, but Mary's son never tired of hearing his father tell it again and again. The story had been told him by his father so many times that He knew it by heart.

"Tell me about Joseph," He would say, as the blankets were tucked around him at night.

"You've heard this story a hundred times," his father always answered with a chuckle.

"I know, but I like it most of all."

So, just a few nights before this birthday, like the loving father he was, the man whom Jesus loved more than any other man in the world, sat on the floor and commenced the story. Jesus' eyes were round as melons as the first word was spoken.

"Old Jacob had twelve sons. Joseph was next to the youngest and his daddy loved him very much. His brothers were envious because their father seemed partial to little Joe."

As always, Jesus would interrupt with childish concern for the eleven older siblings, "Did he really like Joseph more than the others?"

The pat answer was always, "Probably not. I imagine that little Joe was just a more loving and obedient son than the others. And daddies can't help noticing that. The more lovable you are, the more love you get."

"Go on, father," said Jesus, smiling at the thought.

"Well, little Joe kept having dreams about great things he was going to do. When Rachel heard about them, she encouraged him, telling him how very proud she was. But, one day he made a mistake and told his brothers. They were angry with him."

"Because Jacob had given little Joe a long-sleeve coat with bright colors of red and green and yellow and blue!" said Jesus, with the usual excitement in his face. "Right, dad?"

"That's exactly right."

"And they threw him in a pit and tore up his long-sleeve coat!"

"But it wasn't long until some merchants on their way to Egypt came by and . . . ."

"They sold him to the merchants and put goat's blood on the pieces of the coat and told their daddy that an animal had killed little Joe," said Jesus, as He filled in

57

the lines of the story.

"Jacob's heart was broken. He did not know that little Joe had been taken to Egypt where he became a slave to a servant of the king. Joseph was strong and handsome and very bright. Potiphar, the king's servant, liked him at once. He liked him so much that he put him in charge of all his house. Because young Joe was polite, always bowing before his master."

"Then what happened?" asked Jesus, wanting to hear everything again.

"It was then that the worst thing that could happen . . . did happen. He was accused by his master's wife of flirting with her. Of course, he had done no such thing. But Potiphar was so mad that he threw young Joe into the prison where he stayed two whole years."

"Until the butler and the baker of the king were put in prison with him?" Jesus said, as if wanting to be assured that He was right.

"They both had dreams about what might happen to them. When they told their dreams to Joseph, he knew exactly what they meant. Later, after the butler was set free, the king himself had a dream and he was very upset because the wisest men in Egypt could not explain it!"

"And the butler remembered Joseph!"

"Right again. When the king heard about how smart young Joe was, he called for him to explain his dreams."

"There will be seven years of plenty, then seven years of nothing!" said Jesus, as He bolted upright on the mat.

"So Pharaoh knew that he needed help and the best man would have to be . . . ."

"Joseph!" shouted Jesus, clapping his hands for joy.

"And why did this happen to young Joe?"

"Because he was a good man. He always did what was right. And God knew there would be a famine and that Israel would need food. Joseph was made governor so that God could save us from starving."

"You've got it!"

"Daddy, I know that your father named you for young Joe. You are a good man, too. Did you have a long-sleeve coat of many colors?"

"No, I never did. But I want you to have one because I want you to grow up strong and handsome and bright. I want you to be a gentleman who will do the right thing no matter what happens."

With eyes full of excitement, Jesus hugged everybody in the room. "I am the only boy in Nazareth with a brand new long-sleeve coat! What a wonderful birthday."

"I remember how happy you were on your fourth birthday," said his mother. "Do you remember what your daddy gave you then?"

"Sure I do. I've still got that little donkey and I'll keep it always."

What he had gotten was not a real donkey. No

way could the family have afforded that. Rather, Joseph had gone back to the shop night after night to shape and carve a rocking horse out of seasoned oak logs. With all the pride of the master artisan, the carpenter had whittled and chiseled and planed until the little animal was a real work of art to be admired by all.

"Boy, do I remember that night! I jumped on it and wore myself out bouncing to and fro. You know, on that little donkey I felt just like a king!"

Joseph and Mary turned and looked at each other, their eyes speaking of the wonder in their hearts. They were thinking the same thing. Had not the prophet said something like that?

The following day Joseph went to the synagogue to look for the passage and found it in the ancient prophecy of Zechariah, "Rejoice greatly, O daughter of Zion; shout, O daughter of Jerusalem: behold, thy king cometh unto thee: he is just and having salvation; lowly, and riding on a donkey."

Their hearts were filled with wonder, wonder as deep and mysterious as when the angel first appeared to them.

"What does Jehovah God have planned for our boy?" said Mary, more to herself than to Joseph.

After a long interval of silence, during which time they were both deep in their own thoughts, Joseph replied, "God will let us know when He is ready. Just got to be something terribly important!"

The following morning Mary handed Jesus his sack breakfast and He left for the synagogue where he had gone every morning, six days a week, since He was five.

At age five, Jewish boys started schooling with the religious instructors in the local synagogue. They would study daily until noon at what was called "The House of the Book." Their studies would be mainly from the Torah, the books of the Law. At age ten, they advanced to "The House of Learning" where the curriculum would be enlarged. From this moment until their formal schooling ended at eighteen, boys learned the oral law. It was called oral because it had not been written in Jesus' time. Much later it was brought together and written in the Mishnah.

Without question, Jesus was growing in stature and in wisdom with God. Everyone who met the boy knew it, but especially his parents. Most parents think their kids are the smartest and the cutest in town. That is natural. With Jesus, however, it was different.

The House of Learning was to be a new experience. As the varied fathers of the faith added their interpretation, the Torah became much more complicated. It seemed to Jesus that there were an awful lot of things to remember and some of them seemed like nit-picking. Often asked questions about the Law, the growing children were free to make personal comments and ask questions themselves as long as they remained reverent.

The class had hardly started one morning when Jesus asked permission to speak. "Day before yesterday I was in the village where Orthiel lives and some of our kids were throwing stones and spitting at his house."

Now Orthiel was the local tax collector. Nobody liked these people. They were considered traitors to their country because they were always in the despised employ of Rome. If Jews were going to pay tax it should go to the temple, not to the pagan government of Rome. And also, every Jew knew that these people were robbers, taking money by extortion. They were allowed by the government to keep whatever they could collect over and above the set amount for Rome. So they filled their pockets and lived in the finest homes and there was little the people could do about it. Except for one thing. They could teach their kids to hate the tax collector, to rock his house and spit on him if they had the chance.

"Teacher, do you think that is the right thing to do?" asked little Jesus.

The instructor looked a little embarrassed and even more angry that such a thing could be brought up in class. After a moment, he straightened his shoulders and cleared his throat. "My boy," he replied, "these are matters for the elders to decide. When you are older you will understand these things." And with that he moved on to weightier matters.

The remainder of the day was lost for Jesus. He did not learn a thing that day, nor did He recall anything the teacher said except the evasion of his question which was really bugging him.

Joseph was smarter than the teachers at school anyway, thought Jesus. So, when dad returned from work that evening, he was confronted with the unhappy experience at synagogue that morning.

"Did I do something wrong, daddy?" asked his thoughtful son. "Should not the teacher have answered my question? Why do the neighborhood kids treat Orthiel this way? The other day I saw one of them spelling bad words on the side of his fence."

The tired carpenter sat down heavily in the corner of the room. He explained to Jesus why his neighbors hated the tax collectors. "These guys are the most unpopular people in every town," he pointed out. "Nobody ever invites them to be a part of anything. They are outcasts. If anyone gives them the time of day, he risks having his friends turn on him."

"That's not right!" The small boy spoke like someone with authority and Joseph chuckled under his breath.

"You are right, my son. I was only telling you *why* the kids do what they do. The problem starts at home. We claim to be God's chosen people, but there is so much hate in Israel. And we actually teach our children that the thing to do is to hate our enemies. We know why they hate, but that does not make it right."

There was silence. Joseph continued, "Have either I or your mother ever told you to throw stones?"

"You would never do that, daddy. You are the best man I know. Why, you would even stop and help

Orthiel if he fell in a ditch, wouldn't you?"

"My boy, even the Samaritans would do that!"

The conversation ended. The puzzled boy appeared a little more at ease. It was hard even then to get it off his mind. Maybe Orthiel didn't know he was doing wrong. If he has no friends and is unacceptable at synagogue, he probably doesn't know how to be any different. At least, that's the way the boy reasoned with himself.

Life seemed so out of kilter. Everybody was running at break neck speed. Nobody cared about anyone except himself. People wouldn't speak to a tax collector. There were some ladies over at Magdala that people were always saying bad things about. Just about everyone was afraid of the lepers even though they wouldn't hurt a fly. And the blind beggars? Most people didn't even notice them. Just passed on by. Everyone was suspicious of everyone else. The whole village was scared to death that someone would touch some person considered unclean. And why did people hate the Samaritans just because they were of a different race?

These and a thousand other things He saw around him kept annoying this strangely sensitive lad. Why couldn't people get along? Wouldn't it be better to treat each other nicely, even our enemies? If we loved one another, there wouldn't be any enemies left to hate.

Jesus wished He could talk to his grandfather

Jacob again. Jacob was Joseph's father who had died when Jesus was eight years old. He was a kind and gentle man who used to take his grandchildren for long walks in the evening. They would watch the birds, sometimes stopping to talk about them. Within a short time he had taught each child how to recognize the habits of each species and even to call them by their names. On one occasion, Jacob had taken Jesus by himself far out into the unsettled areas where there were wild animals. The wild goats were much like those in the courtyard at home except they were not at all friendly.

The one thing the children shied away from were the snakes. Grandfather tried to make them understand that serpents were more afraid of people than most folks believed. With rare exception, they wouldn't bother boys and girls unless the children teased them. Jesus would invariably think of the first snake mentioned in the Torah. That serpent wasn't very nice at all!

Jacob and the grandchildren also loved the flowers. The blue flax, from which linen cloth was made, was abundant. Of course, the red poppy, used to relieve extreme pain, was gorgeous. The lilies which showed off their lovely pink and violet faces, in random places like the cornfields, were a special delight. Then there was the dark yellow mustard with its proverbial small seed. The children never wanted to leave the lush fields of flowers to return to the drab sights of the village. But grandpa would always get them home before their parents grew concerned about them.

Only once did Jacob return with Jesus later than Mary would permit. That was the afternoon when the conversation turned toward Amos. No one had ever mentioned Amos that Jesus could remember. But Joseph had a much younger brother whom none of the family had heard from for almost nine years. Amos had gotten into bad company and picked up some bad habits. He wouldn't work, yet he never lacked for money. Jacob feared the worst, but whenever the boy was questioned about it, he burst into a tantrum and insisted that it was nobody's business. One morning it was discovered that Amos had left during the night and taken with him some of the family's savings.

Jacob and Joseph searched every nook and cranny in an effort to locate him. It soon became obvious that the much loved son and brother did not want to be found.

"Nobody knows how much I miss him," said Jacob with reddened eyes. "How I wish he would come home."

"You are not mad at him then?" asked Jesus.

"Mad? No. Disappointed? Yes. My dreams for him were so big. Sure I am hurt like any father would be, but I have never been mad."

With an unsure look on his face, Jacob's grandson replied hopefully, "You wouldn't even fuss at him. Right?"

"Fuss at him? We would be so glad to see him that he would be treated like he had never been away. The family would have the biggest party you ever saw. Obed, his older brother, says he won't forgive him, but he ought to be ashamed. Amos knows I love him and that I look down the lane every night in hopes he will be coming."

Jacob died later that year and never had the joy of having his son back home. Many more years passed and none of the kin heard anything about him nor did they mention his name. And Jesus lay awake many nights just imagining what it might have been like if Amos had come home.

CHAPTER THREE

Folks were always moving in and out of town. When a new family, from the not too distant neighborhood of Exaloth, relocated in Nazareth, a local carpenter was hired to oversee the construction of their house. It was an exciting day for Joseph because most of his work was done on small things which could be done inside the shop. This would be a challenge. It was not that he had never built a house before. He had done so a number of times. But it would be a welcome break from the repetitious chores which he could do with his eyes shut.

Day laborers would need to be found, but that would not present a problem since every morning there were dozens of jobless men in town waiting for someone to hire them. These were usually men who had no particular skills, men with strong arms and backs which gave them an edge on being hired when there were jobs requiring more brawn than brains. Some were somewhat shiftless, feeling no particular disappointment if they were overlooked. But others, and these the experienced craftsmen of the town could pick out quite easily, were eager for work since there were families to feed and rent to pay. The anxiety in their eyes and the aggressive way in which they clamored for attention usually gave them away.

Jesus was too young to begin his formal apprenticeship, but often, after morning school, he was in

Leslie H. Woodson

the shop where He watched his father sweat over the small stuff on the workbench.

Something about the place, smelling of seasoned trees, intrigued and fascinated the small boy. It was great fun to play with the wood shavings on the floor, his little mind filled with visions of beautiful things He was building. And the aroma of the logs, as Joseph worked them down to flat planks or shaped turnings, was sweeter than the most prized perfume. At school, in the synagogue during the mornings, He would wish that He were in the shop. Like practically every boy in the group, there was always something far more interesting calling him from outside the windows of the synagogue. Many a time the teacher had to bring him back to attention because He was dreaming of a place He would rather be. After all, any place was better than a school room! Of course, other than hold a piece of timber for his dad or hand him a tool so that he would not have to get up from his three-legged stool, little Jesus did nothing but have fun. And He had a lot of that. Joseph saw to it that his much loved son had every opportunity to remain a child as long as possible.

Being no different than any other growing boy, there was no end to the probing questions asked of his father. Every facet of the shop was like a make-believe world. Filled with wonder, hours were spent visualizing what could be done with the many crude tools hanging on the shop walls. When a customer came in to pick up an order or discuss plans for a piece of furniture which his

70

wife wanted, Jesus was all ears.

"Daddy," he asked, as one of the customers left the shop with a new plow handle under his arm, "how can that man use a plow handle without a plow?"

Joseph laughed, patting his boy on the head as he squatted down to explain. "He already has a plow. One of his boys, too anxious to get his work done so He could go out and play, broke the old handle out of it the other day and I have just made one to replace it. It should be as good as new now."

While Joseph never lost patience with his querulous son, there were times when the constant chatter slowed down his progress. Just when the aging carpenter was at the point of gathering his wits for a compound angle cut, Jesus would shatter his concentration. Nevertheless, he would often stop what he was doing to explain how to put a stringer into a table leg or plane two boards so that no light could be seen in the joint when they were put together. Holding the big hammer in his strong hand, he would explain how one could get the proper swing and more accurately force the nail into the wood by holding the handle as far away from the head as possible. And the bow saw? "Push it forward, letting the weight of the blade do its own cutting," he would explain. "Never bear down on the cutting stroke. If the blade is sharp, it will do its work with very little pressure." The fascination never ended. And it was not all on one side, either. Joseph was as fascinated with the expressions on Jesus' face as Jesus was enchanted with the whole business of

71

seeing the wonderful things which his father could make.

On the day when the stranger from Exaloth, haggling for a while over the cost, struck a deal for the building of his house, Jesus could hardly wait for the man to leave. Not until now was He old enough to be interested in the houses his father had built, but the thought of constructing a big house for somebody to live in was suddenly the most exciting thing in the world. Images of joy and pride, in so grand a thing, filled his thoughts as He anticipated helping with the project.

"Where are you going to build the house, daddy?" He asked, his eyes wide with wonder.

"Over on Yehosef Alley," answered his father. "Not far from the tiny house where the old woman with the wrinkled parchment skin lives. Remember? You asked me about her not long ago."

"Is it a big house, dad? Will it have a room on top? With steps on the outside?"

"No," replied Joseph, "The house will be just one room, nothing fancy. I have never built a house with a stairway. But it will be nice enough for Saller and his family. There are only four of them. They will do fine in one room."

"That's a funny name, Saller." Reaching down, chuckling to himself as he thought of so silly sounding a name, Jesus picked up a small rock and threw it into the distance, watching its gradual descent to the ground.

"Not really," laughed his father. "You just never

heard it before. When you are as old as I am you will know a lot of people with strange sounding names. There used to be some Sallers here in the valley, big family of eight children, but they moved away long before you were born. Have no idea what ever happened to them. Probably related to the man we just talked to today."

The questions went on and on that afternoon. At quitting time, Joseph was worn out, not from the work, but from the thorough investigation!

Three weeks passed and the plans were complete. Designing the house had been rather simple, but good carpenters never began any construction project until it had been thoroughly thought through. The materials had arrived and were neatly stacked outside the shop wall. Some of the poles, which would be used for supports and exposed to the weather, were cedar logs brought all the way from Lebanon. Jesus liked the smell of the cedar logs, sitting atop the pile for a long time just sniffing and feeling the rough bark, peeling it back with his fingers.

It was time to get started. Joseph was noticeably anxious because he loved the out-of-doors and this would get him out of the stuffy shop into the warm sunshine. He had already been out to the hillsides where he selected the young trees, swung his ax, cut them down and carried them home on his shoulder, the larger ones being pulled along by his little donkey. A carpenter had to do it all by hand since there were no saw-mills where one could buy ready made lumber. Once on the building site, the rough trees had to be skinned of their bark and squared, some even flattened into the desired shape needed for the job. It was a rugged life and carpenters, as well as farmers, were bronzed from the hot sun, weather-beaten and physically at their best. They had to be.

Jesus admired his daddy's powerful body. Stripped to the waist, arm and back muscles bulging under the weight of the logs, sweating like an ox, Joseph did not notice his little son flexing his own biceps, wondering if they would ever look like his father's.

First, the ground had to be prepared. It would have to be carefully leveled and compacted with plenty of rocks so the structure would have a firm underpinning. Some areas around Nazareth were so rocky that huge sledges had to be used to break up the more defiant stones sticking through the soil. Others were so sandy that rocks had to be hauled in to stiffen the sandy ground.

As the work got under way, Joseph pulled a small ragged looking scroll from his girdle where it had been tucked away until he needed it. On it he had drawn a rough sketch of what the finished house would look like, its dimensions and openings, noting precisely where the cross-beams would be placed. Sitting on a rock which jutted from the ground, he explained it to young Jesus who soaked up every word, pointing several times to some mark on the scroll and asking what it meant.

"See that hump in the ground?" The master carpenter pointed to a high spot right where the house would be put up. It was easy to see that no one could live in a house with such a bump in the floor!

"Before anything else is done," he continued, "that hump has got to go. Then, if there are any low spots, they have to be filled and tamped hard. You can't build a house on a hump or in a hole."

Staring at the uneven ground, the boy asked, "That sure looks like a lot of work. Isn't that hard to do, daddy?"

"Well, yes. It's hard work to build a house. Takes a lot of time and energy. Anything you do, if it is done right, takes a lot of time and energy. But a good house is worth all the hard work you have to put into it. After all, somebody is going to live in it for a long time.

"And remember, son," continued the carpenter, "If you ever build a house for someone, don't try to build it unless the ground is solid, like a rock. That is probably the most important thing of all. If you build on the sand, the heavy rains will come and wash away the house and everything in it. All your work will have been for naught."

Little Jesus, wide-eyed with excitement, kicked at the soil beneath his feet and asked, "What does *naught* mean?"

Joseph laughed his hearty laugh. "It means that all your work would have been for nothing. Better not to build a house unless the ground is first carefully selected and then properly prepared. Otherwise, it will just fall down."

"That would be awful, daddy! We would never build a house for naught," insisted Jesus, emphasizing the *we*.

"Indeed, it would. Can't think of anything much worse than to lose your house to the wind and rains just because you didn't get the foundation right. Most people around here put their life savings into their houses. They can't afford to lose them. I knew a man a long time ago who did that very thing. Lost everything he had. This is a very important lesson, my boy. Don't forget what I have told you."

And Jesus never did.

After two or three days the earth had been flattened and rocks had been worked into the soil so that the structure could rest on the more rocky substratum beneath the surface. Next came the walls which were made of flat field stones. This was not a carpenter's speciality, though it was not outside Joseph's expertise to supervise the laying of the white rocks. The walls of such a village house did not have to be perfect. Several of the non-skilled men, with whom he had contracted, men anxiously waiting in the village each morning to be hired, got the walls up to his satisfaction without too much hassle. One opening had been left for an entrance and several small slits were provided along the top of the walls to let out the smoke from a heating stove and provide a bit of light and fresh air. Joseph, of course, laid out the openings and placed the door frame, which had been made in the shop, in its appointed place.

Finally, it was time for the roof. The tops of

village houses, where the common folk lived, were flat, or nearly so. They were constructed of branches from trees laid across the wood rafters. Smaller and more pliable limbs were laced into the branches and a thick layer of clay, mixed with straw and twigs, was meticulously worked into the vacant spaces. When the sun came out the clay dried hard and, resisting the intrusions of the weather, provided a durable roof. The same laborers, who smeared and packed the clay on the roof, returned to cover the walls with a similar though thinner coating.

Watching, as the day laborers worked the clay into the roof with their sticky fingers, Jesus inquired of his father whether the roof might leak. It was a reasonable question.

"Not often if it is done right," replied Joseph. "Although it happens very seldom, there are times when it rains a great deal and some of the clay is washed thin. Or the hot sun may crack it following a soaking rainstorm. And too, a relentless wind might break it at the corners."

"Can it be fixed?" asked his son. Without waiting for a reply, the boy, intrigued by all He was learning, added, "I guess you just have to put on a new roof."

"Oh no, most anything can be fixed. The owner has to get up there occasionally and roll the clay, maybe even cramming a little clay back into the cracks. Of course, if worse comes to worse, it is pretty easy to cut a hole in the thatch and fill it in with new material. But you don't have to have a new roof."

Fascinated by it all, Jesus was repairing the roof

right then and there in his little mind. Many years later, He would recall these words of his father as He watched four men chop a hole in the top of a house to gain entrance. So far the boy had done none of the actual labor, but it was all becoming second nature to him. He had no misgivings about whether He could do these things which the carpenters were doing. Jesus was sure that He could. All He needed was a chance.

The new neighbor from Exaloth moved in with his son and two daughters, their mother having died less than three years after the birth of her son, the youngest of the three. Saller was pleased with the builder's craftsmanship and told him so. "May the blessings of the God of Israel be upon you for being an honorable man," said Saller, as he happily surveyed his new home. "And may the God of Abraham, Isaac, and Jacob protect this house from evil," replied Joseph. A friendship was soon to develop between the two families that would endure through the years.

It was late one summer afternoon when Jesus, playing in the yard with his new friend, was startled by what sounded like a heated argument coming from inside the house. This was not the first time He had observed the sisters bickering, but it was all so unlike his own home that He could not understand why families could not get along. The shrill screaming was unlike anything He had heard before.

"Father," Marty was saying, "I have had it with her! Why did the Lord have to give me a sister like this?

What must He have been thinking?"

"Calm down, Marty. You are insulting the Lord. We've been through this a dozen times," answered Saller, reaching out and laying a firm hand on his older daughter's shoulder.

"And it never does any good! We have guests coming for supper and Maria hasn't turned her hand to do a thing. It's always this way. I have meat burning in the courtyard oven and a hundred things to do in here and she just sits there. Since mother died, your youngest daughter won't get off her duff!"

"She's still very young, Marty," explained Saller. "She still misses her mama. We all do. She'll come around in time. Your patience could use a little encouragement."

"How much time is it going to take? Mom's been gone nearly five years. I miss her, too. Maria could help us all if she would stop feeling sorry for herself and *do* something. All she wants to do is sit around and dream about the past."

"Yes, dear, you're right but . . . ."

"Stop defending her, father. Why must you pamper her?" demanded Marty, stamping her bare foot on the earthen floor. "Maria knows that she's your pet. Should she ever marry she won't know how to cook or sew or keep house. Look at the mess in here. Do you think for a minute that she might sweep the floor? Of course not!"

Maria, who had been lying half asleep on her mat, suddenly sprang up and shouted at her older sister, "Why should I sweep the dirt off the dirt floor? Will that make it cleaner?" At that, Marty angrily flung her dust cloth, Mary ducking her head to avoid the dirty rag.

"Girls!" yelled Saller, trying to be heard above the loud clatter, "You are sisters. Have you forgotten that? Maria, what do you sit and think about when Marty needs your help? You really ought to give your sister a hand. It wouldn't hurt you, you know. Might even help get your mind off your troubles."

"I think most about mama and I talk to God about her."

"That's fine, but you know momma would want you to help Marty."

"She picks on me, dad. Marty's a brat and a nag. She cares more about this stupid house and cupboard than she cares about either of us! I just want you to make her leave me alone."

Jesus had heard all He wanted to hear and, since there was every reason to believe that the argument was far from over, He and Flax left for home.

It would not be the last time the son of Joseph was to hear such arguments in Saller's house. The girls were so different in temperament that there was little chance the time would come when tempers would not flare. It all became so irritating to Jesus that He began to insist that his friend, Marty's and Maria's little brother, come to his house to play where the atmosphere was not so charged.

The two boys were about the same age, Jesus only slightly older, and they soon grew very fond of one another. However, as fate would have it, the Sallers lived in the house Joseph had built for them less than four years when a better job opened up farther south. On the day they left, Saller insisted that Joseph bring the children and come to visit. "We have never had such wonderful neighbors before," said Saller. And we do not want our friendship to end just because we are moving away. My whole family will be disappointed if you do not come."

The Saller family would be moving to a village on the eastern slopes of the Mount of Olives near Jerusalem. Although it would not be impossible, such a trip was a long stretch. And Joseph knew that such a trip would not be likely to happen unless they could get together some year at the Feast of Unleavened Bread.

"Maybe one year when we come to Passover," said Jesus, a remark aimed more directly at his young friend than at the older Saller, "dad will let me get over to Bethany to see you."

The two boys hugged one another as did Joseph and Saller. Everyone, including the older sisters, who had come to think of Joseph's wife as their adopted mother, were deeply moved by the farewells.

As the ox cart carrying the family's belongings moved off into the distance, the sisters could be heard quarreling over something of no importance. Young Jesus, choked with emotion over seeing his friend leave, cleared his throat to disguise his red and watery eyes. "See you later Lazarus," He called out, wiping the sleeve of his tunic across his tear-streaked face.

81

The son of Joseph had found his trade early. Every Jewish boy was expected to enter one of the trades because it was considered an unwelcome disgrace to have an indolent son. Quite often, it was the case that boys, following in their father's footsteps, continued in the same occupation. That was not hard to understand since a child would naturally know more about the business engaged in by his father than any other trade. It was just the natural thing to do. Joseph, who had spent all his life working with wood, had felt confident that *all* his boys would be carpenters.

There were many kinds of trades. Everything from stone cutters, masons, wood workers, sculptors, dyers and basket weavers to tanners and dung collectors. But for the elder son of Joseph, nothing was more interesting and satisfying than working with wood. Other fields of endeavor had never held the least interest for him. But, with the smell of wood, He was quite at home. The native trees were sycamore, olive, and oak. Olive trees were abundant and He especially liked their gnarled old trunks with their pronounced brown and tan grain. Cedar and Cypress were sometimes found in the wood shop, but these woods were not as plentiful since they were most often imported from areas other than Palestine.

A carpenter's formal apprenticeship did not come before the age of fifteen, but the less formal part began much earlier. Days passed into months and months into years as the young wood worker learned his trade. There was so much to discover. So many tools that Joseph used so adeptly had to be mastered. Anyone could swing an ax if he had the strength, but the adz was a different matter. And the iron saw, the bow drill, the chisel, the spoke shave, the plane – they all required dexterity and skill.

Like every growing lad in the world, Jesus visualized himself wearing the master craftsman's apron, taking charge of the shop, and doing all the things his father did. He even planned to be better at the trade than Joseph had been. He would build the best construction parts, the best farm tool handles, the best winnowing forks and threshing boards, and the best kitchen utensils to be found anywhere in Israel. No one would surpass him in the perfect fit of the beams, doors, and frames. And no one would even think about building a better table or chair than He. Of that He was certain.

Life for Jesus was not all work, however, lest we think of him as always an adult and never a kid. His childhood was as normal as any other child in the austere world of the Hebrew people. Cousin John was the one who never had any fun. The son of a priest, he never played a game in his life. John was so serious that he could never afford to let his guard down for fear someone might think he was insincere. Not Jesus. He had as much fun as anyone in Nazareth.

Most of the children played a form of hopscotch. They also played a little game in which they would bounce a ball, trying to pick up as many small rocks as they could before the ball hit the ground. Whoever picked up the most was the winner. It was the kind of fun thing that could keep children busy for hours on a rainy day.

When the weather was bad and the chores were finished, the older folks played an indoor game similar to the later game of chess. As an older boy, this was a favorite with Jesus. It was played with a marked board and a number of stones which were alternately moved into position by competing players. While it was actually an adult game, the children enjoyed watching the row created by the amicable arguments and rousing accusations of cheating.

The children also played a form of ball, a fast moving game which had been introduced into Jewry by the Greeks and Romans. This was a summer sport in which both boys and girls were sometimes engaged. Usually, the girls refrained from getting involved since the boys tended to get too rough. Jesus was sorry when the girls refused to play, but there were not always enough guys to get up a good game. When enough fellows could be found, it was a different story. Then Jesus was glad for the girls to sit on the sidelines. The rougher the fray, the better He liked it and his teammates never felt surer of themselves than when He was playing.

Exactly how they organized the game of ball, or what the rules were, we do not know. We can be sure, however, that there were guidelines and that the object of the game was to do something better with the ball than any other competitor. Jesus literally loved the game when He could find the time to be involved, which was not often because after-school hours were pretty filled with chores.

One morning the teacher at synagogue school gave his students a short recess period. That did not happen with any regularity, but the rigors of learning the Torah that day had been particularly demanding. Pairing off into two groups, the children went at a game of ball with such enthusiasm that they momentarily forgot the difficult morning altogether. That evening when Jesus came to supper, He shared with the family some of the strategies of the morning's play.

"Well," exclaimed little brother Simon, eyes sparkling with excitement and having no interest in the strategy stuff, "who won?"

Throwing back his head with an embarrassed laugh, Jesus replied, "They beat us bad!"

Mary felt a strange sensation rush through her body as if she had been shocked. Among the secrets she had pondered in her heart, from the day the angel Gabriel had talked with her, was the promise: "You shall conceive in your womb, and bring forth a son, and shall call his name Jesus. He shall be great, and shall be called the Son of the Highest: and the Lord God shall give unto him the throne of his father David: and he shall reign over the house of Jacob forever; and of his kingdom there shall be no end."

"I am confused," she thought to herself. "He is to reign over the kingdom of David, and He can't even win a ball game?"

85

Had it been a mistake? Had she misunderstood Gabriel? It was all so clear at the time. Does God change His mind? Or was it all a dream?

These were among the mixed thoughts which raced through Mary's mind. And it was not the first time. She thought about it everyday. At night it kept her awake.

"Maybe I am just too anxious," she mused. "After all, He is still just a boy. We have no right to dictate to God how or when He must do what He has promised. I must learn to be more patient. But it is so hard."

There were other games which the smaller children liked to play, noncompetitive things like mimicking the activities of their stuffy parents and grown up neighbors. They pretended to be merchants bartering off to one another their toys and fragments of flat bread and cake which their mothers had baked. Sometimes they played at doctor and patient, the patient plastering his body with white paste to look like leprosy. They played house with the father coming home from work in the fields to a simple supper prepared by his wife. And, of course, the little girls had dolls which they pretended were real babies.

Probably the games most often witnessed by the adults were those of weddings and funerals. While moms shopped in the marketplace, their children would pretend one of them was getting married. They would dress up in colorful rags and parade through the streets dancing and singing and making noises like flutes and harps.

And they were really good at make-believe funerals. More modern children are not exposed to the realities of death as were the boys and girls of an earlier age. Then people died at home in the midst of terrible pain and emotional trauma. Someone would decide on which child would be the corpse, then he would be carried in procession through the lanes. His stretcher would be made of small limbs and sticks and he would be covered with whatever cast off clothes could be found. There was crying and wailing, pulling hair and beating on chests, pouring dirt on heads and chanting dirges as the children shed their sandals and ran barefoot behind the stretcher.

Jesus never got into the wedding and funeral thing. Just never seemed like something suitable for play. But often He watched and it always reminded him of how men and women, as well as children, spend their days playing with sacred things as if they are not all that important.

The game which Jesus recalled most vividly was that of playing synagogue. Everybody would dress up in his best tunic (if he could sneak it out of the house), walk very erect and slowly with the most rigid expression, and attend the make-believe synagogue. One of the children would act the role of the president and lead the group through the recitation of the proper scriptures, reading prayers with their make-shift phylacteries strapped to their foreheads. Some of them thought the phylacteries which their fathers and older brothers wore, at morning prayers, were a little bit silly. But religion was a funny thing anyway and it was all a part of the game.

Jesus would usually give the short lesson on some scripture passage because He never seemed to mind and, even as a small lad, always found a lot of words to use. Then the congregation would break up and the children would walk home, still rigid and somber. No one so much as smiled during the game – that was part of the objective – but when it was over, they would explode with wild laughter.

Days passed into weeks, weeks into months, and months into years. Mary stayed so busy that she did not notice how fast the days were flying by except that her children were growing up so quickly. Jesus, her first-born, was becoming what Mary called proudly, "My Little Man."

It was early spring, a beautiful time of the year in Israel. The almond trees had bloomed in all their lavish beauty, the flax had been harvested, and the barley fields were nearly ready. It was a busy time for the farmer.

Nothing ever made Jesus feel nearer to Jehovah God than when He had the opportunity to walk the footpaths of the grain fields at the edge of the residential district. His farmer neighbors were hard workers. As soon as the first rains had fallen in Tishri, or early October, they were out plowing with their oxen and scattering seed. The interesting thing, however, was that, after the initial plowing, the farmers had nothing much left to do until harvest. They just sat back and watched the seed grow. Of course, they prayed a lot that the weather would be in their favor.

Being a carpenter meant that Jesus was not an expert at farming, but He did observe that the harvest was more plentiful in some spots than in others. One did not have to be an agricultural progeny to see that. When He was still quite small, one of his neighbors, who cultivated a small parcel of land, pointed out the reason.

"See this bare spot right through the middle of the grain field?" said the farmer, gesturing toward the footpath.

When Jesus nodded his head, the farmer went on.

"The reason there is nothing growing is not that it was not sown. When seed is broadcast, it falls on just about everything. No, the reason there is no growth is because the people from the village use this as a short-cut and they trample down the wheat or barley before it has a chance."

The boy nodded again as if that were pretty easy to understand.

"Now look," said the neighbor. "Look at this thin spot here. Very poor chance of harvesting anything to speak of in this place. See how shallow the soil is? See that rocky layer just inches under the ground? No wonder we have a thin spot. The seed can't get any root down. So when the sun comes out, it withers away."

Young Jesus smiled as if He had learned something new.

"Come here, son. Here's another problem. See those weeds? And look at that patch of thorny stuff.

Guess what?"

This time Jesus was ahead of the farmer. With a sparkle in his eye, He said, "Oh, I know about weeds. Dad already told me how they choke out everything as if they own the place."

"Right," exclaimed the farmer. "You are a bright boy. The reason the rest of my field looks good and tall is because the soil is deep and the thorns are absent and nobody walks on it! This part will bring me a lot of shekels. The rest is of little value to me."

That night Jesus told Mary where He had been and how Reuben told him a lot of stuff about farming.

"You know," announced boy Jesus, "I'm sure I'll be a carpenter, but if I do not become a carpenter like dad, it would be fun to be a farmer."

James noticed that his older brother was in deep thought the rest of the evening. He was unusually quiet. There was no way to guess what He was thinking, but it was not hard to see that something important was on his mind.

"What's on your mind, brother," asked James, visibly interested in whatever it was that was bothering him.

"There's no way you could ever imagine all the things that keep going through my head."

The days were jammed full of things to do and things to learn. Everyone else had been asleep for hours when the gallicinium sounded the third watch of the night. Jesus was growing in stature and wisdom and sleeping seemed like a waste of time for him who couldn't wait for morning so He could learn something else.

CHAPTER FOUR

When Jesus was eight days old, the priest had taken him across his knees and circumcised him in a religious ceremony sacred to the Jews since the time of Abraham. The ritual would be forever a sign of the covenant which Jehovah had made with the patriarch. The child screamed with pain as the sharp stone cut into his flesh. And the red serum which dripped onto the priest's apron was red blood – human blood.

Had a modern laboratory technician examined those drippings, he would have found the same substances and combinations which characterize all human blood. It could have been typed and labeled without any question as to its genuineness. And, when the thorns pricked his brow and the lance ruptured his side, the same results would have been discovered had a similar examination been made on anyone else.

Looking at the baby Jesus, no one would have seen a halo about his head. It may have been there, but neither the shepherds nor the wise men from the east saw it. That is because He was a flesh and blood human being as much as they themselves.

It was not what He looked like that inspired them. It was the singing angels in the field and the gleaming star in the sky which made them certain about who this child really was. Otherwise, He looked like any other baby.

And Jesus was no child prodigy either.

Leslie H. Woodson

The infant son of Mary had trouble for a few days getting his eyes focused and accustomed to the sights around him. When He was hungry or wet, He cried, and when the street-hawkers came through selling their wares, He invariably stirred in his basket-sleeper and became fretful on being disturbed.

Bright colors attracted him earlier than anything else and Mary was always amused when her baby's eyes grew big with wonder. The excitement on his face, as He noticed the colorful garments of children who came to the home, made his mother's heart burst with pride.

He learned to walk at the usual age and, being a male child, was a little slow about learning to keep his pants dry.

Shortly before his eight month birthday, Mary noted that He was more fretful than customary. He was a playful infant except when not feeling well. And that was not often. But, this morning, He was not himself. The continual crying and the refusal to be pacified . . . it was too much for a young mother and it was beginning to get on her nerves.

Pacing back and forth in the tiny room, Mary was unable to do anything which helped. If the weather had not been so cold outside, she would have taken the baby to the shop to seek Joseph's advice. Being a new mother with her first baby, every day was a new adventure. And she was growing uneasy for fear her little boy was sick.

A larger than usual amount of saliva had gathered on his chin and its source seemed to be without restraint.

94

The young mother was about to panic. She remembered having seen a child some years before who, during a seizure probably induced by a demon, had acted much like her baby boy. There was a noticeable difference, however. The secretion on the other child's chin was a sort of white foam as though it had been churned by the violent spasm through which the child was passing.

It worried her for a while until a sudden thought occurred. Why had she not thought of it sooner? Sure enough, as she ran her index finger around the inside of Jesus' mouth, she felt the sharp edge of an object which was clearly causing all the trouble. Pulling down his lower lip, she saw the crown of a pearl which had just ruptured the baby's pink gums.

It was Jesus' first tooth! And she ran all the way to the wood shop with the baby in her arms, forgetting about the weather, to show his daddy. Her mother's heart ached to think little Jesus had suffered so much pain when a little terebinth on his gum would have given relief. It was a mistake she would not make again.

The day Mary's boy took his first step was a day to be remembered. For several weeks, he had been pulling up at the edge of the work table where Mary did most of her meal preparation. Invariably, He would laugh at himself when the big chore was complete and He stood, rocking back and forth to keep his balance, holding on for dear life.

Often the baby fell in making the effort and cried

when his mouth struck the corner of the table and bled. His mother always offered her sympathy as she picked up her little one and snuggled him close with unintelligible, sweet nothings understood only by the two of them.

Elizabeth, Mary's cousin, had come from Ein Karem to spend a few days that year. Little John was walking about the room when his cousin, who was six months his junior, inspired by the antics of his kinsman, pulled straightway up at the table and walked right to Elizabeth with the steady foot of a veteran soldier. At least, that was the way the proud mother described the event when telling her friends. And none of them even thought of questioning her about it.

As Mary watched her boy develop, she could almost see him grow from week to week. Each day Jesus learned something new. The first understandable word that He spoke was *abba*, the Aramaic word for papa. Joseph, refusing to admit that such a word was easy to pronounce, often bragged about Jesus' choice. It made him very proud. Like Mary, he never tired telling people it was he whom his little son recognized first.

"No question about it," Joseph would brag, "He's a daddy's boy!"

And the folks would say, "Nobody could miss that, Joe. He looks just like you." Everyone would laugh good-naturedly, including Joseph, as they knowingly stretched the truth.

Before long, Jesus was talking in broken sentences

and noticing everything which happened in the little room where He spent all of his time when not outside under the fig tree. The little fig tree provided him about the only shade from a hot Judean sun. Mary seemed to be busy all the time preparing food for her two men, mending Joseph's tunic and apron, which were forever tearing in the shop, and making new garments for her son who outgrew them faster than she could get them done. Her hands were full, as full as every mother with a growing boy. For Jesus was a normal lad causing his mother as much trouble as humanly possible. Mary was to remember all those trying moments.

When Jesus stubbed his toe that day while chasing a lamb through the meadow, it bled around the nail and clotted with dirt like that which is at home on every boy's feet. It seemed, at times, that He was always into something.

Fortunate for him, He was of a peaceable nature. Otherwise, He would have come home more often with a shiner under his eye like that day when a boy had caught him off guard and let him have it with a biting set of bare knuckles.

"I hope you didn't start this fight," said his mother, as she applied cold compresses to Jesus' face.

"It was Carli, mom," replied Jesus, wincing as Mary pressed too hard on the wet towels. "He really didn't mean to do it."

"I am surprised. Isn't Carli your friend?"

"Sure, mom, he's one of the best friends I have."

"Then why did he hit you?"

"You know what a temper he has! We got into an argument over whose dad was the strongest and Carli just went crazy."

"What did you do? Did you hit him back? Your dad and I do not want you fighting."

"No, mom. What good would that do? He would have just hit me again!'

"Good for you," said Mary, "you are learning your lessons well."

The local doctor at Nazareth had become toughened to his work. He had to. But, it still brought him no pleasure to hear little Jesus cry out in agony as he pulled into place the wrist which He had dislocated while trying to handle one of Joseph's over-size planes. And while He didn't care for the taste of it, Jesus had no choice but to swallow the mustard, which the doctor had instructed Mary to steep in water, to lessen the pain.

Jesus's mother remembered how heavy He was during the last two months before her delivery and how robust and active He was from the very first. She also recalled every incident when her heart had hurt while caring for his childhood pains. Usually his discomfort was brought on by some usual boyish adventure which should have been avoided, but Mary understood and felt every hurt which her boy endured.

She would never forget that day when Jesus had come running into the house with a nasty, lacerated knee injured while playing a rough-and-tumble sport with the boys on the other side of town. Rubbing saliva from her own mouth into the wound and applying what herbs she had available, she nearly lost her mind as the leg became inflamed and fever raged around the infected limb. It was nearly a month before the redness went away and the wound began to heal. Mary was sure that God had answered her prayers for the life of her boy. And she had mentioned her thankfulness more than once when trying to comfort another mother worrying about a sick child.

There had been an earlier time when she had thought Jesus was going to die. He was only four years old. Suffering from an intestinal infection picked up from eating meat which had become contaminated, from hanging too long in the open air of the local bazaar, the chance for survival looked grim. That was the first time Mary had been desperate in her concern for the boy's life. But it would not be the last.

From the time her little boy was old enough to mouth the words, Mary had taught him the prayer which every Jewish mother led her children in saying each night at bedtime. It was from Psalm 31:5 and, having heard it hundreds of times, it had already been indelibly etched on the soft mind of Jesus: "Into thine hands I commit my spirit." That night He was too sick to say the words, so Mary repeated them for him. And the fear which she felt broke her heart.

Mary never quite understood why she felt the way she did when her boy got sick. Like every mother, she worried. But for some reason she felt guilty. God had told her that He would be Israel's salvation. And, if that were so, then Jesus could not die and all her worry was pretty silly. So, during those times of illness, Mary's mind was in a turmoil. There was so much she could not explain about the way she felt.

By the time He was into schooling at the synagogue, Jesus had built up a pretty good immunity against the childhood diseases common to Palestine. Every night, toughened by exposure to injury and disease, He would climb out of the workshop with Joseph, all dirty and covered with chips and shavings, sometimes with cuts on his fingers. He had become accustomed to it from the earliest age. Like all boys from poor homes, He went to work as soon as soon as He was able to produce. There was no other choice. But the boy liked it.

With Joseph, the two inseparable friends would seek out worthy trees, cut them, skin their bark, and drag them to the crude shop. There they would be cut to size with hand tools and shaped into pieces of furniture, implements of toil, and support for animal sheds. When the day was over, Jesus would eat from the modest fare which his mother prepared. He was never quite full – no growing boy is – but He did not complain.

There were chores other than sawing and shaping boards. Early in the morning before sunrise and early in the afternoon before retiring, the lad was tutored by his father. It was Joseph who taught Jesus how to read and introduced him to the Torah long before synagogue school, a formal time of instruction which had been started during the days of Shatah, almost a century before Jesus was born.

At first, Jesus encountered some difficulty learning his letters. Later, when the basics had been mastered, it all seemed to fall into place quite naturally. At times, He got his Aramaic and Hebrew mixed up, but in time both languages rolled smoothly from his tongue. The grade card from school days began to show a gradual incline in achievement and Mary was proud of him. Assimilation of the Torah and its teachings came easily as though He had always known these truths to be evident.

Mary also had noticed that, even as a small boy, Jesus was never selfish with his wood toys which Joseph made in the shop. This attitude about sharing came naturally to the lad, partly because of the influence of godly parents and partly due to the disposition with which God had endowed him.

A sense of pride filled his boyish heart when his daddy befriended some neighbor in need. It just seemed the right thing to do. And when Mary cooked up extra food for a sick friend's household, Jesus felt a kind of warm glow flooding his whole being. His parents had taught him well and it was paying big dividends already.

During the rainy season in Israel, Nazareth always received its share. When the rains lasted very long, the water ran down from the surrounding hills into the village streets below, washing deep ruts into the hillsides. More than once, Jesus had helped Joseph get the timbers and partially completed projects off the ground and onto drier footing. The good part was the way the rushing torrents of water flushed out the smelly sewer which ran day and night down an open gutter in the middle of the road.

There was one season which etched itself into his memory. The rains came down in sheets for nearly a full week and the cold winds made the nights almost unbearable. Many of the sheep and goats of the area died from exposure or drowned in the raging floods. One family of five had been forced out of their quarters when the wind blew away their roof. And the desperate family was given lodging by Mary in the one room house where Joseph and his family lived, Jesus sharing his mat with four strapping boys.

For the duration of the rain plus several extra days, the destitute family stayed with Mary while Joseph and men from the village replaced the roof. Alert to everything that happened around him, Jesus remembered his father's having told him that it was seldom a roof ever had to be replaced since most clay roofs were more than equal to the rain. But this was an exception to the rule.

The maturing young man in Mary's house could not see why people were not always kind to each other like the way his parents had cared for their neighbors. So many folks were so bent on taking care of themselves, on making money, and on having a larger place than the folks next door.

All the folks in Nazareth needed was love. There was not much money, but money did not finally solve anything in the lives of those who had it. He had seen it again and again. On the other hand, in those few instances where He had seen real love at work, even the most stubborn problems had a way of working themselves out. Obviously, it was the love and concern shown by Joseph and Mary for the washed-out family which had made the difference between tragedy and hope. Even as a very young child, this first-born son of Mary showed signs of warmth and concern for people around him, both young and old. And the older He got, the more mellow and gentle He became. Not alone did people notice it. The animals did, too.

Outside the door of the shop, Joseph had hung a little hand-printed sign which Jesus had suggested. It read, "My yokes are easy." People came from afar to buy these superb yokes. Nobody could make a yoke fit so perfectly as Joseph. One reason why there were no better ones available anywhere in Israel was because the able craftsman thought of himself as a servant of the people. His purpose was not only to sell a product, but to make the customer's lot easier and more enjoyable.

There was also a compassion in his heart for the beasts who were forced to wear the yokes. Such a thing should be made as well as possible so as not to chafe the necks of the poor, toiling animals.

The older Jesus got, the more like his father He

seemed to be. It was a known fact that when He wasn't making something to sell, He was making something to give away. How many hours He worked without charge just helping a poor neighbor build a stable or repair a broken cart axle no one will ever know. But there were many.

There was the elderly woman whose household furnishings were all destroyed by a fire which had started when a burning lamp was knocked off its shelf into a straw sleeping mat. Jesus had laid aside all the scheduled jobs and spent almost a whole week building furniture to replace that which had been consumed by the flames. And if a farmer was known to need a new plough, but was honestly down on his luck, he was just apt to wake up some morning to find a plow in his courtyard shed. That was the way Joseph operated the shop and Jesus inherited his father's ways.

And sickness? If there was any thing which upset the growing craftsman, it was the sight of so much suffering across the countryside. Many children died young because of disease and lack of food. Blindness was a terrible scourge and leprosy was a commonplace sight on most any day. Every time He saw a blind man, He wanted to make him see. And the crippled beggars! How He wished there was some way to make them walk.

And those lepers! Why could not someone do something for them? Why must they be treated like outcasts? His insides churned at the sight of their disfigured faces and He desperately wanted to make their hurt go away. The sensation was over-powering as if He might have the power to do what no one else had ever attempted.

Someday He *would* do something! Someday, somehow He would help his people see again and He would restore those lepers to their families. He just knew He could. And the thought scared him.

About a furlong and a half from the house of Mary and Joseph lived a much loved man whom everyone called "Uncle Ezra." He was a herdsman whose duty it was to care for a number of goats which belonged to a wealthy man in Capernaum. Since his work kept him confined to the hills where the herd of goats grazed, he was not at home much.

One late afternoon, just as the day was wearing to a close, he was seen approaching his house. It was obvious that something was wrong. He was stooped and terribly pale from what was soon learned to be some kind of pain in his chest. His breath was extremely short and he found it difficult to speak. When the family got him down on a mat, which someone had hurriedly brought from inside the house, frantic neighbors began bathing his head with cool water.

"The goats! The goats!" he gasped. Those attending him knew he was concerned and fearful for the goats which he had been forced suddenly to leave unprotected on the hills.

When Jesus got word at the shop about his stricken friend, He ran immediately into the country to locate the scattered goat herd. By the time He returned to the village, Ezra was dead.

Jesus was young, but already He had been around a lot of death. Death was the one grim reality of existence which kept him sobered about the sacredness of life. He never really got used to it. However, like everyone else, the saddened carpenter had learned to live with grief and sorrow. It was everywhere. Hardly a day passed without hearing the screams of grieving loved ones in the mournful procession of death through the streets.

As He descended the hill into the valley of Nazareth, the cries of friends who had gathered around the dying man were rending the night air.

"Ezra! Ezra! Do not go away. We will never be the same without you. Our hearts hurt now, Ezra. Please come back." Someone who loved the old herdsman was trying to talk to the dead man – or more likely, trying to reason with himself.

Arriving at the door, Jesus pushed his way through the wide-eyed spectators who had come running from all over town, and knelt beside the lifeless form of Ezra. He could not begin to understand it, but for some strange reason He was filled with an almost irresistible impulse to take the dead man's hand and command him to get up.

So desperately did He want to help that there was the confidant, inner certainty that He could make the man live again. Only with great restraint did He rise from the ground and offer the customary words of love and sympathy to the grieving wife and children.

Afterward, as He walked through the night to his own house, Jesus was filled with thoughts of life and death and wondered what might have happened if He had taken Ezra's hand and spoken his name.

It was a crazy thought.

Lifting his face into the wind, He breathed deeply of the crisp air as though trying to clear his mind of the wild idea that He could actually do something about so final a matter as death. But the dreams never went away. And the day was to come when He would take the plunge and give those demanding impulses a chance.

CHAPTER FIVE

He had been there before but the sights and sounds of the Holy City never failed to excite him. Especially at Passover, when the crowds of men and women from all over the world packed the narrow lanes of the town as well as the fields beyond.

Sprinkled among the teeming masses were colorful sentries on horseback, trained servants of the crown, sent from Rome to keep order. Along the public street, on either side, the shopkeepers were taking advantage of the holiday festivities. They had stacked and stuffed their tiny shops with everything from newly made baskets and woven cloth to dressed fowl and mutton. Of course, there were the frisky little lambs which one could buy for a pittance, but then they would be rejected by the Temple priests who always found some blemish to disqualify them for sacrifice. In this way, pilgrims from afar, who had come to sacrifice, were forced to purchase their lambs from the avaricious priests at an exorbitant price.

This invariably irritated the young boy from Nazareth. Standing among the colonnade of Solomon's Porch, He found himself bristling with quiet anger even as He watched the money-grabbing priests fleecing the flock, a flock so in need of a shepherd. The noise, the confusion, the stench, the circus atmosphere – it was enough to nauseate God. Someone had to do something about it. It just had to stop. Or so He mused silently.

A sudden shiver over-powered the twelve year old boy. The shadows beneath the portico where He stood were menacing. His devout parents had brought him to Jerusalem to keep a custom handed down for generations, but a heavy sense of doom filled his heart.

A boy became a man when he reached his thirteenth birthday. At that time a special celebration would be held for him at the Temple. True, He was only twelve and it was Passover time, but He had matured quickly and Joseph knew that this year's festival would be important for him.

Joseph had tutored him for two years so He would be able to answer the questions without delay. It was certain that, when the time came the following year, He would be ready. The family noticed that Jesus was very pensive as if in another world. He was acting more like a man than during any previous trip to Jerusalem which they could remember. But, then He was growing up. Joseph had spoken to him several times when there was little or no response. That was not like him because He was always respectful toward his parents.

The mood lingered throughout the festival and, as He walked inside the columned court, where Gentiles from many nations were trying to pray amidst the noisy hubbub of what was more a holiday than a holy one, there seemed to be something terribly wrong. It was all smoke and mirrors. The festive event was like a dramatic performance in one unclear act – part comedy and a bigger part tragedy.

The traditional activities felt so hollow, so pretentious, so unreal. There was an instant when, as the whole structure appeared to shake, the wondering lad darted off the sheltered pavement. For a moment it seemed that the Temple itself was about to collapse.

"Are you all right, my boy?" asked an attending Levite who had observed his sudden movement and the frightened look on his face.

"I'm not sure," gasped Jesus. "Did you feel that?"

"Feel what?" replied the Levite with a quizzical stare, obviously having noticed nothing out of the ordinary.

But what the boy had experienced had left him dazed with an uncanny feeling that He was not dreaming or imagining something. "The shaking! The Temple was shaking! I thought it was going to fall!"

Just then, a fellow Temple attendant, standing at the far end of the porch, cupped his hands around his mouth and called, "Ananias, you are needed in the Levites' quarters. Come quickly."

Pulling up the skirt of his robe as he prepared to heed the summons, Ananias grasped the lad by the shoulder with his other hand and assured him, "No, no, my son. I felt nothing. If there were an earth tremor, I didn't know it. Don't be afraid. This is God's house. Nothing can ever happen to God's house. You were just imagining that the Temple was shaking."

As the Levite moved quickly away, Jesus was not so sure. What had happened to him was more than He

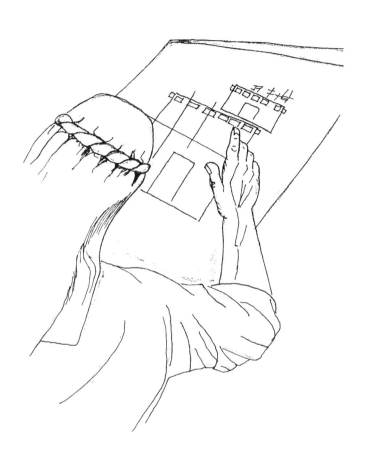

could understand. But it was real enough that the memory stuck in his head for days like a haunting dream. A dream, however, was the one thing it was not!

The Temple on Mount Zion was the holiest place of all to the descendants of Abraham. It had been the center of worship in Israel since the days of King David. Long before that, it was the belief of the religious teachers that the first Temple had been built by Solomon on the exact spot where Abraham went to offer his son, a hill commonly referred to as Moriah.

The Temple of Solomon was one of the wonders of the Roman world, so wonderful that the queen of Sheeba acknowledged it to be twice as magnificent as she had been told. Jesus knew all that, having been well versed in Judean history by his father.

The maze of buildings, upon which the twelve year old boy looked, was not the holy place of a thousand years ago. Solomon's Temple had been burnt to the ground by the Chaldeans nearly six hundred years earlier. Zerubbabel had rebuilt a makeshift kind of worship center when the captives returned to their homeland and his poor copy of Solomon's lavish Temple, though much larger, had remained until the time of Herod the Great who leveled it around the year 20 B.C.

Jesus remembered well the story of Judas Maccabeus who restored Zerubbabel's Temple following its desecration by Antiochus Epiphanes nearly two hundred years prior to his own birth. But the glory, which

113

had once flooded that mountain in Jerusalem, had remained a distant memory until recent times when the new edifice had been constructed by Herod.

"Could it be that it is being desecrated again?" said the boy Jesus to himself. "No pagan king is defiling it, but anyone can see what's happening. Those of us who ought to know better are allowing the Lord's House to be defiled. Where is God in all this? Are we going to destroy this holy place ourselves? Are we about to become our worst enemy?"

The boy was full of questions. The great Temple which stood atop the sacred mount was still under construction. It was not completed until the time of Agrippa II and the procurator Albinus in 64 A.D. In fact, workmen were continuing with the final touches until only a few weeks before the Roman Titus destroyed it six years later.

Herod, the proud and tireless builder, was an Idumean, a descendant of Esau, the worldly brother of Jacob. Esau had been denied his rightful inheritance as the older son by the deceptive partnership of Jacob and his like-minded mother, Rebekah. John Hyrcanus brought the Idumeans into Palestine from their desert land of Edom, which lay between the Mediterranean and the Dead Sea southward, about 130 B.C. It was at that time that they embraced the Jewish religion.

As a proselyte to Judaism, Herod was a Jew in name only. Actually, he was no less than a pagan monster who, with nearly a dozen wives, had his favorite,

Mariamne, put to death along with his brothers, Aristobulous and Alexander.

Five days before his death, he ordered that his son Antipater be slain. He had even commanded that thousands of Jews be put to death, at the time of his own funeral, so there would be people to mourn his passing. Jesus was only twelve, but He was aware of all this.

He was also cognizant of the fact that the tetrarchy had been given to Herod by Mark Antony and that later, in 37 B.C., the Roman Senate declared him a king. Known for his insatiable drive to build memorials to himself more than for any reverence for Jehovah, Herod razed Zerubbabel's Temple to its foundation and began construction of the gleaming edifice known to Jesus and his generation. Ten thousand skilled craftsmen were hired to teach the priests the arts of stone cutting and carpentry and at least a thousand stone masons worked continuously on the project.

Always in awe of the magnificence of the place, the boy was struck again and again by the foundation stones of white stone, some of which were seven feet high and sixty-seven feet long, all of them ornamented with gold.

"Behold," He thought, "what manner of stones are these? Nowhere else in all of Israel are there such monster rocks. I must ask dad how they got them up here."

Beautiful as they were, it was a puzzle to him why the house of God should be as cold as the limestone in its walls. The deceptive magnificence sent shivers up and down his back.

Passover had ended and the crowds of Jews, who had come from every corner of the earth, were returning to their homes. Life would soon be returning to the humdrum style so prevalent in a city where every move was prescribed by written laws, laws which were enforced by religious police unyielding in their authority. Jerusalem was beginning to thin out and the Temple precincts were almost empty. Only here and there could be seen small groups of people, mostly travelers from afar who were loathe to leave the many new friends they had made since arriving.

Mesmerized by the massive structure, Jesus had wandered deeper into the interior courts. He had stopped in the Court of the Jewish Women where several local wives and daughters had gathered around him. He had attracted their attention by asking two of them why they were not allowed to go beyond the marked boundaries of their court. They had explained what the boy already knew, that the Law established certain levels for different groups of people. Jesus had asked the question, not for information, but in order to spark a conversation.

"So, to put it simply, you can't go into the men's court because you are not men?" continued the boy. "Does that ever bother you?"

"No. That's the way it has always been," replied one of the women. "But we don't mind," chuckled another, "our husbands will instruct us when we get home." Several of them smiled, shrugging their shoulders and rolling their eyes in disbelief that anyone should think their husbands would tell them anything.

By this time a number of priests had come out of their isolated quarters, having heard the commotion, inquiring as to what was going on. When the women told them what the boy had asked, one of the older priests scratched his head, breathed a deep sigh, and asked him who He was.

"I am Jesus bar Joseph," was the quick reply. Of course, none of the holy men ever heard of Joseph. No one expected holy men to know everybody, certainly not peasants in a musty little town far from the grandeur of Jerusalem. But, there was something captivating about this radiant boy in his white tunic and red sash with the little black capstan.

"So you are interested in learning about the Temple? You are to be commended," remarked the priest, patting the boy on the shoulder, noticeably patronizing such an arrogant lad. "Holiest place on earth. But, then, surely you know that!"

"Yes, I do. It just seems to me like everyone should be treated alike in the house of Jehovah," Jesus said half-questioningly, looking first at the women, then at the priest.

Knowing that a complicated situation was developing, with numbers of people stopping to listen, the priest beckoned for the crowd to disperse and led the boy away to a low stone ledge just outside the priests'

117

Leslie H. Woodson

quarters.

"First," said the older man, who was obviously the head priest of the ten or twelve robed younger men, "why are you asking these questions? We don't need any unhappiness among our women!"

"I don't know exactly why," answered Jesus, "but who told us that Jews are better than Gentiles, that men are better than women, that priests are better than ordinary folks? Doesn't Jehovah treat everyone alike? And why were all those animals in the place where Gentiles need to pray? I thought the Temple was a place of prayer, but it is not much different than the marketplace. No way could I pray in all that hubbub."

They were not very successful, but the priests tried to explain. In their hearts, they knew the boy's questions were valid, that the holy place had degenerated, and that once such a thing happens, it is like a cancer. It is almost impossible to stop. So they had become proficient at putting on a show and they were not about to change.

But the boy from Nazareth was not finished. "It's so lonely feeling here at the house of Jehovah, as if God isn't home, like He has gone away because He doesn't like what goes on in here. I am only a boy and Joseph taught me to respect my elders. Maybe I ought not be saying these things, but I mean no harm. My parents always come here at Passover, but everything seems so empty."

The holy men looked at one another in disbelief as they listened to the intensive lad. After an uncomfortable pause in the conversation, Jesus continued.

118

"There are no smiles on the people's faces. The people are loud and noisy, but no one looks happy. Feels like the party is over. Today, as I walked in the portico, the gloom was so heavy it was scary."

"Young man, we perceive that you are sensitive beyond your years. Most boys your age are not bothered about these things. These are matters which were never supposed to concern the thinking of children. Why, most of our Hebrew men leave these things up to us here at the Temple. They never give them a thought. And incidentally, what you have described as coldness here is not that at all. You are too young to know it, but what you have felt is reverence. Jehovah is an awesome God and there must be no levity or light-hearted approach to holy things." Feeling his superiority, the cleric rambled on until the young boy dared to interrupt.

"Forgive me, holy father, but isn't Jehovah God our friend? Does He want us to tiptoe in the Temple, or would He rather we rejoice and be glad? Would He not be revered more if we were less rigid in our worship?"

Not only was this boy sensitive beyond his years, but the Temple priests found him wise beyond his age as well.

During those solemn trysting days of political and religious debate, there had been hectic disagreement among the Sadducees and Pharisees over a number of controversial concerns. The wisest sages of the ancient world had gathered in Jerusalem to listen and wonder.

119

But as Jesus questioned them, they felt annoyed. Yet, with their aged brows bent to a frown, they sat spellbound and unexplainably speechless. The subtle arguments of the ages, theological issues which had been tumbled about mercilessly by the wisest sages among them, were coming to the fore again. And they were baffled by a boy.

CHAPTER SIX

"How I do wish that we lived closer to Jerusalem," said Joseph. "Can you imagine what it would be like to work on the new Temple? To have regular work everyday without wondering whether there will be enough to keep food in the cupboard for more than one day at a time?"

"Now Joseph," replied Mary, "we have been through this before. We surely have learned by now that God will provide us with daily bread. He never promised more than that, but what more could anyone need?" Noticeably showing her disappointment in her husband, she added, pointing an accusing finger at him, "Where is your faith? After all, what fun would life be if it were not for the struggle? Have you forgotten that arriving at your destination is not nearly as exciting as getting there?"

"I know! You are right. But I keep wishing that I could provide better housing and just a few of the nice extras for you and the children. Sometimes, when I look at this shabby little room, a feeling of failure rushes over me. It just seems like no matter how hard we work, there is no way to get ahead. Every morning, I have to start all over." Looking at Mary's worn-thin dress, his expression filled with inner pain, Joseph continued, "You are bound to think . . ."

"You are a wonderful husband and no child ever had a better daddy," interrupted his wife, leaning toward him with her hands on her hips. "And here you are feeling sorry for yourself. Let Herod have his Temple. The Lord will take care of us. He always has, just like He cared for our ancestors in those hard days in the wilderness. When they complained because they had no food to eat, God rained fresh manna from heaven every morning. And He told them not to gather enough for tomorrow. There would be enough for every day, but those who were greedy and without faith discovered that what they had collected for the next day rotted away. Joseph, God will take care of us!"

Jesus, who had been listening from his stool in the corner of the room where he had been reading by the flickering lamp light, broke in with his own comment. "Mother is right, dad. Look how our heavenly Father cares for the sparrows. You don't see them fretting around or worrying about whether there will be enough to get them through the winter, do you? And there is something else . . ."

"Not so fast," said Joseph, striking the heavy adz, which he had been resting his chin on, into the hard earth floor. "You both know very well that my faith is strong. That's why I married you, Mary. Remember?"

Flax, the dog, sensing the irritation in the air, showed his displeasure with a guttural growl and a loud bark.

"It's all right, Flax; everything is fine," laughed young Jesus, as He roughed up the hair on Flax's head.

For what seemed like a long time, nobody said anything. The wrinkled leather around Joseph's eyes made him look older than his years. The gnarled fingers were those of a man who had endured long hours turning rough olive trees into graceful pieces of furniture and oak boards into well-fitting yokes. Even when he was sitting, his stooped shoulders betrayed the fact that the years had taken their toll.

Finally, wrapping his time-worn hand around his beard, Joseph pushed himself upright with the aid of the adz, which was still burrowed in the floor.

"Out of the mouths of babes," he said, half-jokingly, "but I'm the breadwinner here and it would be great to have a chance to be master carpenter at Herod's Temple. If we just didn't live so far away."

During the entire incident, Jesus' mother had been preparing the mats which had to be rolled out every night. The thin mats, which lay rolled together in the corner of the room, were the only things which came between the children and the hard ground. When Mary got through with them, she always had them fluffed up and inviting. No one understood her magic with those old mats, but then nobody ever thought much about it either. That's the way it is where tender love and care is taken for granted.

That night, Joseph could not get to sleep. Flashbacks kept coming one after another. He remembered how the angel had warned him to take the newborn baby with Mary and flee into Egypt. The same Herod who commanded the construction of the new Temple had also killed all the infant boys two years of age and under. He had hopes of destroying the young king about whom the Wise Men from the Orient had told him. Years had passed since the death of Herod, but would it be safe to work at the Temple? Would the identity of Jesus be discovered? Perhaps the authorities would find out that Jesus was missed in the massacre. Thousands of thoughts, heretofore buried in his sub-conscious mind, surged to the surface and haunted the troubled carpenter.

The idea of working at the Temple site might not be such a good idea at all. He had been afraid to remain in Judea during those earlier years and it was probably the better part of discretion to stay in Galilee now. It could not be overlooked that Archaelaus had only recently been deposed and there was no guarantee that the present procurator, Coponius, might not continue the vicious rule of the Herods. Though not as politically smart as his father, Herod the Great, Archaelaus had been even more cruel and vicious. Nobody knew about Coponius.

"Well, enough of this day dreaming," thought Joseph as he rolled restlessly beneath the covers on his mat. "There are more important things than my job right now. And it will soon be time to get up. Better get some sleep."

Only two days remained before the annual festival of Hanukkah was to begin. There would be eight days of celebration in every Jewish home. Even though it was disturbing to have to think about the hard struggles of their ancestors, there was great joy during this week of remembrance.   It was a time of celebration as each household relived an event which had taken place over a century and a half earlier. And every child knew the old story.

Antiochus IV Epiphanes, the Syrian oppressor, returning home after his invasion of Egypt, passed through the despicable little parcel of land known as Palestine where he decided to vent his wrath by ordering his army of 22,000 to destroy Jerusalem. Adding insult to injury, the city was invaded on the holy Sabbath while the people worshiped in their synagogues. Many of the men were massacred and the women and children were taken captive. Burning the city and defiling the Temple by offering swine's flesh on the altar, the soldiers set up an image of Jupiter and allowed the precincts to be used as a brothel.

When a decree was issued for the remaining Jews to conform to the religion of Antiochus or be put to death, devout Hebrews had taken all they could. The Maccabees, members of the Hasmonean family, initiated a rebellion. It was Judas Maccabeus who brought deliverance to the Jewish people in 164 B.C. Ever afterwards, this great triumph was commemorated by the lighting of lamps for eight consecutive days beginning on the twenty-fifth of Tislev, usually early December. It was a time of joy and dancing, feasting and general merrymaking.

Each day Joseph would call the family together and light the candles, explaining the story of the Feast of

Lights.

Looking wide-eyed at the hypnotic tapers of flame, Jesus commented on the wonderful story. "Our forefathers were great and dedicated men, weren't they?"

"Had it not been for men like the Maccabees, we would be a land of misguided people serving some fabled god of our pagan neighbors," announced Joseph, still holding the straw with which he had started the flame.

"We must never forget. As you have told us the story every year, so we must tell it to our children. Right, father?"

"Again and again," replied the proud father.

"But, dad, I need to know how we are to understand the meaning of the lamps. How does the light fit into the story?"

Joseph leaned back against the wall, stroked his graying beard, and began to speak. "Some of our people still fail to see the connection of light with commitment and victory. That is more than unfortunate." Reaching for the papyrus scroll, on which he had entered passages of scripture and personal notes on his most favored, he rolled it open to words from the prophet Isaiah and began to read: "For Zion's sake will I not hold my peace, and for Jerusalem's sake I will not rest, until her righteousness go forth as brightness, and her salvation as a lamp that burneth."

"The lighted lamp then, is a symbol of our deliverance," said Jesus, as though the connection of light with the Maccabees was becoming clearer.

"That is the idea," said Joseph, leaning forward for emphasis. "Whenever people live in oppression and away from Jehovah, who is our light, they dwell in darkness. Only when we take our stand for God, willing to die for him rather than live without him, do we live in the light."

Jesus knew that God is light and that everything else is darkness, but it was a gradual thing for him to get it all together. Once he had it worked out, the truth was locked firm in his head.

"Another question," said Jesus, after a long pause in the conversation. "Is it always all right with Jehovah God for us to kill our enemies?"

That was a tough one. There are two sides to just about everything. As a responsible father, Joseph was struggling with the response. Exactly how could he explain this enigma?

"What about Judas, the son of Ezekias?" inquired the boy. "I guess I am just too young to understand it, but adults talk about these things all the time and we kids overhear them."

"When the Roman emperor Augustus, who claimed to be a god, demanded another census in 6 A. D., the Jews were outraged. It meant that Caesar thought he owned everybody and that he, as a god, could determine a person's taxes and his right to citizenship. The result was that Judas of Galilee and a man called Zadok, both Torah instructors and political revolutionaries, called on the people to resist," explained Joseph, fighting his way through what he feared was hard for a child to fathom.

"Warring against Rome, with the most primitive kinds of weaponry, was irrational if not insane. As would be expected, Judas was slain and no one knows what happened to Zadok."

"Was Judas wrong, father, in killing Romans to defend Jehovah? Or was he right? I'm kind of mixed up."

"My son, there can be absolutely no one in all of Israel who despises the galling Roman occupation of our land more than I. We have been over-powered and abused throughout our history. Our ancestors believed that God must be defended no matter what the cost. Because of that conviction, they jumped on their enemies and killed as many as they could. They never hesitated to murder even innocent people in the name of Jehovah, God of Israel. Many folks have never learned that Jehovah doesn't need our defense. He is perfectly capable of taking care of himself."

"But there is one thing that keeps rambling around in my head. Our scriptures tell us that Jehovah commanded our ancestors to get rid of the wicked. And He was angry when they did not do what they were told. Even when the wicked were destroyed, there were others to take their place. Wasn't it all a losing battle?"

"God's ways are not our ways and God's thoughts are not our thoughts, my son."

"Maybe God was trying to teach them a lesson like the lessons you are always teaching me. Maybe we are supposed to learn that no one wins in war, no matter in whose name we are fighting. Maybe it was because our people failed in their mission, to persuade the nations to turn from their idols unto the living God, that they ended up having to kill them!"

Joseph smiled as he tried to ravel out the mysteries of what he himself did not fully grasp. "You are probably on the right track. I know all this sounds like double-talk to you, but we have yet to fully understand the ways of the Lord. Sometimes it is helpful to think of the whole human race as a spoiled, disobedient child. No father can deal with a three year old like he does with a thirty year old. The race learns as it grows, or it should. But apparently the race, and especially Israel to whom Jehovah has been so gracious, is still not grown up. We are all so immature."

"Do you mean that Judas of Galilee was wrong in defending Jehovah God against His enemies?" interrupted young Jesus.

"Look son," remonstrated Joseph with a wrinkled brow, "how can we be sure who God's enemies are? There are times when the enemy may be religious folks! In times of holy war, like those of the scriptures, the question is not whether God is on our side, but whether we are on His. And the answer is not always clear."

"I wish He would tell us for sure what is right and what we should do."

"Well, it is certainly time," answered Joseph, clearly revealing how weary he was with people like Judas of Galilee. "Remember, he was one of our own! Maybe God is telling us, but we don't listen."

Jesus looked at the ground wistfully. Then, lifting his eyes, He smiled a boyish grin and said, "Maybe God will come and tell us something soon. And maybe we *will* listen."

Mary had supper going when the two of them arrived. She was putting the last loving touches on the meager fare she had prepared. That evening it was lentil porridge with onions and cucumbers. As always, there was plenty of flat, hot barley bread. It was a staple and they could fill up on the bread in case the porridge ran low. Would have been nice to have had some fish, but that was the kind of thing reserved for special times.

The family's sleepy-eyed donkey was enjoying the idle moments when there was nothing tied across his back for transport to somewhere else. Flax, the family dog, was sound asleep in his favorite spot. And there was old Esther, the pet sheep they had procured when she was a frolicking lamb. The life was about gone now from Esther, and she would not survive many more winters to provide the wool so important to all of them. Was sad to think about. Esther was like a member of the family.

There were goats – three of them – but soon there would be some more because two were going to be mommies. Hopefully, they would be girl goats since the family could use the extra milk and cheese. Scattered across the courtyard were five or six scrawny chickens pecking their way to bare survival. At least, there would be a couple of eggs each morning.

Mother Mary was stirring the pot and keeping a watchful eye on the bread rising in the courtyard oven. Meals were prepared in the out-of-doors where most homes had clay, mud brick ovens for making bread and cooking meat when it was available, which was seldom. As Mary poked the bread to see whether it was done, Jesus was intrigued by the way it fluffed up while hot. His mother said it was the leaven. He knew nothing about leaven, but Mary said that when He was older, He would understand it better.

The welcome meal was as satisfying as if they had killed the Passover lamb. Mary and Joseph were simple people who did not demand much. While Joseph would have preferred living conditions for his family to be a little better, he was always grateful to God for what they had. And Jesus loved them both and would not have had it any other way.

Nothing was more pleasant for a Jewish child than the sheer delight of being safe at the supper table when the shades of night began to fall. The little house in Nazareth was so tiny that no one had to work at being cozy. When more than six or seven people were in the room, each person was forced to like the others whether he wanted to or not. It was always snuggle time. Jesus, however, never complained about the cramped quarters because He got attention from every side. And He also loved people, a trait which would accompany him throughout his entire life.

Of all the people He loved, there was one whom

the boy Jesus absolutely adored. When his mother could arrange it, she invited Heli over to share the evening meal with the family. Mary would laugh and say, "There's always room for one more." It lifted her spirits to see little Jesus so happy when she could tell him his grandpa would be with them at table.

For a small boy like Jesus, Heli seemed like a very old man. Being somewhat stooped, he walked with the aid of a staff which Joseph had made for him and, when spoken to, cupped his ear in his hand lest he miss what was being said. Mary's mother died shortly after the birth of Jesus, so He didn't remember her, but it was interesting to hear Heli talk about her. And he did often.

Grandfather had white hair except on the top of his head where his toughened scalp glistened in the lamplight. A long white beard graced his wrinkled face and his beady little eyes sparkled with an impish kind of joy. In spite of the rough times he had been through, his heart seemed to bubble with excitement. Everybody called Jesus by his given name except grandpa Heli who had affectionately nicknamed him *Boy*.

That night, as he stooped even more to enter the low doorway, he glanced toward Jesus and, with a chuckle in his voice, said, "Hey Boy, how you like my sandals?" In his hand he carried his old sandals which he had dyed a bright red. Grandpa was a fun guy and he enjoyed making the children laugh. It worked. Jesus thought the sight of an old white-bearded man in red sandals was a wonderful thing. And He slapped his knees in laughter.

The next thing grandpa said was, "Mary, forgive me for being late. First thing I need to do is get this mud off my feet." As he spoke, Heli was leaning down to put his red sandals, which he had removed that evening as he stood in the doorway, on the floor. His bare feet were covered with mud and, though Heli had scraped the worst of the mud off his sandals, they were a sight to behold.

"Neighbor Huri was taking a load of firewood to the other side of the village when the ox slipped and got the load stuck in the ditch. We had to unload the cart stick by stick, dig the cart out, and then reload it."

"Sit down, dad, you must be worn out," said Mary as she pushed a stool toward him.

Grandpa welcomed the chance to rest as he slumped down heavily on the stool. Jesus ran for a basin and a towel and, after making certain Heli was not ill, began washing the grime from his beloved grandfather's feet.

"You're a good one, Boy," laughed Heli. "Your daddy has taught you well. So many young folks these days have no manners and little respect for their elders."

"Grandpa," replied Jesus, as He reached for the dirty sandals, "I'd wash your feet anytime just to get you to dance in these crazy red sandals."

Everyone laughed with Heli who, in spite of his weary muscles and the pain in his back, was full of his usual merriment. "Not much dance left in me tonight."

When the family moved toward the table where Mary had set the steaming bowl, Heli lowered his voice

and said, "You won't believe what I am about to tell you. We were up to our ankles in the mire when my old friend, Gaddi, happened by. It was a welcome relief when I saw him because I knew Huri and I would never get that cart out of the mud by ourselves. The three of us had a better chance now of moving the cart. But it was not to be. Gaddi had never been like that before, but he quickly apologized about something that couldn't wait and, pulling his tunic tightly about him, left us with our problem." Mary gasped and covered her mouth with her hand.   Heli, sensing her displeasure, quickly continued,"But, wait until you hear what happened next!"

Captivated by the story He was hearing, Jesus blurted out, "What happened grandpa? How did you get out?"

"I'm coming to that. We were huffing and puffing with little luck when I suddenly sensed someone pushing beside me. When I looked up – well, how can anyone explain the way I felt? – when I looked, there was old Orthiel giving it all he had!"

"Orthiel!" shouted his grandson, "The tax man? Dad, remember the talk we had one day about him! He's the man my school friends threw rocks at, father!" Pausing in disbelief, Jesus, sensing that the story was almost too good to be true, said to Heli, "Orthiel helped you?"

Flax, sensing the excitement in the air, leaped to his feet, barking for joy.

"Yes. Believe it or not, the town's untouchable

was giving us a hand when my friend didn't have the time. Wonders never cease, but who would complain at a time like that?"

Jesus leaned back against the stone cold wall and smiled.

CHAPTER SEVEN

Among the most interesting experiences He could recall were the hundreds of times when He just sat around the wood fire and listened to the old folks talk. Sometimes it was just Joseph and Mary. At other times it would be Joseph and a few of his close friends. The conversation took turns in every conceivable direction. Regardless as to what it was about, it was always interesting, sometimes even spell-binding.

There were times when they talked about the strange weather. Often it related to business and the economic conditions which were never very good. Or it might be some sudden tragedy in the community which left everyone dazed for months. Of course, there were always the angry discussions surrounding the occupation of the land by Rome. That was a subject that never went away. And it was always a night filled with wonder when the old folks talked about deceased relatives whom Jesus had never known. It was an education in itself.

There was one subject, however, which never failed to leave Jesus under a cloud of strange hypnosis. Everywhere, across the world of his day, there was an over-powering awe which filled the air. It just felt like something was about to happen, something of momentous import. No one could state precisely what it was that they were expecting, but Jew and Gentile alike felt it. And they talked about it all the time.

Some were afraid of impending disaster. Others were filled with undefined hope. The world was in a mess and, even though the Roman Empire seemed to be at its peak of power, Rome was beginning to lose its grip, starting to fall apart. If any person or group sensed anything specific which might develop, it invariably had something to do with the Hebrews in the little nation of Israel where Jesus lived.

Their prophets had told them for a thousand years that one day Jehovah would send his anointed King to establish righteousness over the whole earth and that He would reign from Jerusalem. For many Jews, the hope had grown dim. After all, it had now been four hundred years since the last prophet had spoken. These had been hard times. The Hebrew people had suffered terribly. Where was the promise? What had happened to the glorious predictions made by the prophets?

Now, maybe out of desperation, there was a kind of rebirth of hope. Many of the poor folks were talking about the coming of a Messiah again. For them great anticipation filled the air.

Joseph, who was an avid student of the sacred scriptures, would often recite from memory the words of the prophet Isaiah: "And it shall come to pass in the last days, that the mountain of the Lord's house shall be established in the top of the mountains, and shall be exalted above the hills; and all nations shall flow into it. And many people shall go and say, Come ye, and let us go up to the mountain of the Lord, to the house of the God of Israel; and he will teach us his ways, and we will walk in his paths; for out of Zion shall go forth the law, and the word of the Lord from Jerusalem. And he shall judge among the nations, and shall rebuke many peoples; and they shall beat their swords in plowshares, and their spears into pruning hooks; nation shall not lift up sword against nation, neither shall they learn war anymore."

Invariably, these ancient words would produce heated discussion.

"But, Joseph," someone would say, "that was seven hundred years ago. Seems to me that just the opposite has been the case. There were the Assyrians, then the Babylonians, then the Persians, then the Greeks, and now the Romans! Where is this mountain top experience for Israel?"

And Joseph would argue that Jehovah was probably taking a long time to get his people ready for that superior place of world power. "It won't happen over night," he would say.

All of the men of the village respected Joseph as a trustworthy business man and as a wise, devout student of the word of God. But then, most men were alike. They were so busy with secular things that there was hardly ever time to think about religion. That being the case, they argued, but they listened to Old Joe almost as if he were a rabbi.

Not even the rabbinical leaders, who had been to theological school and should have known, were abreast of the situation enough to prepare the nation for what was happening.

Across the nation, whose founding promised such potential greatness, there was, beneath the hopeful surface, an ancient pessimism and despair. The future was bleak and faith in the coming of a royal deliverer was, for most of the people, becoming weaker every day.

"What really do you think is going to happen?"

Jesus had heard that question asked of Joseph more than once. And on this particular night, Joseph, leaning forward with elbows on his knees, answered as he always did. With a certainty born of a life-long search for the coming kingdom, he simply stated what he envisioned as a fact, "Why, men of Nazareth, this is the time. Our king is coming. Mary and I are more sure of that than anything in the world. Every day moves us closer to redemption."

One of the neighbors, normally more vocal than most, yawned in a kind of cynical way. Recovering from his boredom, he drawled, "Joe, you are so naive! You are a good man and you know the scriptures better than any of us here. In fact, I don't know anything about religion. Never really cared much about any of those fairy tales we keep hearing at the synagogue. The priests have got us all under their thumbs. We all know how rich they get from their dominance over the rest of us. As long as they can keep us ignorant and superstitious, they've got it made."

Jesus was hearing all this and, even though He was now a young man and welcome to join in such a

140

discussion with his elders, He was quietly taking it all in and coming to some conclusions of his own.

"It will be a sad day for Israel," replied Joseph to his yawning friend for whom he felt such pain, "a sad day, indeed, if we lose our faith in the covenant which Jehovah has made with our fathers. The reason Israel has had such hard times is because we keep disregarding the covenants with Abraham, Moses, and David."

Several men tried to speak at once, but one voice was heard above the rest and the other men turned in his direction. He was expressing a question which was nagging at each of them. "How on earth, Joe, can we expect to over-power the mighty force of Rome. We have no military with which to fight. And you know what Caesar does to anyone who claims to be some kind of Messiah! He doesn't last long enough to pick up his spear. We've just got to quit dreaming. Got to wake up and admit that there is not going to be any way out of this."

Joseph's knees popped as he got up and slowly walked to the little table where Mary had left some hard bread under a clean cloth. He removed the cloth, picked up a broken piece and smeared it with a little butter. Taking a man-size bite, he turned back toward his friends and said, as he chewed, "Who ever said this would be easy?"

Swallowing hard, he gestured with his big, gnarled hand and continued to speak. "It's difficult for me to understand why our scribes and elders talk all the time about how we will trample down the Gentiles and they never say a thing about what it may cost us. They make it appear that all we have to do is just sit around and wait and we will walk right in and scare the nations into submission."

"What do you mean, Joseph? Sure, that's what I've been told all my life. Are you saying that is not true? What are you trying to tell us?"

"I guess that I'm telling you that God has not forgotten us."

"Sure looks like it to some of us."

"He never breaks his word. And He has made us a promise. But we seem to be expecting something He never promised at all."

"Wait a minute, Joe. You are getting crazier by the minute. What are you talking about?"

Raising both his hands for quiet, Joseph went on with the most intent eyes Jesus had ever seen. "Israel has been so unfaithful to the covenant. We are always making it hard on ourselves. Jehovah has to keep sending the Gentiles to discipline us and we have yet to learn anything. We are no different than God's enemies. Why should He put up with us? If any one of you, my very dear friends, were king of Israel, how would things be any different?"

Every man in the room realized that what he was being told about himself was true. Young Jesus, who remained quiet throughout the evening, knew that if He were king, everything would have to change. The rest admitted quietly to themselves that they had no idea what would be required to alter the course of the nations.

"You see, my good friends, we are so stiff-necked that the discipline is going to have to be increased. When God made a covenant with us as a nation, it was for the purpose of making us his servant people. Somehow, we think Jehovah likes us better than the other nations. Well, that has never been true. Jehovah loves everybody and He made a contract with us to let the world know it. We have really never done that. Right now, if we were in power, everybody would suffer at the hands of the Hebrews!"

The room had taken on a quietness like that in the synagogue when, on a Friday evening as the Sabbath began, the Torah was removed from its shelter under the holy hush of God.

"Look," said Joseph, "look again at the words of Isaiah. We are so accustomed to hearing the prophet announce the glory of the kingdom that we never hear him when he talks about the need to sacrifice ourselves in service to our enemies."

"How's that? What are you talking about? You must know something we do not know. What did Isaiah say?"

"Those beautiful words are ever in the forefront of my thoughts. Listen!" And with that, Jesus leaned forward to look into his father's eyes as the old carpenter, turned teacher, spoke the words of Isaiah: "He is despised and rejected of men, a man of sorrows, and acquainted with grief, and we hid as it were our faces from him; he was despised, and we esteemed him not."

Joseph's shaggy head was visibly trembling as he continued: "Surely, he hath borne our griefs, and carried our sorrows; yet we did esteem him stricken, smitten of God, and afflicted. But he was wounded for our transgressions, he was bruised for our iniquities; the chastisement of our peace was upon him, and with his stripes we are healed. All we like sheep have gone astray; we have turned everyone to his own way, and the Lord hath laid on him the iniquity of us all."

When Old Joe stopped, the air in the room was so heavy that the men noticed they were getting their breath with difficulty. The neighbor sitting nearest the door pushed it ajar as the fresh, welcome air surged through the opening.

"It seems to me," said Joseph, after a long period of silence, "that Isaiah is telling us God's people must suffer in service before we can ever know the glory promised. When I read that scripture in Isaiah, it is almost as if each one of us is destined to suffer. Or maybe it's the coming king who will suffer as our representative. And in it all, one can clearly see that God is suffering most of all."

"Why don't we hear this on the Sabbath at the synagogue?" piped up one of the men who had not spoken a word until now. "What you are saying is so completely different than what our people are taught."

With obvious modesty and deeper humility, Old Joe clasped his head in both his hands and said, "I do not know the answer to that question. I am just a carpenter, but when I read God's word, that is what it says to me."

It was getting late and most of the men would have to be up early. Their heads were so full anyway that there was no room for any more ideas. So they left in deep thought, some of them even forgetting to say goodnight.

After most of the men had left, Jesus, who had said nothing during the whole discussion but had soaked in all the wisdom which had fallen from his godly father's lips, said to Joseph, "Father, how long have you felt this way?"

"A long time now, my son. Actually, I began to seriously study the prophets about the time your mother and I married. There's no way to explain it to you, but it just seems that new insight came to me gradually after your birth."

"I guess having a son is a pretty life-changing thing for anybody, isn't it?"

Old Joe folded his son in his arms and, with the bear hug this big man had come to be known for, kissed the auburn hair on Jesus' head and said, with great emotion, "My son, you have changed my life forever. I have not been the same since you came. Everyday I thank Jehovah for sending you to us and I keep wondering how we deserved such a son."

Still thinking about the words He had just heard, words about the pain of being God's servants, Jesus asked, "Father, why are people so afraid of being hurt? Why does everybody feel threatened, like nobody can allow himself to be vulnerable? It may hurt to do good things, but it is worth it. I just cannot fathom why our friends pull away from each other as if caring is too risky."

Joseph was so proud at that moment.

"And father, when Jehovah sends the long-awaited One, the government will be on his shoulders. What an awesome job to even think about. Look at all the kings we have had through the centuries since David and the country has always been in a mess."

"When Jehovah sends the Anointed One, He will not be like our previous kings. Some of them were pretenders whom God never put on the throne; some of them went bad almost immediately; and some were just incapable of the responsibility. None of them, none of them ever grasped the real purpose of his kingship. They called themselves the servants of Jehovah, but they acted like any other ruler among the world's nations. They were proud, self-centered, easily compromised, and never dedicated to being servants at all."

Stopping to clear his throat, now choked with emotion, Joseph went on with his explanation. "All the prophets, whom God sent to keep the kings straight, knew what our failure was. Again and again they warned us about coming judgment unless the nation changed its ways. We abused some of them, even killed them, rather than listen to the truth. Daniel wrote about this."

Clearing his throat again, with a far-away look in his eyes, Jesus' father began reading the prophet's confession from far away Babylon. Jesus was forever amazed at how much his father had written in his own scroll from his days of schooling at the synagogue. "O Lord, righteousness belongeth unto thee, but unto us confusion of face, as at this day; to the men of Judah, and to the inhabitants of Jerusalem, and unto all Israel, that are near, and that are far off, through all the countries to which thou has driven them, because of their trespass that they have trespassed against thee. O Lord, to us belongs the confusion of face, to our kings, to our princes, and to our fathers, because we have sinned against thee. To the Lord, our God, belong mercies and forgiveness though we have rebelled against him; neither have we obeyed the voice of the Lord, our God, to walk in his laws, which he set before us by his servants, the prophets."

The hair stood up on the back of Jesus' neck as He listened to his father read those sacred words. It was almost uncanny, and He surely could not understand why, but the prayer of Daniel was like the ringing of a bell on a clear day. He could have sworn that He had heard that confession when the prophet offered it to Jehovah. In the back of his mind, there were visions of the heavenly Father being moved with compassion as He listened. And Jesus thought He remembered having heard Jehovah God assuring Daniel that Israel's day of glory would come, but it would come through a period of great trouble.

"Do you think, daddy, that the Messiah will come in your lifetime?"

Joseph shook his head vigorously, not that he did not believe such a thing could happen, but to acknowledge that no one could really know that.

"Everything is ripe for the fruit to fall from the tree," answered Old Joe. "There is something in the air. A lot of us sense that the night is about over and that the day star will soon rise with healing in his wings. With God, however, time is of little concern. A day with God is as a thousand years and a thousand years is the same as a day. Jehovah has all eternity to work out his plan for us. And He will do it, son, He will do it in his time."

Nothing else was said that evening, but there would be many other nights.

It was the best of times, thought Jesus to himself. But it was also the worst of times. The storm in Israel was tearing away the bulwarks of a nation. Every night the darkness was thicker and deeper. But lately, every sunrise seemed a little more promising.

Jesus stretched out his arms every morning and breathed deeply of the fresh, clean air, thanking God for the beauty of the day and the promise of good things to come. Thinking ahead, He had lately come to the place where, as He rubbed the sleep from his eyes, He would say to Jehovah, "Perhaps today, Lord?"

CHAPTER EIGHT

Joseph was always tired. He had to work very hard just to keep bread on the table.

It was not unusual for Mary to act like she was not hungry when the cupboard was nearly empty. Often the children went to sleep wanting more to eat. And that made her cry. On the few special occasions when there was a chicken on the table, Mary would eat the neck or the back all the while insisting that they were her favorite pieces. The children would laugh and poke fun at her for eating those old bony things. And she would laugh with them. But no one was fooling anybody. She loved chicken as much as anyone else. She just loved little boys and girls more.

Lately, Joseph was more weary than his wife had ever seen him. Added to the work itself was the worry about his business. There had been a notable slump in income as of late. Business had slowed for no known reason. It had happened before and every time they had managed to pull through. This time, however, the prospects did not look good.

A larger number of customers than usual owed him money. But there was no way he could run a business without giving people time to pay for what they purchased. Some had promised to pay later, However, the time for payment had come and gone with no sign of the money. Joseph felt sure that his customers, most of whom he had done business with for many years, were good for their debts and that they would eventually be in to settle their over-due accounts. But that did not put bread and fish on the table at the moment.

Mary was troubled, too. Every day pushed her stress to the limit. But she had an uncanny way of keeping her anxiety to herself and making her husband feel better with her words of encouragement. The children had noticed how Joseph's spirits were lifted after Mary had talked to him. And they loved her for what she did to help their daddy through the tough times.

Jesus had overheard them talk before, often discussing the usual business and household pressures, and He always sensed when something was wrong. That night Joseph had said something about money being so short that he could not buy five sparrows. These little birds were the cheapest of food and were bought for two farthings. Actually, the market price was two for a farthing. They were so plentiful that, if a customer would buy four, the shop keeper would throw in an extra free of additional charge.

It was all the family could do just to make ends meet. Other homes in the neighborhood were having similar problems, but Joseph took little comfort from that. When supper was over in the evening, there was never anything left on the dish because someone didn't like that day's menu. Every child in the household gladly ate what was set before him without question and with much thanksgiving.

Joseph and Mary knew very well that they were not the only poor people in the world. In fact, no place on earth was more economically deprived than the rustic village where Jesus lived. Nazareth was a backward little town where almost everybody shared the same impoverishment. The wealthy lived far away where they enjoyed the luxuries of multi-room villas, several wives, many servants, and the most exquisite food and wine. Few people in Nazareth had ever seen inside one of these rich houses. Among the poor there were no servants, but there were numerous neighbors. And they all needed each other.

How well Jesus recalled that midnight when a neighbor came knocking at the door. A relative from Capernaum had just arrived and the neighbor had nothing to feed him. Joseph was nearly destitute, too. So he went running to a half dozen other neighbors. Together they made up enough to set a little bread before the new-comer. Everybody wanted to help, but it was reluctantly that any one of them surrendered what he was counting on for the morrow. Joseph remarked, remembering the incident with humor, that he had acquired the bread mainly because his friends had to get rid of him so they could get some sleep!

Jesus had never known the luxuries which the priests at Jerusalem enjoyed. His father had been galled by it and even complained about the hypocrisy to his friends, people like himself who were working their fingers to the

Leslie H. Woodson

bone. Young Jesus wondered what it might be like to
dress in such finery, to have enough to eat with some to
spare, and never to feel the cold night wind because the
house was always warm. His own house, although it was
made of field stones and clay, was never comfortable in
the winter. Some mornings He would wake up and see
the steam from his own breath.

"Don't fret about it," Mary would say. "Don't be
anxious. Anxiety will only tear your insides out. God
knows what we need better than we know ourselves. We
don't need to inform Him and we certainly can't let Him
hear us complaining!"

She just had a way of making her family face up to
things. Her words did not make them warmer, but they
made the children *feel* warmer. And that was no small
accomplishment. Sometimes she would pull the little ones
up close and spread her own thin tunic about them,
tucking it tightly around their necks. The tunic did not
help much, but her warm arms embracing them helped a
lot.

That composure of spirit and immunity to worry,
which was so evident in Mary, became a model for the
whole family to emulate. Jesus did better with it than the
rest because He could see the wisdom in the way she
lived. Things just seemed to work out for her. All his life,
He had lived from hand to mouth with his family. Often
the next day's meal was nowhere in sight. Yet, though He
was seldom full, Jesus could not remember a time in his
life when God had failed to provide, as if by miracle, what

was needed at the time. While the needs of tomorrow were not met until the morrow arrived, there was no reason He could think of for anyone who trusted in God to concern himself about those needs today!

Jesus knew what it was to wear patches on his garments. There was no such thing as purchasing new clothing when one grew tired of the old. Nothing ever went out of fashion. An item of clothing had to be worn until it was threadbare. Even then, it was usually handed down to the younger child, restored to use again and again by Mary's ingenious needle. Mary had patched her children's tunics so often that she had found herself patching the patches.

One afternoon, when Jesus was eight years old, He caught his tunic on a thorn and literally tore a plug from it. Knowing how displeased his mother was when extra mending was required due to carelessness, He slipped into Mary's sewing basket and sewed a patch over the rent. His efforts only aggravated the hole. Before the week had ended, the patch had pulled the edges of the tear and the hole was larger than ever.

That night, Jesus' mother got her sewing basket and sat down with her son. While she repaired the rent which He had made far worse by trying to hide what had happened, she explained what it was that had gone so wrong.

"When you are patching a garment," she said, "the cloth which is used for the patch must be as old and as dry as the garment being repaircd. If you use a new piece of cloth which has not had time to shrink, it will draw up in the sun and rain."

Jesus was listening, but his mother could see that He was unfamiliar with what she was trying to describe.

"Why does that hurt anything?" asked the boy. "Won't the cloth in the garment just move with the new piece? Look, I can move my tunic anywhere I want to."

Mary smiled and tried again.

"The material in the old weather-beaten garment has shrunk as much as it is going to and when the new piece begins to draw up, the old clothe will give way to the pull. And when it lets go, there is a bigger tear in the old cloth."

As she explained all this, Mary was pulling and stretching both the old and the new material.

The boy was interested, but only to a point. Sewing was not his thing and, while He sat still as his mother taught him about the nature of cloth, He was glad when the lecture was over. But He never forgot that homey lesson. Actually, He never forgot anything.

Work had picked up again in the carpenter's shop and living was a little less pinched than it had been. The family had survived once more. And it could not have happened at a better moment, because it was Adar, or February, and one of Israel's sacred festivals was about to be observed.

Being among those who took the traditions of

Israel seriously, most of the holy festivals were observed in some way by the family of Joseph and Mary. The feast of Purim was a time of general merry-making in remembrance of the deliverance of the Jews as described in the book of Esther. The people were not required or even expected to come to Jerusalem for Purim. It could be celebrated anywhere. And devout Jews scrimped and saved in order to celebrate the historical event which, when remembered, brought great rejoicing.

Mary had prepared a succulent portion of goat meat surrounded by baked apples and smothered with an almond sauce. Four of the close neighbors had gone together and bought the goat which had been equally quartered. Such a wonderful meal was a real treat because of its rarity. Jesus had smelled it cooking, or thought He did, all the way up the village street to the shop where He had been helping Joseph after school hours. Needless to say, it was hard to keep his mind on his work. For a climax to the meal, his mother had fixed a large bowl of fig jelly which happened to be one of her son's favorite dishes.

Everyone enjoyed the festivities as much as did Jesus himself. It was not often that the family had such a feast and the boys took advantage of it. Mary had hoped that some of the goat would be left for lunches during the coming days but, seeing her boys' happy eyes and endless appetites, she did not have the heart to suggest that they ration the sweet morsels.

And it was all eaten. The clay plates were licked

clean and the bones looked like they had been bleached in the mid-summer sun when the family finished with them. As Joseph watched the quick disappearance of the supper, he was careful not to let anyone detect his concern. But he wondered where he would ever get enough to provide for all the continuously hungry mouths in the weeks to come.

After dinner, Joseph retold the story of Esther, the Jewish queen of Ahasuerus, the Persian king. Had it not been for this dedicated Hebrew maiden, whom God had sent to do a special work for His people, the Jewish race would have been wiped out. When the story was finished, the furniture was pushed to the side and there was dancing and singing as the family held hands and gleefully worked off the sumptuous meal they had just completed. Jesus cherished the memory of that wonderful day. Even more, He cherished his god-fearing, hard-working parents who gave so completely of themselves for their family.

Joseph had always been honest. Jesus had observed that he would rather lose a whole day's work than to have a customer think him guilty of cheating. The family never had much, but what they did have was honestly earned. In that, there was joyful contentment.

There were numerous occasions when an opportunity arose for him to cut corners. Had he been of a mind to use inferior woods, in places unseen in the finished product, no one was likely to know. And by being a little careless about the manner in which he constructed his work projects, the volume of production could be greatly increased. This would mean more profit and, as a result, more supplies, on the bare pantry shelves, for the struggling family.

"But Joseph would know. And God would know," the carpenter would say to his boys when someone laughed at him for being so meticulous and honest.

"There's not a man in town or in the surrounding countryside who can say that he has ever been cheated by Joseph or his son," proudly insisted the carpenter, as he drove home a tenon into its well-fitting mortise.

These shop-worn principles of ethics in business were soaked in by Joseph's children like water in a sponge. Later in the life of Jesus, people were to see these admirable qualities and positive attitudes come through time after time. The meaning and value of responsibility, which had been exemplified before him as a child, became second nature. Joseph deplored pretension in any form believing that the fundamental prerequisite for maturity is always honesty and trustworthiness. And he further denounced any talk about religion which ignored one's personal responsibility to his neighbor.

Down the lane from the place where the family lived, there dwelt a farmer and two sons whom Jesus knew very well. The boys were near his own age, one slightly younger and the other about two years older, who often wandered into the shop. Their father had done business with Joseph on a regular basis. It was always

157

strange to Jesus how two brothers could be so completely different.

One, the older boy, was an extrovert, talking loudly and bragging about what he could do without ever doing anything at all. A decent enough fellow, but all mouth, the sort of guy who easily got on your nerves. He had been named for his uncle Joed who, according to the neighborhood grapevine, had been a loud-mouthed blacksmith whom nobody could stand to be around. The uncle had been dead for a long time, but he lived on in his nephew.

"What a relief!" Joseph would sigh, on those occasions when Joed would leave following one of his irritating visits in the shop.

The younger boy, on the other hand, was very likeable. His disposition was more that of his dad who was rather quiet and spoke slowly. Eli, the younger son, and his dad were liked by most all the working men of the village and an atmosphere of comradery prevailed when they were around. Good natured joking and laughing were the order of the day.

That was why Jesus was so shocked to hear that Eli had that very morning flatly refused to work with his father in the fields. The reason was unknown, but no one could remember a time when Eli and his dad were not together in the field either sowing or reaping or clearing out rocks. At the moment, when Jesus heard the news, Eli could not be found. And in a tiny village like Nazareth, where everyone knew everybody's business, the entire community was upset about old Eli's boy.

Joed, who was usually unreliable, had agreed to anything his father wanted. Trouble was that nobody could ever depend on his word. It was as if he did not know the difference between a lie and the truth. He could, as he had done that morning, look straight into his father's eyes and lie with absolutely no embarrassment.

By late afternoon, the boys' father returned home disconsolate because he had not found his youngest son anywhere. As he wandered into the field, hoping against hope that something tragic had not happened to him, he saw that the work in the fields, which needed attention, had been done. His first thought was that his neighbors had gotten together and completed the job for him. That was the way poor folks were. When a friend got into a hole, they dug him out.

What had happened, however, was something quite unexpected. The younger son had returned, repentant of his rebellion, and had completed the entire task by himself. Joed had not gone near the fields, but had wasted the whole day in town. Once again he had conned his patient father into believing that he could be trusted.

The incident had made a deep and lasting impression on Jesus. And Joseph had taken advantage of the situation to draw an important lesson. "Responsibility," he noted, "is not something we say, but something we do! Unless a man builds confidence by his integrity, his word means nothing at all."

It was an ever-recurring thing. Each night,

159

whether the lesson was learned in the morning at school or in the afternoon at the wood shop, some new idea about the business of living occupied the serious mind of the young apprentice carpenter. And each morning, following those nights, He would be up before the others, alert and anxious to discover and experience some additional knowledge.

Hardly had he roused himself from sleep that mid-summer morning when Joseph, rubbing the night out of his eyes, announced with a loud voice, "Grab your gear, boys, we are going to visit Zeb."

Zeb was what Joseph called Zebedee, husband of Salome, Mary's sister. Father of James and John, he and his family lived near the Sea of Galilee, about thirty miles northeast of Nazareth. They were engaged in a fishing business which supplied food for towns around the lake as well as villages to the south. While the carpenter's shop was seldom closed, once in a while it was smart to take a few days off. Such was a necessity for the sake of sanity alone.

Jesus liked to hunt and fish as much as any boy. But as He grew older, He found himself being drawn to the mountains and lakes for other reasons as well. The serene lakeside was so peaceful and the white-stone mountains were alive with voices of the patriarchs and the prophets. Life was becoming such an adventure of excitement for him that it seemed almost sinful to waste time netting fish and snaring game. The mountains became a growing addiction during his late teens. Prior to that time, there was nothing He liked more than to go fishing with Joseph and the boys. Due to the rigors of school and shop, however, there had been little time for the much-needed togetherness with his younger brothers.

In a way, these cousins in the north country seemed as much like brothers as his own family. Salome, Mary's sister, was such a sweet, kind aunt that He thrilled at the thought of seeing her again.

Drawing near to the lake, the big fishing boats could be seen in the distance. There were dozens of them strung out across the gleaming waters. Zebedee owned four such boats, and printed on the side of each one were the words, "ZEBEDEE AND SONS–WHOLESALE FISHERMEN." Zeb was a veteran fisherman, toughened and calloused by the demands of the sea. And he had done well in his business, very well, indeed. One had only to look at the spacious house where he lived to know that Zebedee had arrived.   James and John, his partners in the family business, were indispensable to him.

Maybe it was partly because of the sea-going men he had to work with, but Zebedee was not very religious. No one had ever seen him at the synagogue. His language wasn't always fitting for a gentleman, but the big fisherman was not particularly interested in being a gentleman anyway. And when things at work did not go right, he would explode all over the place with profane expletives which made even the fish blush. No one called

him by his name anymore. Everyone felt free to call him "Thunder." And he didn't mind. Come to think of it, he was a bit proud of his reputation.

The day after arrival, Jesus accompanied his cousins as they rowed out onto the lake with Zebedee. They had not been out long until a sudden squall arose and the wind became furious. As the boat rolled with the waves, Jesus stumbled and fell against the side of the boat, knocking some of the rigging into the swirling waters. Old Thunder was so enraged that he swore at his young nephew with words which Jesus had never heard and the meaning of which He could only imagine. While such treatment could have made him despise his uncle, Jesus felt nothing but sympathy for him.

Suddenly, Jesus shouted, "John! Look at the fish!" Turning quickly in the direction of the voice, John saw his cousin leaning over the side of the boat, looking into the blue waters.

"What is it?" cried John as he ran forward and stretched over the boat's edge. "What are you talking about?"

Pointing at the clear waters rushing past the moving boat, Jesus excitedly said, "Look at the fish! Did you ever see so many fish? There must be a thousand of them!"

By this time, James and Zebedee were peering into the deep with them. "Don't see a thing," said Zeb. And James replied, "Neither do I."

Just then, reaching his hand into the water, Jesus

pulled up a live and wriggling fish big enough to make supper for them all. Foul-mouthed Zeb said nothing as James and John looked at him with wondering faces.

CHAPTER NINE

Mary and Joseph had four sons and two daughters who were born to them after the miraculous birth of their first child. The other six births were as ordinary as those of the masses which swirled around their little neighborhood in Nazareth.

James was the oldest, born twenty-seven months after Jesus. Even as an infant, James had a thick crop of black hair which was always unruly. His skin was lighter than that of Jesus, a contrast to the shinny black hair which grew low on his forehead. Like two dark spots in his face, his eyes were captivating, penetrating right into your soul. People usually felt exposed when in his presence and were sometimes seen pulling their clothing more tightly about them.

Complementing the authoritative demeanor of this youthful Nazarene was his deep, guttural voice. More than once neighbors suggested that James would miss his chance if he did not become a religious instructor, maybe a rabbi. He not only looked the part, but he talked quite a lot. At times Jesus thought it might be better if James said a little less and thought a little more. But no issue was ever made of it and, frankly, he was Jesus' favorite brother. That would be natural as they were nearer to one another's age than were the others.

There were moments when the conversation of these two brothers turned to religion, but those serious discussions became less and less as they grew older. At times, Jesus gave James reason to believe that the subject of religion was all He ever thought about. And James was by nature not a religious person. Mary often remarked that he seemed more like the son of Zebedee than of Joseph. Not that he was a bad boy – far from it. Growing up, he was obedient and respectful toward his parents' deep beliefs, but his interest lay elsewhere. The younger boy was more intrigued with camels and silks and caravans and a pocket full of shekels. It was Mary's guess that he would one day be a successful merchant bringing priceless things to Nazareth from afar, perhaps enriching the entire family.

Joses had been named for his father, the shortened Greek form of Joseph being Joses. Under more normal circumstances, the son born first would have been given his father's name, but the name Jesus, the Greek equivalent for Joshua, had been decided by the angel who announced his conception. Joses' invasion of the family came soon on the heels of James who was only fourteen months old when the third member of the family arrived. Mary had a hard time giving birth to him even with the help of the Hebrew midwives. No one ever knew why. But by the time Joses was two years old, it was noticeable that he was a frail child subject to ever-recurring bouts with childhood diseases. Seemed like it took much longer for him to recover than was the case with the older boys. His mother became so solicitous of the health of little

Joses that James was clearly envious. The attention given to Joses was eagerly soaked up, but Jesus kept reminding James that, even so, he had no reason to dislike his brother.

Little brother, as Jesus always referred to him, was not at all like his older siblings. His hair was brown with a reddish streak on the left side. And, by the time he was six, it was always neatly kept in place with a hair band around his forehead. He just liked it that way and was never impressed by James' mat of black, wiry stuff.

Joses learned his daily lessons easily, as if figures, words, and thoughts came naturally. The whole family found the child's bent to learning a bit uncomfortable because he out-classed just about everybody in the household. Joseph spoke the Aramaic of the common folk but knew hardly any Greek. Mary, of course, had little time for studies of any sort with all the work of caring for her growing family. James and Joses were both highly intelligent, although James had a battle with grammar and Jesus struggled with math. As Joses developed into a teenager, Mary decided that here was her rabbi.

There were two baby sisters. One was called Rachel, in memory of an ancestor's beloved wife, and the other was given the name Elizabeth for Mary's cousin. The mother of John the Baptist, Elizabeth, was honored by her namesake. Both the girls had smooth olive skin and auburn hair. But that is where the similarity stopped. Rachel was hyper, loud-talking, and impulsive. As would

Leslie H. Woodson

be expected, she was in daily trouble. She found it very easy to sass her mother. And her demands for freedom from the rules caused her parents more than a little grief.

For one thing, as she developed into a beautiful young woman, Rachel allowed herself to mingle with the town's seamy side. More than a few times, she returned home late in the evening having drunk too much pomegranate wine. The local beverage was not expensive and her wealthier friends made it readily available to her. Since she always seemed to have money, Mary feared that she was being paid by the rowdy boys for her favors. It was not a pretty sight. Elizabeth, on the other hand, was quiet and every bit the little lady. She was proper and refined and the entire neighborhood was impressed.

Zacharias, the father of John the Baptist, told all the honorable bachelors he knew that one of them was going to be a lucky man. "That little Elizabeth is going to make some man a wonderful wife," he would say, as proudly as if she were his own child.

And the boys all knew that old Zach was telling the truth. The problem was how to get her attention since she was so quiet and shy. Her mother never worried about young Beth. If anything, Mary wished that she were a little more social and out-going, but then there was Rachel! What could a mother do?

Jesus instinctively reached out to Beth because of her sensitive soul. But, He also felt a deep sense of disappointment as Rachel continued her frivolous ways.

Again and again, He had stretched out his arms to her, but she always turned away. The pain in his heart was more than anyone knew.

Elizabeth was to be the nearest thing to a rabbi that the family would have. When old enough, she called her beloved papa to a private corner of the little house and opened her heart to him. She had always been close to her daddy and felt free to share anything with him. Rachel hardly ever talked to him and it broke his heart. But, since the day when Elizabeth began to form sentences, it was to Joseph she ran when she wished to bare her soul.

"Daddy," she began, "I am now a woman on my own. You have been a great father. You have protected me, provided for me, listened to me, understood me, and loved me. And I will never forget. Your life has been lived before me without pretense. I have watched you every day. Now I want to thank you for not only teaching me about God, but for showing me the way. There must have been times in my growing up when I disappointed you, but I never forgot what you taught me."

The huge brown eyes of Old Joe filled with tears. As they began to trickle down his cheeks, he wrapped his big muscular arms around his baby girl and, with broken voice, said, "My child. You have never disappointed me. Your affection has kept me going when everything looked bleak."

Joseph, soft-hearted and sentimental as he was, wiped his eyes and blew his nose. "You never begged for

169

those things which I could not afford. You always understood when you had to wear your sister's out-grown tunics. And I never heard you complain when she ran off with the last fragment of barley bread and you were still hungry. Little Beth, you are my pet. I will do anything for you. And I am not fearful now that you will ask something that I cannot give."

"Daddy, daddy," broke in Beth, "there is nothing that I want you to give me except your blessing."

Surprised and thinking that some romantic young man had suddenly swept her off her feet, he could not believe that she had said nothing about it before. It was not like her to be impulsive yet, try as he might, he could not think of a single village boy she might be considering.

"I want to be a Nazarite," she blurted out.

It was not at all what Old Joe had expected. And he was visibly shocked. While women could dedicate themselves to be Nazarites, such a role was customarily assumed by men like Samson, and her cousin, John the Baptist, who would one day take the vow.

Beth was asking permission of her father, who would be the head of the family as long as he lived, to enter the lifestyle of those who, in consecration to Jehovah, renounced the world with its pleasures and defiling influences. As a rule, the vow was taken for a period of time, but Elizabeth said, "Daddy, this will be my life from today until the hour of my death."

It took no time for Joseph to grant his blessing. The next day, beautiful Beth, who everyone knew would make a good wife, gave herself body and soul to God. She would never be anyone's wife except God's. She would never know the joy of having children. Being a Nazarite did not prohibit marriage, but for Beth it did. In her heart of hearts she knew that.

That night Mary tried to console her husband who was so choked up with ecstatic sadness that he could not sleep.

"Life plays such tricks on us," Joseph explained. "There's sweet little Beth who will never know a man. And there's Rachel who has known them all."

Stabbed to the heart, Mary shuddered and blew out the lamp.

But there were two other children, both boys, and they were twins. Their names were common enough. The little fellows were dubbed Judas and Simon. Probably no two names were found more often in the annals of Judaism than these. Judas was rather fair complected and Simon was a shade darker. Both had the typical Hebrew features with similar dispositions. While not shy or introverted, they were not hyper like Rachel either.

Jesus was past seventeen years of age when the twins came to live in the little house in the valley of Nazareth. Being the oldest of the children, He had already attained the demeanor of an adult. Times were hard and everyone had his assigned chores, that of the elder son always being a bit harder. No one complained.

Considering the attitudes of the two sisters, no one

171

was surprised that it was Elizabeth who, while still living at home, took the twins under her wing. "I can't imagine what I would do without my little Beth," Mary would say. Beth's sister resented such remarks, but they were noticeably true. Relatives and friends were forever shaking their heads at their inability to tell the twins apart. Nonetheless, while they were identical, Beth could tell which was Judas and which was Simon in a second. There were little things like a small wrinkle in Simon's left ear and the more subtle nuances in the way Judas formed certain words. Only a mother – or a dotting older sister – would notice such things.

Joseph had been busier than usual in the carpenter's shop and he lamented the fact that he did not have more time to spend with the twins. Like every father, he worried when the work got slow. And it did at times. Right after the birth of the twins, however, it had picked up and there were more orders than he could handle. His reputation was growing. The news had gotten around that Old Joe made the best yokes and plow handles in Galilee. The yokes never chafed the oxen and the plow handles seemed never to break. Young Jesus was fast learning the trade working with his father every day after finishing his studies. He was becoming quite adept with the adz, probably the most difficult of all the tools to master.

Some days He and Joseph worked late, so late that everyone but mother Mary was asleep by the time they dragged themselves home. Tired or not, Jesus would always make his way to the straw mat where the twins lay and, leaning down, kiss them gently. Then, without fail, He would whisper, "Sweet dreams little lambs and may the Good Shepherd shield you from all harm 'till the shadows of the night give way to the morning light."

The years were flying by and the children were growing up. Judas and Simon were not infants anymore. They were now into everything and a real handful for their mother. James was nearly fifteen and very handsome. And Old Joe? Well, Joseph was not as ancient as old Levi, grandfather of Carli, Jesus' best friend in the community, but he was considerably older than Mary. At fifty-seven his body was showing the stress and strain of his large family. The young apprentice son had noticed that his dad was more stooped than He remembered. Never could He recall hearing the aging carpenter complain. Nevertheless, it was lately impossible for Joseph to hide his shortness of breath as he handed the bow saw to his boy.

The day began like every other workday. It was mid-morning and the carpenter's shop had been open since dawn. Several customers had been in and an old friend, who had not been seen around for a while, had dropped in for a chat. Finally, there was a lull in the traffic and the shop was now empty save for the stooped, brown-skinned proprietor and his boy apprentice. Supporting himself

173

with the wood handle of the adz, Joseph raised himself slowly from the three-legged stool where he had been sitting throughout the earlier conversation. Without a word, Joseph fell face down on the hard-packed earthen floor.

Rushing to his side, Jesus dropped to his knees and rolled his father onto his back. His eyes were barely open, but he was not dead. While it had never been obvious before, Jesus noticed the wrinkles, the lines nestled behind his father's beard, the jagged scar on his left jaw

"Papa! Papa! " shouted the aproned lad, horror all over his face. "Can you hear me? Papa, you must not die! We need you. What would mama do? And the twins? Papa, please talk to me!"

Flax, who often wandered in and out of the shop, had just appeared at the door and, sensing that something was wrong with Old Joe, began to bark wildly.

With much effort, Joseph tried to speak. The words came slowly, with much effort, deliberate emphasis being placed on each word.

"Something . . . I must . . . tell . . . you . . ." whispered the old carpenter. "Lean down."

"No, No, Papa," cautioned Jesus as He placed his fingers on his dad's lips. "Maybe you should save your strength."

Joseph rallied a bit and continued barely audible.

"My boy . . . you have been like a son to me." His voice grew stronger. "It has been . . . a joy being . . . your dad. No one could . . . no man could . . . be so blessed.

But I must . . . tell you something which . . . you do not know. Your mother has pondered this in her . . . heart since before you were born. But now . . . now it is my duty to . . . tell you the truth. I . . . I am not . . . I am not your father."

For some reason, the young apprentice was not surprised. No one ever told him, but somehow He knew. Not until many years later did the lad, who loved Joseph more than any man on earth, begin to understand what Old Joe meant. And the clearer it all became, the deeper grew his love and affection for his mother's husband.

The family came for Joseph. His body was laid to rest on a sloping little limestone hill near the family house in Nazareth. All the children were there. Zechariah and Elizabeth, who had been visiting friends in a near-by village, came with young John. Jesus and John felt a bond that day they had not known before. Yet, what John would discern thirteen years later, on the banks of the Jordan, had not so much as entered his mind. Even for Jesus, the vision was blurred.

During the coming years Jesus, as the first-born son, would fill the shoes of Joseph. The family's well being would be on his shoulders until every child could shift for himself. The responsibility was a frightening one to confront, but being the elder son insured not only special blessings, but an extra load of terrifying obligations.

Now that He had become the chief carpenter in the

tiny shop, working hours would be even longer. What two had done before must now be done by one who was still a novice in the trade. There would be a little help from the younger brothers, but the burden was his alone.

Trees had to be felled and back orders had to be filled lest the business fail. That was a real possibility, but one which could not be permitted. Three months before Old Joe died, the sign over the rough wooden door had been re-worded. For years it had read JOSEPH'S WOOD SHOP. Now it said JOSEPH AND SON – CUSTOM WOOD PRODUCTS. Jesus was proud of that sign and never considered altering it after the death of his father. Not once did the seventeen year old feel sorry for himself for having such awesome responsibility. After all, the oldest son knew from the time He turned twelve that He was a man.

About five months had lapsed since the death of Joseph and young Jesus was having real problems in caring for grieving Mary, the younger children, and the shop. Creditors were pressing for unpaid funeral bills and, in spite of himself, the junior carpenter had almost more than one person could handle.

The single incident in his life which made the deepest impression on his vulnerable mind happened right in the midst of all this tension. There was a knock on the door of the little shop and Jesus, laying aside the ax handle which He had been shaping, opened the rough-hewn door only to be met by the landlord who had come for the rent which was a month overdue. When the boy tried to explain the problems which the family was facing, the greedy property owner was unmoved. He threatened to evict the whole family unless payment were received within ten days. Jesus could not understand how anyone could be so in love with money that he had no compassion.

The rent was paid in time to save the embarrassment, but nobody ate well during that period while the money was being saved.

During the years which were to follow, Jesus could have walked off and left his mother and her children to survive as best they could. That would not have been the first time such a thing had happened in Nazareth. Everyone knew suffering families which had been abandoned by a father or an older son. But, with his growing sense of adult freedom, there was also a relentless demand for personal integrity. To be free was not for him the same thing as being irresponsible. Jesus talked a lot about freedom, but He was never thinking of a license to do as one pleased. Being free meant being able to decide what direction life must take, rejecting any course which would militate against fulfilling the plan which God has for every person. If it were to be meaningful to himself and to others, among whom He lived and to whom He was obligated, life had to embrace more than interest in oneself. To be free was not synonymous with being selfish. It was identical with achieving the ideal ingrained by God within us all.

If He were to be honestly free, Jesus knew that there would never be time to live for himself. His life would be one, long day of giving and sharing and serving – first his family and then the multitudes. Through all those days of arduous life at Nazareth, God was preparing his Son for the day when He would open the door to emancipation from bondage for the whole world, a door which had been shut tight for centuries by the political and religious bureaucracy in Israel, as well as Rome. It was far too early for young Jesus to understand how these things could happen. Nonetheless, the wistful feeling haunted his every thought, night and day, as He mused upon the steps which must be climbed if He were to make a difference.

CHAPTER TEN

John was born in the year 5 B.C., six months before Mary gave birth to Jesus. The two boys were second cousins. Their families were close-knit as were all Hebrew relatives. Even though they saw each other seldom, blood ran thick and often the boy Jesus questioned his mother about John and the fascinating story surrounding his birth.

Zacharias was a priest who was married to a cousin of Mary. Her name was Elizabeth and she was considerably older than young Mary. In fact, Elizabeth was barren and too old to have children. This was a burden almost too heavy to bear, especially for Zacharias, because not having an offspring was the next thing to a curse. And, in addition to that, a man's immortality depended on fathering a son. We die and are soon forgotten unless we have children. In them we continue to live. Grandchildren are an even greater asset. They carry us even further into immortality. As long as there is someone alive to call your name, you will never die. But without children . . . well, it would be better not to be born. At least that was the way the priest in Ein Karem saw things.

Every day, several times a day, Zacharias lifted his hands to Jehovah in prayer from a heart crammed with frustration. How could he be an effective priest if a curse of God were upon him?

"Lord God of Abraham, be not grieved by the prayer of thy servant."

His habitual communication with Jehovah always began with those words. If the Lord were grieved with anything, it was probably this vain repetition lifted day and night, sometimes with inconsolable weeping. After an interval of mournful self-pity, the old priest would ramble on, oblivious to everything around him. Weaving back and forth with near despair, his prayer would continue. "Our father Abraham was granted a son in his old age. Sarah was old and beyond child-bearing and they both had given up on hope. But, Jehovah be praised, when she was older than Elizabeth, You blessed her with Isaac. May my beard turn snow white and my hair fall from my head, but let me not depart this earth with no seed."

The old priest would often stop and wipe a mixture of tears and perspiration from his face. Then he would return to his pleading. "You, O Lord, are a God of miracles and your servant is only a man. You have all power in heaven and earth and I have none . . ."

On and on the heavy hearted priest would ramble. And God heard him. It never felt like anyone was listening, but Someone was.

Zacharias was in the direct line of descent from the priestly family of Abijah and his wife was of the daughters of Aaron, the very first high priest appointed by Moses himself. Surely, such a family would not be denied an heir! So reasoned Zacharias in his more hopeful moments. Actually, there was no more reason why a priest should have a son than any other man. God treats us all alike. Zacharias knew that in his heart. Yet, it is all too human to think that servants of the Lord ought to receive special consideration.

But that was not why God granted the priest's request. Mary had explained that carefully to her inquisitive son who heard the family retell the story again and again. "The Lord is concerned about all people's problems," explained Mary. "He doesn't bless us because we are good or rich or of the right color. And He doesn't judge anyone for those reasons either. The sun shines on the just and the unjust. And everyone gets rained on, too."

Jesus would always act as if his mother had cleared up a great mystery for him. But really, although there was yet no fully developed theology about such things, He had known in his heart that God loves everybody the same. What Mary was telling him was certainly no new revelation.

One day, while Zacharias was bemoaning his fate, even as he officiated in his role as priest, he was interrupted by an unearthly voice.

"Zacharias," said the voice, "Where is your faith? How many times have you asked for a son? Once, you know, would have been enough if you were not so slow to leave it in God's hands. Well, your prayer has been heard. Not because of you, but because of Elizabeth. She is a god-fearing woman, just what Jehovah needs to mother a child whom He will use in a mighty way. She never wore God out with her begging. She just quietly waited and trusted Him to do the right thing. You, Zacharias, are an irritation!"

The old priest was struck speechless.

"Very good," noted the angel – by this time the priest could see his visitor as well as hear the voice – "You talk too much. Because you have this fault, you will remain without voice until the child is born. Then, you will humble yourself by insisting that the boy be named John, not Zacharias."

Try as he might to respond, no sound came out when he opened his mouth. The walk home was fitful – excited, embarrassed, confused. How could the news be given to Elizabeth? He was struck dumb. Would she ever understand?

Jerking on the leather door latch, the priest kicked his way in. Elizabeth dropped her broom. Never had she seen anything whiter than her husband's face. Evidently, something awful had happened. He looked like a ghost.

"Quick! Here," she said, shoving a stool toward him. "Sit down. Let me get you some warm milk. Tell me what is wrong."

The frantic wife was trembling with emotion as Zacharias pointed to the heavens and then to his ear. Apparently, there had been some message from the Lord. Again the finger was raised and lowered again as he tenderly touched Elizabeth's flat belly. It was uncanny. Could it be that Jehovah had promised them a child? It had happened to Sarah, but that was a long time ago and things like that were never heard of anymore.

Nine months later, the aging priest and his older wife welcomed a bouncing baby boy into their home. No question about it. Everyone in town was talking about the miracle at the house of Zacharias.

Instinctively, as the angel said he would do, Zacharias opened his mouth and said, "His name is John. And God has great plans for him!"

Feeling the welcome relief which had suddenly come to him in the return of his speech, Zacharias opened the scroll of the prophet Malachi. He read aloud. His voice was strong and reassuring. Tears streamed down his scraggly beard. "Behold, I will send my messenger, and he shall prepare the way before me: and the Lord, whom ye seek, shall suddenly come to his temple, even the messenger of the covenant, whom ye delight in: behold, he shall come, saith the Lord of hosts."

Jesus had heard the story many times as his mother told it to some new friend. It never failed to intrigue him and fill him with wonder. What exactly did God have in store for John?

When Jesus was about five years old, Mary had taken him and little James to visit Elizabeth in the hill country, a modest lean-to hut where Elizabeth had taken her son immediately after his birth. The need for privacy was a demanding one and the family remained there until John was grown. Jesus recalled the visit and remembered playing with his older cousin. No great impression was made, but He did think at times about the fun they had.

Twelve years had passed since that day. When relatives from surrounding villas arrived for Joseph's funeral, Jesus was delighted to discover that John was in their company. He was now a man of eighteen years and looked very much like a younger version of his dad. Under his nose and around his chin, John wore heavy patches of black beard. No question but that it made him look much older. Young Rachel, Jesus' sister, was in love at first sight, but disappointed that he rebuffed her flirtation.

The trip to Nazareth, from the home where they had been visiting with friends, was a grueling one of several miles, but Zacharias had brought the family as quickly as possible so the young ones, who had not seen each other for a spell, would have some time to get reacquainted. While the old folks talked about things of no interest to the younger set, the kiddies went into the fields to play, the maidens got together under a fig tree to talk about boys, and the young fellows wandered a distance away to one of their more manly sports.

When the games broke up, John and Jesus remained behind. It was dusk and the sun had already begun its drop over the western hills. The cool of the coming night was a welcome relief from the heat of the sun-scorched afternoon.

"What have you been doing with yourself?" asked John of Jesus. "We are grieving with you over the death of Old Joe. I know how this has broken the whole family. Will you be handling the shop alone? Is there any chance that James and Joses might give you a hand?"

"James has already been learning a little of the trade and I think Joses will help some," explained Jesus. "He is not very well, you know. Mom needs a lot of help around the house and the boys will have plenty to do there. Anyway, the job is mine and I am ready to get to it. Dad and I had talked about the business and where I would fit in when he was no longer here. We all knew that day would come."

Turning his head away from the sunset, at which He had been staring as He talked, the young carpenter looked straight into the eyes of John and asked, "And what about you? Are you going to be a priest like your father? Most people are saying that you would be good at it."

Knitting his brow into what appeared to be a grimace, John protested strongly. "Never! That is not for me. Mom and dad keep insisting that I was born for the ministry, but having lived in that atmosphere all my life, the whole thing has left me with doubts. Father is a good man and very careful about his duties. But I get the feeling at times that his work is not very satisfying. What's more, you know as well as I that I could not be a priest if I wanted with this flat nose! The Law disqualifies me because of that alone."

185

His cousin laughed good-naturedly, making no comment on the flat nose.

"Why do you think that?" asked Jesus.

"Think what?"

"Why do you think that your father's work is unsatisfying?"

"Well, for one thing, as I see it, every day is gray for him. There is nothing exciting, nothing to give hope in what he does. Mom and I have often overheard this futility expressed in his prayers. Regardless as to how hard he works for the people, nothing changes. The people look sad. Their lives are hollow. Often we hear them pleading with dad to ask God to send the long-awaited One. Our land is under the gall of Rome and the common people have about given up on ever seeing the kingdom of David restored to them."

With a far away look in his eye, Jesus glanced away again at the sinking sunset, which had now turned into an afterglow of incomparable glory.

"It's getting dark, John. We need to return to the family. The coming night is especially hard when someone has died. Mom needs all the help we can give her. Just knowing that we are there will be a big help."

"That's exactly my point, cousin!" exclaimed John, jumping to his feet. "The night is coming in Israel. I am just a boy, but even I can see this. Things have never been so dark. The darkness is so thick you could cut it with a knife. Our political overseers are vassals of Rome. And the priests, most of them at least, have no courage to speak out."

The boy from Ein Karem was pacing back and forth and gesturing with his hands as if he were deeply distraught about what he was describing. "And how long has it been since the voice of the prophet was heard in the land? Four hundred years! That's how long. Jehovah? Where is He? Why has He abandoned His people? Something has to be done soon and I can't see the priesthood's being the answer."

Everything John said made a lot of sense to the seventeen year old carpenter who was wise beyond his years. There was a moment of silence. Slowly, Jesus stood and, with a twinkle in his eye as if great hope were springing up inside his own heart, commended his older cousin. "You have spoken like a prophet yourself. What will you do if the priesthood is not for you? And you have apparently already decided that it isn't. I have been wrestling with the same dilemma. Not that I ever thought of becoming a priest. But, deep inside my soul there is something forever tugging at me." Jesus paused, looking intently at John. "Mom says it is Jehovah speaking. But how can I know? And what can I do? Do you think the two of us could do anything that would make a difference? After all, who do we think we are anyway?"

The two boys starred blankly at one another. John turned away in thought, then suddenly shifted his body back and looked into Jesus' brown eyes. "Zacharias is always talking at home about the scriptures and the coming Messiah. That's preacher talk, you know," John

187

said with a chuckle. "You cannot count the times he has read the prophet's words to me. He always *read* them, but he did it so often that I can quote them."

At that, the young son of Zacharias sounded more like a priest than his father. With much feeling, he began to recite the words, "Behold, I will send you Elijah the prophet before the coming of the great and dreadful day of the Lord: And he shall turn the heart of the fathers to their children, and the heart of the children to their fathers, lest I come and smite the earth with a curse."

While Jesus could not quote that particular verse as had John, He had learned enough from his carpenter father to recognize that the teachers in Israel expected the prophet Elijah to come back to earth. He would announce the arrival of the Messiah and the restoration of the kingdom of David. Elijah, prince of the prophets, had been dead a long time, but his spirit of prophecy would return in the latter days and prepare the nation for the promised king of Israel.

"What do you think Malachi meant?" added the boy from Ein Karem.

John listened with eager interest while the younger lad explained the content of Malachi's prediction. That was the way Zacharias had understood it, but John had never been sure that there might not be something else there which his father did not see.

"Maybe I'll be a prophet rather than a priest," laughed John. Jesus chuckled with him. "Prophets have never been popular like priests. The priests never upset the people, you know. But the prophets startled and irritated everyone, even the kings! What we have got to have now is not a priest to comfort us, but a prophet to challenge us! I think maybe I could do that, don't you?"

Nodding his head approvingly, Jesus replied, "You've got the guts for it from what I can see. But you know I can't tell you what to do. That's between you and God."

Children from more devout Jewish homes knew a lot about their religion before they were old enough to read. That was true because of the curriculum which was used by both teachers and parents. The bigger part of learning was done at home. The Law and the Prophets were an indispensable part of every lesson. When John mentioned Elijah, Jesus immediately visualized what the old prophet was like. It was as if He actually *remembered* him as a recluse, seldom appearing in public except to announce a word from God. Existing on the barest necessities, Elijah had no time or taste for life's delicacies. His message was one of judgment. And Jesus could not help noting how much like him was John.

Still a growing boy, this cousin had lived in the desert since his birth and no one ever heard much from him. He was studious in the scriptures and seemed, it appeared to Jesus, to have absolutely no interest in the lifestyle of his peers. He was contemplation, deeply serious all the time, about weighty matters. Young Jesus had not realized that until his older cousin appeared at the funeral in the crudest of apparel and consumed none of the spread of food. And, what was most noticeable of all, he scowled and turned his head away when he saw the guests drinking wine.

When Jesus asked him about it, John admitted that his thoughts lately had been turning in the direction of being a Nazarite. When Jesus heard that, He remarked that the news was quite a coincidence because sister Beth had only recently committed herself to the same devoted service.

The two boys, who had now begun to feel more like brothers than cousins, turned their steps downhill toward the house where Mary and the relatives were keeping watch. Members of the family were at work washing and preparing the body for burial. The heavy aroma of spices and perfumes filled the air as they were dumped freely upon the body to retard the smell of decaying flesh.

Joseph's body would be wrapped in long strips of cloth and laid on a makeshift stretcher. Come morning, he would be carried to a ready made hole in a limestone hill. Prayers would be offered by Zacharias and the local priest. It was to be a long night, some of the guests dozing fitfully wherever they could find a spot to lie down or just sit. The one room house was so small that none but the immediate family could stay inside. Some made their way to the courtyards of neighbors to wait.

At the proper time the following morning, the men

gathered up the remains and the procession to the tomb began. All along the way was heard the mournful chanting sound of ritual prayers. One of the friends of young James followed the stretcher playing doleful notes on his homemade flute. There were no professional mourners, since they were too expensive for poor families and Mary did not want them anyway. She didn't need them. Many friends walked beside her and they were all heart-broken. There was enough grieving without paying anyone to wail.

At the door of the tomb, John's father read from the prescribed ritual for the burial of the dead. The readings offered little comfort. Women were all about Mary, holding her up and offering encouragement in the midst of the greatest hurt she had ever known. No one wanted to leave.

It was at that moment that Jesus beckoned to the crowd. He had already started talking and some missed his first words. ". . . and mother wants you to know how you have helped her by being with us during this tough time. As the oldest son, I want to speak a word for my dad. Old Joe, as all of you knew him, was a bigger man than any of you can think. My mother and I know how big he really was. His heart was so big that there was enough room for everyone, especially his wife and me, his first-born. Old Joe always trusted my mother even when he did not understand. And he believed in me, believed that the shop was safe in my hands, and the family as well. Today, out of love and respect for my big-hearted daddy, you are witnesses to my vow to support and protect mom and my brothers and sisters as he did so well."

A shuffling noise was heard in the crowd of spell-bound listeners. One of Joseph's admiring customers shouted, "Hear! Hear!" With that word, the hands of many of the people went up with their response, "Amen! Amen!"

When the noise died down, the young speaker continued. "It occurs to me that such a man as Joseph ought not to die. I know He *looks* dead. But . . . and some of you are thinking that I am just a kid and shouldn't be talking like this . . . but I think maybe he is not dead at all."

A mixed sound of unbelief and hope filtered through the crowd of listeners.

"Maybe he is just resting for a while, or sleeping. With his heavy work load, he never seemed to get enough of it. Or maybe we are just dreaming. Could it be that we are the ones dead rather than my dad? It's hard to explain, but something inside me says that he has slipped away from us to a larger life, a place much better than here. It seems to me that I have seen it myself."

By this time, the crowd of listening people was in the palm of the boy's hand. No one could bat his eye for fear he would miss something. Older people cupped their hands behind both their ears for fear some word would pass them by. You could hear people gasping as though they had caught their breath.

"Who is this lad? Who has he been talking to?" someone whispered in the awkward silence.

"I know that none of you have ever heard such things before, but you have thought about them. Go home now. And don't worry about us. We will be all right. And don't worry about daddy. Somehow I *know* he's all right."

The people disassembled scratching their heads. Even Zacharias was seen thoughtfully stroking his beard. The women folk were quiet as they were expected to be. Only young John, the priest's son, dared break the awesome silence. With both arms above his head, fists clenched, he leaped into the air and shouted, "Thus saith the Lord!" The aging priest was a little embarrassed by the outburst of his son, but down inside his own heart he felt much as did young John, moved nearly to tears.

Since custom required that the house where one had died be considered unclean, the family remained in the open as much as possible. The evening meal would be eaten in the courtyard. That night when mother Mary, Jesus, James, Joses, Beth, and the twins reclined at supper – Rachel had come to the funeral but left immediately – they could not believe their eyes. The neighbors had prepared a sumptuous feast of green vegetables, boiled eggs, goat's cheese, bread with butter, wine, nuts, and fruits in abundance. Few of the native people in Nazareth had much, but when they pitched in at a time of sorrow, it was amazing what they could do with so little.

"Look!" shouted Joses with delight, "We've got chicken and fish both." Seldom did the struggling household have either.

It was their first supper without Joseph. Now the head of the house was Jesus. He was expected to take the lead. And He did. Reaching out for the hand of Mary and James, who in turn took the hands of the other children, this vibrant young man lifted his sun-tanned face toward heaven and offered praise.

"God of our fathers – Abraham, Isaac, and Jacob – our brokenness is not unknown to you. Your eyes are always upon us and your arms around us. Only those who are blind and insensitive would not know You are here. We praise your holy Name for letting us have Old Joe for these many years. I am sitting here in his place tonight, a place much too big for me. What he has done for us, and for You, Jehovah God, will never die. And somehow we believe that he is not dead either. He provided well for us all. Without him, we will all be more dependent upon You. For these reminders of your grace now set before us, we give You praise and glory now and forever. Amen."

Everyone was pleasantly surprised when James added his own "amen" for, even outside the family, it was old news that this younger son was an agnostic.

On the other hand, Mary's first-born was so religiously inclined as a boy that there were times when Joseph had thought He would profit greatly by being exposed to the nurture and discipline of the ascetics who lived near Qumran. The Essenes, as they were called, pursued a rigorous life and, even though the people did not understand their asceticism, they did respect them.

It was known that the community was willing to accept on probation any boy who had reached his twelfth birthday. Mary had discussed the possibilities with Joseph several times. She found it difficult to imagine how life would be without her eldest son and her mother heart drew back from the thought. But, if it were best, she could reconcile herself to it.

When Joseph died, it all became an exploded dream. The situation at home was now grave and there would be little chance to devote his life to anything but the carpenter's shed. All Jesus could do was hope that the day would come when He could lay aside the hammer and apron for something which would satisfy the deep longing of his soul, the desire to do something for the people of Israel who were suffering in poverty and hopelessness.

The responsibilities would mushroom. When James had become old enough to come into the shop, it became the task of Jesus to assist Joseph in teaching him what He himself had learned from their father. And the task was harder than it would have been if James had been more interested in the work of woodworking. Later, when Joses, Simon, and Judas got into the business, the older brother had his hands full. Just teaching them and guiding them in the craft of woodworking took most of his time. The whole business was in the hands of the young carpenters with the oldest son – barely a man – in full charge. Neighbors in Nazareth watched the young carpenter with much admiration and respect, but the honor due him was far less than He deserved. For the most part, people simply accepted what He was doing as being that which was expected.

It was quite a responsibility for so young a man. There were days when Jesus refused to eat in an attempt to get a farmer's plow handles repaired before night. It was not unusual for customers to come into the shop at closing time, sometime to discuss an order and other times just to talk. He just kept going. It was as if He had meat to eat of which the others were not aware.

The days were long and the work was arduous and Mary, though she hated to see her boys work so hard, was proud of the way Jesus accepted the responsibility.

One thing Jesus would have changed if He could. He would have made the days longer so there would be more time to study. About the only chance He had was very late at night after everyone else was asleep on the straw mats. And then, with his lamp in one hand and his notes on the Torah and the oral law in the other, He often had to go out to the shop in order to read and think.

On mornings after He had studied beyond the midnight hour, the young craftsman was usually very tired and sleepy. Though his intentions to quit at a reasonable hour were good, He would have become so absorbed in the scrolls as to be still reading when the first tints of day colored the Judean sky. The more He read, the more excited did the son of Mary become.

God had a message for the whole world and very few people seemed to get it. Everybody made religion a mechanical thing. It appeared to Jesus that God had planned history so that all man had to do was get into the stream of the Spirit. Once in that stream, man learned to live and life became an enriching and meaningful thing. Why did not someone make that clear to the people? God only knew how hard He had tried, talking to his neighbors as well as strangers in the hills, but most of them just plowed laboriously on in their depression.

The kingdom of God, as Jesus was beginning to understand it, was not a political enclave like Israel within the borders of Rome. It was not political at all. Most of the rabbis continued to leave the ignorant masses under the impression that the kingdom of God was a Hebrew regime to replace Rome. But Jesus knew that the kingdom of Jehovah was the *reign* of God in the hearts of men, a rule of justice and righteousness which was present wherever men and women embraced it. Romans could be a part of it, too. It was everywhere, all over the earth. People just could not see it.

It was true that the prophets wrote of a day when the glory of Israel would return. In no way, however, did any of those wise men think of Israel's place in the future as one of military might over subject peoples. The coming glory would be the rule of Jehovah over *both* Israel and the nations, Israel itself being the heart of that benevolence.

Surely someone, thought Jesus, will point it out.

197

Surely, someone besides me understands this. Thus far, however, the whole wonderful truth had been kept a secret and Jesus wondered how long it would be before a much-needed prophet would get the nation back on track.

CHAPTER ELEVEN

Excitement was in the streets. The birth of a baby was everyone's business in a town of three hundred people, all of whom considered everyone's business to be the rightful possession of everybody else. Nothing was secret. No one wanted it to be. There were a few nosey meddlers, but most of the folks felt like family, and the neighbors cared for one another.

Ben Haggi, the stone cutter's son, had married one of the town's most likeable girls and the morning grapevine tingled with the news of a new daughter at the Haggi house.

Mary was drying her hands and untying her apron. No sooner had she heard the joyful news from the town crier, her next door friend, than she was off in a run. By the time Mary arrived, there were so many women already there that she had to force her way into the room. Every woman in the room had to hold the little girl, touch its tiny nose, and speak some nothings to her in a squeaky little voice just right for the baby's ears.

As Mary's turn came and she held the soft infant in her arms, the memories came flooding back, memories from that courtyard stable where she had held her own. All the way home, she relived that holy night so many years ago in a town far away.

Coming in from the shop at even time, Jesus and the boys had heard the news and were inquiring about the child. In those days, everyone had a soft spot for little babies. Of course, as would be expected, the men were disappointed that the newborn child was not a boy.

The custom in Palestine was for friends, neighbors, and musicians to gather at the house where it had been announced that a child was about to be born. When the birth finally took place, if it was a boy, the musicians broke into music and singing. If it was a girl, the musicians went home! So, while the family and friends remained to congratulate the mother, the festivities were short-lived.

During dinner, the conversation at Mary's house was almost entirely restricted to discussion about the Haggis. Nothing was said, however, about the disappointment. Finally, weary from another day of sawing and nailing at the wood shed, the boys drifted off to bed. That is, with the exception of Jesus who was, as a general rule, the last to collapse on his straw mat.

"What was it like when I was born?" He asked his mother.

Not until that moment had Jesus ever asked about the times of his life which He could not remember. He did know that He was born in Bethlehem where his parents had gone to pay their taxes. And He also knew that the town was so crowded that Mary gave birth to him in a stable behind the town's inn. That, Jesus had heard. But nothing else.

Mary had never found the right time to share the details with her son because it was all so hard to explain without sounding unbalanced. But, now that He had asked, she decided to tell her son about his birth.

She began at the beginning.

"When we found out that we had to go to Judea to be enrolled in the census and pay our taxes, we didn't know what we were going to do. It's a long way from Nazareth to Bethlehem. Your father's people were all from there, so there was no choice. We had to go."

"Why didn't you stay home and let dad go by himself?" Jesus asked.

"It was our first baby and we wanted to be together when you were born, and Joseph would not have gotten back in time. So we took our chances."

"Sounds like an ordeal to me."

"It was worse than that. I rode the burrow up the hills and walked down the other side. Just bouncing on that little donkey was enough to have brought you early. The trip itself was uneventful. Didn't have any trouble, but it took several days and we were worn out by the time we arrived."

"You've told me that I was born in a stable."

"Oh, son, the town was filled with people like us, people who had come to be enrolled. The town's one little inn was full up to the brim. Other than being irritable from the pressure of tired people wanting a place to sleep, the keeper was polite and helpful. We were fortunate to be allowed in the stable. Never thought to complain."

"Wasn't it cold," asked Jesus.

"Very cold. But we were out of the wind and

there was a lot of straw and hay, so we snuggled and kept warm. Anyway, it wasn't for long. In the early hours of the morning, before daybreak, you were born. You were an easy birth. The Lord saw to that and we were grateful."

Mary told him how beautiful He was lying there in swaddling clothes with the hay pulled close around him to keep him warm. She mentioned the pink of his cheeks and the beautiful brown eyes which finally opened on a brand new world. And what a sweet thing it was to hold him in her arms, so warm and cuddly, and nurse him until He fell asleep. There was no child in the whole world so loved.

"Did a lot of people come when I was born like that crowd over at the Haggis?"

"We were in a strange town, son. Nobody knew us. And no one knew that you were born. The three of us were kept company by the cattle and sheep which spent the night with us in the stable. It was very quiet and, for some reason, the little stable was full of light from somewhere. I don't remember any lamps, but then I was pretty pre-occupied!"

"So nobody came? Did that make you sad?" asked Jesus with a kind of melancholy in his own eyes.

"Oh, no," replied Mary quickly. "I haven't finished my story. You were only a few hours old when several peasants suddenly appeared at the door and asked if they could come in. Joseph and I thought they had been unable to find shelter and needed someplace to spend the rest of the night. Your father began to clear away a spot where they could sit down when one of them said, "We are not here to stay. Do not bother."

"Your daddy and I looked at each other. We had been so startled by their sudden appearance that we had not noticed that they were shepherds fresh from the fields nearby. One of them even carried a little lamb on his shoulders. Their tunics were dirty and they looked very tired from the walk through the fields to the stable. They didn't smell very nice either!

"Determined to show hospitality, Joseph stroked the little lamb's soft wool and insisted that they were welcome to stay. But, three of the shepherds joined their voices to tell us the most amazing story. It was as if they were hypnotized. They spoke in unison the words I shall never forget."

Jesus was wide-eyed as his mother repeated the message brought by the shepherds from Bethlehem's fields, "The angel of the Lord came upon us, and the glory of the Lord shone around us, and we were afraid. But the angel said, Fear not, for behold, I bring you good tidings of great joy, which shall be to all people. For unto you is born this day in the city of David a Savior, which is Christ the Lord."

"And son, Joseph stood like he was in a trance," Mary said, interrupting her own story. "But the shepherds had more to say."

"This shall be a sign unto you; ye shall find the babe wrapped in swaddling clothes lying in a manger, and suddenly there was with the angel a multitude of the heavenly host praising God and saying, Glory to God in the highest, and on earth peace, goodwill toward men."

At this point, Mary paused in her story to explain to Jesus, "Had we been in Nazareth the musicians would have burst into music at the birth of a man child. But we were in Bethlehem where no one knew us. So, I've always thought that God sent His own heavenly minstrels to do what no earthly singers could do!"

"When the shepherds had finished their message," Mary went on, " they bowed low toward your manger and explained that they had come to see for themselves. Now that they had seen you, they would leave and go tell their shepherd friends what they might not believe."

Jesus had never heard the story before. Floating before his mind were all kinds of strange images. What did the angels' message mean? Who were those lowly shepherds and why did the angels pick them? What did others think when they heard the story from them? And did people think they were hearing and seeing things that were not there?

"Do you mean that the angels were saying that I was to be some kind of savior?" asked Jesus in disbelief. "What do you think that meant? And why hadn't you told me about this before?"

"Wait," said Mary with excitement in her eyes, "there is more, much more. Now that we have started, I must tell you everything.

"We rented a little house and stayed in Bethlehem for about four months. Joseph did not want to make the long trip back for circumcision and presentation at the Temple at near-by Jerusalem. Really, there would have been no way we could have gotten home and back in eight days. The prophetess Anna and old Simeon, who were seen regularly at the Temple, told us that you were born for the fall and rising again of Jerusalem. It all mystified me. Still does.

"While we were in Bethlehem, some wealthy men from the east – Babylon or Persia – we never knew, arrived at the door carrying gifts. There must have been over a hundred of them. We soon found out that they were wise men who studied the stars to tell what was going to happen."

"Well, what did happen?"

"Son, they were riding on the biggest camels I had ever seen. They told me that they knew Israel was expecting a king and they had seen a brilliant star in the sky which they had followed to the holy city. Having inquired of king Herod where the new king was born, they came to our little house in Bethlehem."

Mary stopped and breathed deeply as if she could not believe her own story.

"Go on, mother, go on."

"They bowed low and then walked right into the house and laid their gifts of gold, frankincense, and myrrh at your feet. When the men straightened themselves up, they said that they had come to worship the king. I knew they meant God, but what I did not know was why they came to our house to do it."

"What ever happened to the gold and frankincense, and myrrh?"

"Your father and I knew that we could not keep it. We sold some of it to pay the rent and buy food and, of course, we needed some for the long journey to Egypt. But there was a lot left and we felt so strongly about it that we gave it to the Temple."

Finally, his mother dropped her head into her hands and began to weep. Jesus, who had listened enraptured to every word, asked in a soft whisper, "Did you ever see them again?"

"No, we did not. They climbed on their camels and left as quickly as they had come. But they did tell me that Herod knew about you and was so angry that he had demanded every male baby under two years old be killed. They said that the king was afraid of you. Can you imagine? A grown man afraid of a baby!"

Jesus swallowed hard. "What did you do?" He asked.

"I told Joseph what the wise man had whispered to me. So many strange things had happened in such a short time. Maybe this was a message from God! So, quickly as we could, we got the donkey and what few things we had and left for Egypt. Joseph said we would be safe when we got across the River of Egypt because Herod's authority stopped there. We stayed several months in Egypt until the news reached us of king Herod's death. You were nearly eighteen months old when we got back here to Nazareth."

"You never found out why he was afraid of me?" asked Jesus, as if the whole idea bordered on lunacy.

"Not really," replied Mary, shaking her head in amazement. Some people said that he killed all those children because he was losing control and just went mad. I have wondered if the wise men warned him that some child had been born who would someday take his throne away from him." Mary covered her mouth and laughed. "I guess we'll never know for sure."

Jesus sat for a long time in deep thought. Never in a thousand years would He want to take the throne of Herod even if He could. Anyone would be crazy as Herod himself to get tangled up with Rome as the king had done. The whole thing was unbelievable. Yet, He knew that his mother was not lying to him.

"Why had you never told me these things?" asked Jesus of his mother.

Mary said, "You have been too young to understand. Had I told you when you were very small, you would have believed me, but you would have seen the story as just another nursery rhyme like those which I used to tell you at night. I wanted you to be old enough to think seriously about what I have told you. I still do not understand and I am your mother. Even now, I can see that you are confused. It may be that I should have kept this to myself and pondered it longer in my heart. God knows I have pondered and pondered again and again and I am yet baffled."

207

"Mother dear, I am not confused at all really. It all makes sense to me. It is just that I do not know *why* it makes sense."

Mary threw her arms around her son's neck and kissed him on the brow.

"My dear Jesus boy, you know your mother thinks that you are very special. Even before you were born, there was never any doubt. The Lord has a plan for everybody. Most of us never find it. But I am one of the lucky ones. I know why God has put me in the world. He put me here to help Him have you. And what He plans for you, I can only guess. Whatever it is, it has to be very important!"

"I sure don't know yet, mother. There are strange stirrings, but there is never any clear call."

Mary hugged him again. "You will know when the time comes. Be patient. Just live every minute ready to do whatever the Lord wants and one day you will know without a doubt!"

Talks like this always left Jesus probing in his soul for answers.

He was remembering the days in synagogue school when the class learned by memory the prophet Isaiah's promise of the coming Messiah. Joseph had helped him get the words right and explained their meaning, pointing out that he had learned the words himself as a boy: "The Spirit of the Lord is upon me, because the Lord has anointed me to preach good tidings to the poor; he hath sent me to heal the brokenhearted, to proclaim liberty to the captives, and the opening of the prison to those who are bound; to proclaim the acceptable year of the Lord."

In his heart, as best a boy could, Jesus believed that the Jews were a chosen people and that one day their king would come. But, why these words of the prophet kept ringing in his ears He did not know. And why it was that they seemed so personal, so challenging, was beyond his wildest imagination.

Would the Messiah come in his lifetime? Or was Isaiah's prophecy for a time in the distant future? There were those who were sure the time was ripe. Joseph was one of them. And if it were, the son of Mary had decided that He would do whatever it took to be useful in the kingdom which the new king would rule. Maybe all these mysterious things were Jehovah's way of preparing him to serve Israel's long-awaited Savior. All He could do at the moment was keep his eyes and ears open and wait.

Just then, Flax roused himself from his slumbers in the corner, knocking a wooden mixing bowl off a table onto the floor. The bowl rolled half way across the room, Jesus trying to stop it. In a flash, Jesus was brought back from his concentration. Tomorrow was another day and the shop would be opened within six hours. Kissing Mary good night, Jesus crawled onto his mat and was soon fast asleep.

Early the next day, Jesus stopped by the Haggis on his way to school at the synagogue.

"Good morning and peace be with you," he said,

209

as grandmother Haggi unlatched the heavy, wooden door. Ben had already left for the stone cutter's shop where he worked with his father. Hannah was holding her newborn in her arms, the glow of motherhood surrounding her. Although still just a boy, Jesus was not embarrassed as He reached for the sleeping baby. Nestling the tiny thing in his arms, Mary's son smiled into the angel face of the child and said, more to the babe than to others in the room, "You look just like God!" Hannah was never to forget those words.

CHAPTER TWELVE

At night He wondered why He felt so close to the stars. Why there seemed to be such familiar acquaintance with the anemones in the fields and the swift-winged, clear-throated birds of the sky. Why everything seemed so hauntingly familiar as though He had seen those fiery mists of the morning long ago when the world was young and the earth was still warm from creation.

There were times when He felt like a stranger, times when He could have sworn that He was a visitor from outer space with citizenship in some other realm.

Men and women about him gave the impression that they felt perfectly at home, that they belonged to the earth. But, while Jesus knew full well that He was a member of the human race at that moment in history, He also perceived a transitoriness about the whole thing which caused him to feel a part of something far more permanent.

Jesus knew the old theory of reincarnation. With merchants traveling into Palestine from the Orient had come ideas foreign to Hebrew thought. The theory that men had lived before in other bodies, and that they would be permitted to do so again in ever-recurring incarnations, had been around for hundreds of years. The kind of body was said to be determined by the good or evil of one's previous existence. It was an intriguing idea, but the Jews had never accepted such a theory. And it was not an area

211

where the young Jesus felt comfortable.

And yet, He felt as though He had really witnessed everything going on around him in some prior age. When He gave serious thought to it, which was often, it was not so much like having been an actual part of the human race as it was like having been acquainted with the whole panorama of human history. The events of Hebrew tradition were more than history in a book. Jesus could have sworn again that there were details which He could remember that were not in the stories.

He seemed to recall the discussion in heaven when the Godhead trialogued about the creation of man. One would have thought that He was there himself. And when the rabbinical fathers debated the details of the act of creation, it all sounded so unnecessary as if He knew first hand how it all happened. The mists had rolled across the warm earth and the light had streamed in on a darkened universe. The emergence of the mountains was like some volatile explosion which punched up the crust of the earth and left low-lying holes into which the frenzied waters surged from beneath the surface. When He closed his eyes, He could see it all.

On clear nights, when the heavens were bright, Jesus felt the urge to talk to the stars, to call them by name, but He shrugged it off as some sentimental obsession. Certainly, He never breathed a word about these feelings to anyone else.

And the angels? The Sadducees, who made up the priestly class of religious conservatives in Israel, were known to treat the existence of angels, as well as demons, with skepticism.

Jesus could never understand why anyone would have doubts about the angels when both his parents and cousin Zacharias had seen them and even talked with them.

And why, He wondered, would anyone doubt the reality of demons if he had ever once tried to resist the attacks of the devil and his fallen ones? As a boy, Jesus was a bit frightened when He saw people roll on the ground and foam at the mouth, uttering strange guttural sounds like mad men. Joseph had explained the demonic spells to him, but the sight of these incidents left a lasting impression on him. The boy was convinced that his father knew what he was talking about. Nothing like that could happen unless some evil spirit were in control of the man's life.

Adam and Eve were like members of the family. He thought of them not as figures of the ancient past, but as living contemporaries whom He had known for centuries.

When Abraham talked to God about Sodom, Jesus could have staked his life on the fact that He heard the conversation even as He witnessed the breaking of the tablets of stone by Moses at the foot of Sinai.

The preaching of Isaiah was not nearly as exciting to read as it had been when Jesus heard it straight from the prophet's lips!

And the Maccabeans? Joseph had told him their

213

Leslie H. Woodson

story, but it sounded vaguely like something which He already knew. They had meant well and the Jews nearly worshiped them for their courage and loyalty to Israel. Jesus knew, however, that their zealous and excessive devotion to the letter of the Law, rather than its spirit, had brought about their final undoing.

Jesus remembered it all as if it were yesterday. And yet, how could it be? It was all so incredible – so awesome and frightening.

Once, in the company of some of his less pious neighbors, Jesus grew disturbed to hear several of the men arguing about the historicity of Jonah.   They were suggesting that the whole thing was a myth, a story with a very real truth in it, but not something which really happened.

It was hard for the young carpenter to comprehend. His father had always accepted the story as an historical fact and, furthermore, it seemed that Jesus could remember having known Jonah. Of course, such an idea was so out of the bounds of reason that He was certainly not going to say anything about that! But, the feelings which He had in his heart were so strong that there was no way for him to doubt the existence of Jonah.

The fields, with their precious grain and budding flowers, never failed to remind the young nature lover of the plenty and beauty of the heavenly world. While He had never experienced, in Palestine, a land that flowed with milk and honey and where the grapes were as big as pomegranates, it was certain that He had seen it

214

somewhere.

Possibly every sensitive spirit felt as He did. However, there was something more for him than just a sensitive response. Rather, it was as if He had been in those same fields in some previous existence, that they were a kind of replica of heavenly meadows which served as the perfect reality for which earthly forms were only copies. Even the lilies, so colorfully arrayed, recognized him as his feet moved across their peaceful fields. Everything in the Father's world was like a page from the past which had been read many times before.

Time and again, He asked himself why, when others talked and prattled about religion as though it were a matter of laws and holy days, did He feel so close to Jehovah and so sure of His love? Why was the air around him so charged with divine energy as though something great was about to happen and He was somehow a part of it?

There was always a kind of spine tingling sensation of being drawn more to the heavens than bound to the earth. As others trudged the beaten lanes with backs bent and faces toward the ground, He hardly seemed to notice where He walked. Inside his heart, there was another voice which kept calling him from the heights. And when He said his prayers, He was almost frightened with the over-whelming sense of Someone listening. Someone whom He could not see.

Shortly before his visit to Jerusalem for the Passover at the age of twelve, Jesus had tried to talk to his

215

mother about these strange things. Mary had become so excited that the tears streamed down her cheeks as she choked back the emotion which she felt in her heart. All that day, she had acted like there was some big secret that could not be shared. Mary was unusually quiet, obviously pondering something in her head, something too good to keep but too intimate to tell.

At first, Jesus had felt a little embarrassed for fear that He had invaded some private corner of Mary's heart where no one was allowed to go. But she had not gotten angry and she seemed more pleased than annoyed when He brought up the subject. It was more like being reticent about talking of a happy secret which was too delicate to discuss with a twelve year old boy. He had hoped she might talk more about it later. But she didn't.

More than five years had passed. One night after Jesus' seventeenth birthday, Joseph, who had died only a few months earlier, occupied his thoughts. He had always loved Joseph and respected him highly. Joseph had been a faithful husband to Mary and had taken good care of his big family. A devout man, who frequented the synagogue and prayed often, Joseph was the kind of man any Jewish boy would be proud to call father.

Try as he might, He could not rid his mind of what his dying father had told him. The blunt words, "I am not your father," had not surprised him for some unknown reason, but still they were puzzling.

For a long time, Jesus had been haunted by a

question which lingered in the shadows like a bad dream. Every time He encountered it, the boy attempted to brush it aside, but it kept coming back.

Some of the people in Nazareth were reported to have spread rumors about his mother. He knew that. A few times He had been called a dirty name which reflected more on Mary's honor than on himself. Although Jesus refrained from verbal retaliation, He never understood why anyone would say such things.

There was no way young Jesus was going to believe that Mary could have been familiar with anyone but her husband. Joseph had told his boy that he was not his father, but there was no time to explain before he died. Why had he said nothing earlier?

Yet, there were a few neighbors who referred to him as Joshua ben Miriam and never as the son of his father, which would have been the commonly used reference.

It was on that night, when Jesus' mind was in a quandary about the identity of his father, that He dared to mention the subject to Mary. He tried to be tactful and not say something which would hurt her. Nevertheless, the burning question which He wanted to ask was who his father was. So he began.

"Mother," Jesus asked, "where is father?"

She did not answer for a moment. In her heart, she knew exactly what her son was wrestling with. On the surface of things, it was a common enough thing to ask.

When her own father died, Mary had wondered the same thing. People just go away and we see them no more. But where do they go?

A soft, luminous light played around her eyes. Reverently and lovingly, she replied, "Your father is in heaven."

The answer sounded right. It was as if there were a double meaning to her response. It was not exactly what He had meant. Or was it? Yet, there appeared to be no cause to press the matter further. Mary had said more than she comprehended and more than her son, as mature as He was, could understand at the age of seventeen.

Almost a dozen years had lapsed since that night under the stars when Jesus had asked his question. The nagging uncertainty refused to go away. He was now a young man and entitled to a fuller explanation of the concern about his father which He had tried unsuccessfully to get cleared up.

The years had eased the situation around town and people had more or less forgotten the rumor about Mary and her boy. Jesus was now accepted as one of the young, well-skilled artisans of the village. Time has a way of taking care of many of our problems. Even the town's gossip had found other more recent and promising victims for her slanderous tongue.

No one had heard the rumor mentioned for several years. But, it was still in the back of the young carpenter's mind like some unsolved mystery waiting for new light.

And Mary knew that He must be told.

One morning as she prepared breakfast, Mary chanced to drop a dried fig onto the earthen floor of her kitchen. Jesus, who was standing in the doorway, stooped to pick it up. All his life He had been gathering and eating figs as a part of the staple diet of Jewish families, but this was the largest single fig He had ever seen.

Calling attention to the size of the fruit, He pointed out to Mary how God is always out-doing himself. And Mary had laughed with some kind of answer about God's being full of surprises. Reaching out, she took the luscious fruit in her hand.

The time was ripe, as ripe as the fig, and the subject was a good lead into what needed to be said.

With the big fig still in her hand, she sat down on a low stool near the door and beckoned to her son to join her. Folding his legs under him, Jesus sat down on the dirt floor and waited for his mother to speak.

Mary started by reminding him that He had once asked her about his father. Jesus nodded his head as she continued.

"I have never seen your father," she said. A startled, half-knowing expression broke across the face of Jesus. But He made no reply.

"That's right, son," explained Mary, nervously clutching the fig in her fist, "I have never seen your fahter. God *really* is full of surprises and the biggest surprise of all is you! Can you imagine how I felt when the Lord sent Gabriel to tell me that I was to bear a child? You see, son,

I was unmarried and had never known any man, not even Joseph."

Jesus' mind exploded with light. "So that's where Gabriel had gone!" he said loudly.

"What? What did you say?" said Mary, startled by his remark.

Sensing the awakening of dormant brain cells in her son's head, she went on.

"I reminded God of this. Fear filled my heart as I thought of Joseph. And my parents. And the neighbors. What would people say? Joseph would reject me. Then the angel assured me that the Spirit of the Lord would overshadow and protect me and that my son would be special, holy. He would be God's Son."

Jesus said nothing. He did not move nor did He once take his eyes off his radiant mother.

"Joseph was a good man and afraid to marry me when he discovered that I was with child. But the angel explained to him that you were to be a special baby and that there was no reason for him to be afraid. You must always respect the memory of Joseph. He knew you were not his child, but he welcomed and loved you as if you were his own flesh. He and I both believed that you were to be the deliverer of Israel!"

Although, for some unknown reason, the news did not really take him by surprise as He thought it might, Jesus did ask whether the villagers knew this to be the case. When Mary explained that they had assumed many bad things about her and that such a story would have made matters worse, Jesus admitted that the news which He had just heard was enough to make anybody wonder.

No one could ever believe such a tale! No one! Still it did not seem the least bit difficult for Jesus to accept. If what Mary was saying were true, it explained a lot of things which had long troubled him. The way He felt when He prayed. The closeness which He felt to the stars. The feeling that He had been here before, even at the very beginning. Could that be the answer?

That day, when Mary let him in on her long-guarded secret, Jesus did not make any chairs, or ox yokes, or anything else in the little carpenter's shop. No, He walked into the hills and spent the whole day thinking thoughts which no man before him had ever dared. They were frightening, but they were exciting and promising, too.

Late that night, his face drawn from the emotional experience through which He had gone, Jesus returned to Nazareth. His whole being was alive with the conviction that there was something God had for him to do. It was more than an ordinary job. Something special. Many shared this feeling of divine vocation in their work but, with Jesus, it was different. And it was not just a difference in degree. God was leading him in a path on which none had ever walked.

As He looked up at those stars, which had always seemed to be his kinsmen, He muttered to himself. "My Father is in heaven! So that's it! Well, Mary is not completely right. My Father is also right here on earth

221

with us all!   And I now know what He wants me to do. He wants me to spend my life telling people about his love and showing them what He is really like!" The joy which filled his mind was sobered by the pain in his heart.

And so it was.

CHAPTER THIRTEEN

When Joseph died, Mary was more shaken than she had been by any other one thing that ever happened in her life. Her husband was considerably older than she and the family knew that he could not live forever, but Mary made it perfectly clear that she would never be ready to give him up. She loved him too much for that.

Never would she forget how kind and understanding he had been with her during her pregnancy with her first-born. And that was reason enough to love him passionately since the child she was carrying was not his. He was a just man and believed in Mary's role as the one chosen to bear a servant of the Lord.

On the night of his death, no professional mourner could have wailed so loudly as she. Her world caved in and it was as though she could not breathe. For months afterward, Mary could talk to Jesus about nothing else. And when her first-born was not there, she stayed busy and spoke very little.

How often Jesus relived the day when they came home to their empty, little house after having buried Joseph in the village cemetery. Mary cried all that day and night. Elizabeth and Salome both stayed with her for several days until she was able to face her loss. Nothing seemed right to anyone in the family. Nothing could ever be right again without Joseph.

From that day, Jesus knew that his first duty would

be to his mother and her children. Whatever might have been his dreams was all canceled by this tremendous task which lay before him.

When the relatives left for their houses, the men had embraced the elder son, kissing him on both cheeks, and telling him of their confidence in his ability to assume the role of his deceased father. The shoes which He would wear were awfully big.

The day following the funeral, Jesus had gotten up very early, much earlier than usual, and gone out to the shop. There he knelt by the old battered bench where Joseph had spent most of his life. Every nick and scratch on the bench was a reminder of the old carpenter. And Jesus was thankful for the man who had prepared the way for him and tutored him in the skills and crafts of his artistry in wood.

As Jesus prayed for strength and direction through the dark and strange path which He was destined to tread, He was sure that the spirit of Joseph was in the room with him. But, above all, there was the presence of the Lord God and it was as real as the tools which lay on the workbench before him.

From the darkness of the shop came a voice which was familiar to the grieving boy. "Do not be afraid, I am with you. You are my very dear Son and I am pleased with what you are doing."

It was not Joseph's voice, but the words sounded like something a father might say to a boy who had a man-size job to perform. The sound in the room did not frighten Jesus. Under normal circumstances, it would have been eerie to hear so distinctly an audible voice in a room where there was obviously no other person present. But, for some reason, the resonant voice was reassuring to the praying boy.

In the coming days, Jesus was to become more and more sensitive to death and the sight of grieving loved ones. When he saw Jewish men neglecting their responsibilities at home, by claiming that all their possessions had been pledged to the Temple, it was appalling to him how commonplace it had become to rationalize around responsibility. They were insisting that this kind of vow freed them from the care of their parents. And Jesus knew, even as a youngster, that this was just a loophole created to release one from his obligation to aging parents.

The main reason why He would be unable to do more walking and talking with the people of the soil, about things which had become so important to him, was because He couldn't neglect the business at the shop until each person in the family was on his own.

Joses was now a big boy and James was more and more restless with thoughts of leaving home. Rachel had abandoned the family before her father's death for life on the streets. Elizabeth had become so absorbed in her work as a Nazarite that she was pretty much on her own. Judas also had married and Simon had agreed to take over the shop when Jesus decided to leave. Having become quite a craftsman in his own right, younger brother Simon was the right one to take over the role of master craftsman.

Nazareth was not the most desirable place in the world in which to live. No great prophet had ever come out of Nazareth and it had the reputation for being a town of loose morals. The men were vulgar and some of the women were known to entertain Roman soldiers on duty in the area.

That didn't make Jesus' hometown any different than most towns in Palestine. It was just more noticeable to the people who lived in Nazareth. A few of the men and their wives had even been rumored to swap spouses with their neighbors. There was nothing new under the sun. Jesus, as a boy running errands for his father, would often hear the men in the marketplace laughing loudly as they told of their escapades of the night before.

When He would tell Joseph what He had heard, the shame could be seen in the old carpenter's face and he would apologize to his young son that he had to live in a place like Nazareth. The town had its own way of embarrassing him.

Joseph, while yet alive and able to work in the shop, often explained to his son that he had tried to get away and move the family to Sepphoris where grandmother Anne lived, but finding new work in a strange community was not easy. More than once, he had known of families who nearly starved to death trying to make such a move.

Now that his father was gone, Jesus could recall

vividly a lot of the things He had learned. He remembered how quickly the local men and boys found out that Joseph would not allow any profane talk or dirty jokes around his place of business. Some of the shops were known as hang-outs for vulgar stories. From the earliest days of Jesus' recollection, however, He had admired his father for his clear cut stand.

One morning, when Jesus came into the wood shop, He sensed the addition of something new. A hand printed sign had been posted just over the workbench. His father had printed it in both Aramaic and Greek. Most of the people who came into the shop were Jews and spoke Aramaic. But, apparently Joseph had feared that some foul mouth Roman soldier might wander in and contaminate the place with abusive language.

The sign read, *God is listening.* When his father died, Jesus kept the sign in its place and no one failed to respect the suggestion. Neither Joseph nor Jesus understood the full truth which the sign conveyed.

It was one of those beautiful days in late spring when everything had come to life or was in the process of nature's resurrection. Birds were singing, the grass had greened, trees were budding or in full blossom, and the air was fresh. Little children were frolicking in the lanes and Jesus felt like He could jump clear over the hills which surrounded the quiet town of Nazareth.

The boy carpenter was rapidly becoming a man. He was now nineteen years old.

Several of the younger men appeared at the door of the shop and reminded the youthful craftsman that a fellow should not work his life away. A guy had to have a little fun. They were all taking the day off and were on their way to Magdala Two, which was what the makeshift tents just outside Nazareth were called. Women from Magdala were all business, setting up wayside substations which could be taken down in minutes at the first sight of religious authorities. They knew there was no need to ask Jesus, but why not lock up the shop and come along?

The young men about town often accused Jesus of being a slave to his work, his family, and his ideals. But, He had noticed how they found it impossible to say no to the lusts which surged in their hearts. They could not make their own decisions. Someone else held control over them and made their choices. They were like animals following their natural instincts rather than men made in the image of God. Jesus knew who was the slave!

Men who were going to Magdala Two could have been making such a trek for only one reason. The town on the west shore of the Sea of Galilee was notorious as a bed of harlotry. These small substations set up for a night here and there made it possible to enjoy Magdala without the long trip. True, there were willing women in Nazareth, but the guys were looking for new girls.

The carpenter stood, hammer in hand, looking with pity at the grinning faces in the doorway. After a moment of silence, he asked his friends if they had forgotten what happened to king David. They all laughed with disbelief that Jesus was about to preach them another sermon.

"How long will it take," asked the young man in the hot little shop, "how long will it take you fellows to grow up? You have too much idle time on your hands."

The men laughed and slapped one another on the back. Without comment, they were soon on their way to see what Magdala Two had to offer.

Some of the women of the city of Nazareth had thrown themselves at Jesus on several occasions. When they saw him coming their way with a load of wood products He had made, they would lie in wait until He returned from his journey with an empty cart. Then, assuming that He had money from the sale of the wood goods, they would approach him with an offer to exchange their love for what He carried in the money bag.

These incidents always saddened Jesus.

He never wanted these women to think that He condoned their sin, but neither did He want them to feel that they were deserving of his scorn. The men who frequented their hovels were just as guilty as they and possibly responsible for what the women had become. Women were considered property, the playthings of the males. No one seemed to think much about the indecency of the men.

Usually, Jesus walked right on by the women without censure or approval. One day, when interrupted by a young woman plying her trade, He paused to speak to her, a thing for which He knew He could be criticized.

His heart was beating wildly because He knew that to stop was dangerous for any man. Furthermore, He did not want her to think that He had ulterior motives. Yet, for a reason known only to God, He had to say something to her.

"Woman," He said, "who brought you into this life of shame?"

Flippantly, she replied, "A bad mother and a number of men!"

Looking deep into her dark eyes, Jesus said, "You were never meant to do this. I am sorry about your mother and apologize for what the men have done to you. But you do not have to do this. God has better things for you."

"What could be better than this?" she teasingly asked. "We never lack customers. The money is good. And the work is easy."

"No, you are wrong. It may be easy now, but it will become a crushing load as you get older."

"You some kind of priest?" suddenly asked the woman as she pulled away in fear that he would report her. "Priests come here all the time. Some of my regular customers are priests."

"I am not a priest. And I am not going to report you. Please, don't do this. You are too good a person to wreck your life."

As He walked away, the woman stood gazing after him.

"What a strange man," she said to herself, walking

back to the perfumed hovel which served as her temporary place of business. Inside she felt strange as if someone had just tried to sweep the cobwebs from her soul.

That very day, what He feared might happen did happen. One had to be so careful.

A good man never dared to stop and talk to a woman of the streets. Not for any reason. Most men of character, and there were a few, went out of their way to avoid them. If accidentally confronted by such a woman, they were careful that she did not touch their garments lest they be rendered unclean.

Sometimes the more pious men, most often older ones, would spit at the village strumpets. The only men who ever took a chance on stopping in conversation were those interested in what the women had to sell. Therefore, when the village gossips managed to get hold of the juicy story of Jesus' having been seen with one of the lecherous females, the scandal soon spread all over town.

It was only the beginning.

Long after He had commenced his ministry of reconciliation, those who should have known better still enjoyed casting reflection upon his character because He went to be guest of those who were sinners, publicans, and harlots. Even his closest friends had been surprised to find that He allowed himself to be caught off guard in conversation with a woman of ill fame at Sychar.

One former prostitute, from the red light district of Magdala, later became a devoted follower and the more

231

vicious tongues made capital of that. The very fact that such a sinner would be welcome in Jesus' circle of friends was enough to discount his wisdom, much more his holiness.

Mary had told her son, while He was still quite young, about the day when Joseph took him to the Temple and dedicated the screaming boy to God. In his heart, Jesus was always proud that He had been made a part of the Hebrew covenant by parents who believed deeply in the value of infant dedication.

The circumcision was only incidental as a symbol, but what was important to him was that this action of his parents was their visible way of declaring their hopes and aspirations for the growing infant. There was nothing magical about it. Joseph and Mary had been faithful across the years and the nurture by devout parents had much to do with his later life and mission.

Coupled with this direct influence was the impressive and moving ritual which surrounded his coming of age. The Temple ceremony was again incidental, but the whole event was to serve as a guideline in later years. At times, He mused on the fact that there was no way for him to remember these things which happened when He was an infant, but there seemed to be some recollection of the whole thing.

These two incidents were like a beam of light which kept him on course when temptations came to yield to the pressures of conformity.

During all those formative years, before the

baptism by John in the Jordan River, Jesus had an unshakeable conviction that the way one lives his life is of eternal significance. His upbringing at home by devout parents had laid a foundation for manhood which would stand the test of time.

Moral looseness was everywhere around him and it became a constant source of embarrassment that so many were easily duped, so easily led astray, so prone to weakness. Such men insinuated that fellows who did not share their moral laxity were not men at all, but Jesus noted that it took far less courage to submit to lewd suggestions than it did to resist them.

What took all the energy one could muster was the dedication to principles of living which required resistance to anything that would make one less than he was before. And He had observed that, each time He said no to the seductive voices, He grew stronger for the next round of conflict. The hard bumps on the by-way, though unwelcome at the time, seemed to leave him a little stronger than before.

There were times when Jesus thought no one was tempted by the world around him so forcefully as He. And, as time approached for his leaving the shop to share with the people what He had learned about life, the possibilities open to him were like an alien onslaught.

When the divine Spirit led him into the wilderness, following his baptism, to think through the choices open to an itinerant preacher, the devil enticed him to think first of himself. This was not the first time Jesus had entertained these thoughts, but they had never come with such force before.

"You have power to become great," whispered the voice which had been first heard long ago in Eden. "If you are who I think you are, turn these stones into bread! You don't ever have to want for anything."

It was not just a voice. The shadowy figure, grinning and majestically erect, was visible to the carpenter. He had seen him before.

The scene shifted. Jesus was seeing the Temple precincts filled with teeming multitudes. All of it was in living color, breathtakingly beautiful.

"Look," insisted the devil, "Go over there on a feast day, climb up to the highest point and jump off! God will take care of you. You believe that, don't you?"

Fearing that his alluring offers were not getting the job done, he continued.

"You will sail through the air like a butterfly. The people will be spellbound. They love a good show. Think how much money you could make."

Both times Jesus recited scripture which did not begin to deter this demonic spirit who was set on side-tracking the teacher who posed the greatest threat to his worldly power.

"All right, All right," replied the pleasant and reasonable sounding voice. "Maybe that's not your thing. Tell you what! If you will let me be your public relations front-man – if you will listen to me and give me freedom to run this campaign – I will put you into the greatest office in the land. You will be king of the world! Think of it . . . Joseph's boy, king of an empire bigger than that of Tiberius. Your daddy would be proud."

No stone was left unturned in the determination to seduce Jesus into a self-centered life which totally ignored service to others. But that was not the first time.

Perhaps one reason why He felt the temptations so keenly was because Jesus was so everlastingly sensitive to good and evil. Joseph had wrestled with the problem again and again and his family had watched, with wonder and pride, as Old Joe invariably won in the fray.

The voice of God, which called to him more and more as the years sped by, was so noticeably different than the sultry voice He had heard in the wilderness. God's voice was forever insistent that Jesus respond to the highest which was in him. Therefore, when some outside force tried to cut into their channel of communication, the interference was easily recognized.

The older He got, the more frequent were the interruptions. They were relentless. Ignoring them was not a solution. They literally refused to go away. As would be expected, He was never left unmoved by the strange, alien whispers and usually had to fight pretty hard to get the lines clear again.

Not for one single moment, though the struggle was always there, did Jesus ever come close to surrendering his deepest conviction that He was sent to do something more.

And when the seductive voice began to speak, it

235

Leslie H. Woodson

was helpful to recall the words of grandpa Jacob. "It takes a live fish to swim upstream. Any old dead one can float down." And if there was any one thing which Jesus would never be content with, it was floating!

CHAPTER FOURTEEN

The mother of Jesus was always uneasy when it came to her children. What mother isn't? James had never given her any serious trouble, but she just knew in her mother's heart that the potential was there. Lately, when there was a knock at the door, she was afraid that it was bad news about James.

Then there was Rachel, the older of the two daughters. She had come to the funeral where the whole time she stayed in the shadows by herself. Any effort to get to her only drove her deeper into her wretchedness. Joseph had been seen weeping for her before he died.

Beth was a joy. As a dedicated Nazarite, she did not see the family much, but all concerned were aware that there was a good reason. And the twins? Maybe it was because they were still quite young, but they were the least of her worries.

Although a genuinely good boy, Joses was the child which caused Mary the most anxiety. Since the hard time she had in his delivery, Joses had not been well. In comparison to the other boys, good health had been a constant struggle, always alluding him for some reason unknown to his mother. God was good, in that Joses had a way of licking his health problems each time, but the respite was commonly short-lived.

In the house four doors away lived a beautiful and wholesome young woman called Abby. Her real name was Abigail, but nobody called her that. Abby was fourteen years old, with jet black hair and the longest eyelashes in Nazareth. Joses, who was now nearly eighteen, was smitten. Although he had known her as a playmate for many years, it had just struck him that she was not a kid anymore. She was the most gorgeous woman he had seen in all Galilee.

Abby's father was a smith whose shop was directly across the downtown lane from "Joseph and Son." The dirt lane between the two shops was trodden down by the coming and going of the two proprietors. While there had never been any formal partnership, Joseph and Ahaz had worked hand in glove for at least a dozen years when Joseph died. The carpenter shop would make the handle for the ax or sickle which had been forged by the smith. Or the smith would provide the rim for the ox cart wheel which Joseph had made. It was a great arrangement and they got along well. Ahaz was pleased and proud when his daughter showed an interest in Joses.

The relationship had been growing for several months during which time Mary and Abby spent considerable time together.

The September rains were splattering on the thatched roof as Joses crawled off his mat, rubbed his eyes, and decided that it was time to tell Mary. It was the time of year when the rains were normal and invariably welcomed as they softened the ground and made it pliable for the plow.

Mary was getting Joses' breakfast together, a kind

of sack lunch which he would eat later in the morning where he worked in the tanner's shop.

"Mother," he said, as he reached out and gripped her by the arm. "Mother, for several days I have waited to tell you. Abby and I are going to be married. We pledged ourselves to each other only minutes before the last Sabbath began. I love her more than anyone on earth."

His mother was not stunned by the news, but she pretended to be shocked. Her mouth flew open and she raised her hand as if to cover it. Few moms fail to perceive what is happening to their children even when no one has told them. It is just a mother thing.

"My dear boy, nothing could ever bring me more happiness. She is a wonderful girl and you have made a very wise choice. Your daddy would be very proud," said Mary, with pent up emotions, a tear glistening in her eye.

Joses tried to explain. Shaking his head vigorously, he said, "Forbid it that any son should ever make his mother cry."

"No, no! These tears are tears of joy. I can't wait to be a grandmother."

"It will not be for a while. We plan not to marry until next year. It's too early to firm up the time. There are so many things which have to be done before we can ever think of marriage. We do not want to move in here with you. So we have to find a place to live. And I need to save some money so our start will not be so hard. We'll need to buy a couple of goats for milk. And Abby wants to do everything just right." Joses hoped that his explanation satisfied his mother.

From across the room came a voice. It was that of Jesus who, contrary to his habit of rising before everyone else, had just been awakened by the conversation.

"This is an answer to prayer. Somebody's got to keep the family going and you are the one God has appointed. Good choice, too. You will make a great daddy."

Joses looked a little embarrassed.

"Sorry to make things harder for you, brother," he said. "But I will be here for a year or more until the wedding, so you'll have a little help around the house with the chores."

"Don't worry about it. We'll work it out."

"And there is the bride price. I'm sure that Ahaz will not expect much, but I have to do something. Now that dad is gone, I'll have to scrape pretty hard."

When a father gave his daughter in marriage, it was considered a loss and he should be compensated for it. The two fathers would get together and work out an agreeable settlement. Now that Joseph was dead, the contract would become the responsibility of the oldest son. It would be drawn up and witnessed in the presence of at least two witnesses. Then, in front of these persons, a betrothal ceremony would take place. During the next twelve months the couple would be thought of as married, but not until the wedding night itself did the woman take up residence in the man's house.

"We'll work together, little brother," Jesus said,

placing his hand on Joses' shoulder. "I will speak to Ahaz myself and see what can be done."

Weddings were routinely planned for the season of fall after the harvest was gathered. This was a more leisurely time when guests would not be so pressed. A village marriage was the last thing a Hebrew wanted to be hurried.

Jesus began immediately to plan for the wedding. He and Ahaz came to an agreement on two goats and a replacement part for a threshing board.

Zacharias had agreed to come and officiate at the wedding. Mary busied herself helping Abby make her very special embroidered nuptial garments. Together, she and Abishag, Abigail's mother, worked for months making a list of friends to invite so that no one would be accidentally omitted. And the festival, which would last for days, had to be well thought through lest the food and wine give out before it was over.

Neighbors were called on to arrange for distant guests to have a place to stay. A few, who were a bit more affluent, had an upper room, a box like room set squarely atop the one beneath it and accessed by an outside stair. These families could accommodate a half dozen.

Others would make their courtyards available and there was no one who objected to sleeping among the animals. Finding places to house the visitors was probably the easiest part since eastern hospitality was never questioned by the gracious people of small villages like

Nazareth. Most of them did not have much, but what they had they shared freely.

All the expected guests had been informed of the wedding, even though the date was still not fixed, with the understanding that they should be ready when the final invitation was issued. Nobody refused because it was an insult ever to do such a thing.

The day for the wedding was finally set for the last week of the month Marchesvan or mid-November. Everything was readied and the guests were called. In great numbers they descended on the little lane where the couples' parents lived to await the coming of the bridegroom to the bride's parents' home. In their hands were timbrels, harps, and flutes as well as torches.

Weddings were most often set for night. The bride's female attendants waited with their lamps burning and extra oil just in case there was a delay. When the groom, in the company of his male companions who carried their own torches through the street, arrived at the home of the bride's parents, he asked for his wife-to-be. Upon her appearance, her veil was lifted and the groom expressed loudly the joy of finding such a priceless treasure.

The procession from the house of Ahaz to that of Joseph and Mary was no more than a few hundred cubits, but no one was in a hurry and the waiting guests were loud and rowdy as they lined both sides of the street.

Jesus was waiting at the door as the happy couple approached. The joy on his face was evident. God had planned for the marriage of man and woman since the beginning of the world. It was Jehovah's way of continuing the human race and insuring the care of children and the building of family. Joses was doing what God wanted him to do and that always pleased his older brother.

As the evening progressed, those who had offered to help with the meal were kept busy bringing fresh food, which had been sent in by many relatives and friends to the festive bunch of men, women, and children. Laughter filled the air as riddles were offered and games were played. The red wine was especially good and some of the guests overdid it. But, it was these who kept the celebration from dying. Everybody danced, even those who knew not how and those who had come on canes and walking sticks.

Late that night, before the party broke up for the first day of celebration, Zacharias tried to quiet the loud crowd. It was time for the blessing which would complete the joining together of Joses and Abigail. Raising both his hands, the priest thanked Jehovah God for the two people who had pledged themselves to one another. He implored God's benedictions of grace upon them. Then he laid his big wrinkled hands upon their heads and affirmed that, in the sight of God, this couple had become one flesh. And he insisted that once such a union was made, it was to be forever. Joses kissed his new wife and they danced before the enthusiastic friends who had come to launch them on their life long adventure together.

After the crowds had left, Jesus warmly greeted his new sister-in-law and welcomed her to the family.

"Now Joses," he strongly insisted, "you are no longer just my brother Joses. You are from now on Joses and Abby. The two of you are one, no longer two, and God forbid that you should ever break apart. For if you do, you will never be whole again. You and Abby will be two halves, never complete without each other."

Joses nodded. His family training had driven that deep into his head. Furthermore, it was not hard to accept such truth because he loved Abby so much that the thought never entered his mind. Jesus thought of his younger sister, Rachel. How different it might have been.

There was never any privacy in a one room house where a large family lived. For a newly married couple to be added to the very public room was more than a little awkward. James, a little embarrassed, but recognizing the need for Abby and his brother to be alone, suggested privately to Jesus and Simon that they sleep that night in the courtyard.

"What about mother," asked Simon.

"We will fix the best spot of all for her," replied Jesus.

He knew that she wouldn't mind, because she had told him that she once before had spent the night in a stable!

Life went on pretty much as usual while James and

his brothers continued work on the modest house at the end of the lane which was not quite completed when the married couple moved in with Mary.

It was Joses' plan to take his bride to their new home for the wedding, but it had taken much longer to finish the house than he had counted on. Finally, the day came when Joses took Abby by the hand and together they sat on the dirt floor in their brand new place.

One afternoon sometime later, Jesus was struggling with a spoke in a cart wheel which was defying every effort to slip into the prepared hole in the hub. In the doorway stood a stranger inquiring for Jesus.

"I am He," said Jesus, wiping the sweat from his brow.

"Greetings in the name of Abraham. I am Shachia from Bethel. I am traveling to Cana," explained the weary stranger at the door.

"What an arduous journey. You are bound to be in need of rest," exclaimed Jesus, rising from the three legged stool which has father made and used when building cartwheels. "Come! We will go to my house. I will wash the dust from your feet and you can sleep while Mary warms some fresh milk."

The weather beaten traveler shook his head and thanked the shop keeper for his generosity.

"There is no time. I have much distance to cover. A young man, dressed in camel hair with a leather girdle about his loins, passed through Hebron a while ago. Said his name was John and that he was on his way to Engedi to study with the Essenes. Asked if anyone would be traveling north who could give a message to his cousin in Nazareth."

"So that's where he is," reflected Jesus aloud. "Doesn't surprise me, really. What is the message?"

"He said to tell you that he is preparing himself for whatever lies in the future. Didn't say much else. He acted as if you would know what he meant."

"Well, my thanks to you for coming out of your way to bring me this great news. If you cannot stay with us, let me offer my blessing as you move on."

Nodding graciously, the stranger turned from the shop door and was not heard from again.

The Essenes were ascetics who had formed a monastery near what is known as Qumran at the north west end of the Dead Sea. The order had developed sometime in the second century B.C. and disappeared after the destruction of the Temple in 70 A.D. Men who joined the monastic life were abstentious, simple, and honest. They lived celibate lives, ate the simplest food, wore plain garments and sandals until they were threadbare, rejecting everything sensual. Living in the wilderness made such a lifestyle seem even more correct.

"So John is studying with the Essenes," mused Jesus, continuing to work on the defiant spoke. "God works in mysterious ways, performing wonders which none of us could anticipate. John never did care for all the pomp and display of the priests. The crude and simple life of the prophet is just ingrained in him, I guess. It will be interesting to see what comes out of this."

Toward the end of that same week, Joses came running into the shop and announced, "Big brother! How would you like a surprise?"

"Two in the same week!" exclaimed the carpenter. "I hope it is a happy one."

"O, it is, it is! Abby is with child. We just found out and I wanted you to be the first to know."

Jesus congratulated his baby brother. In his heart, there were questions as to how Joses would provide. He was so young and, in many ways, so immature. Although big brother was glad, He had developed much since the death of Joseph and knew what a hard time lay in store for this young family.

The little girl, whom they called Miriam, was beautiful. She became the center of attention for her uncles and her aunt Beth who, though she did not see her often, loved and spoiled her when she could.

Miriam was nearly three years old when Joses came in early from the tanner's shop. He complained of feeling ill with terrible pains in his stomach. The local physicians were called, but there was little they could do but apply potions and provide a mixture of herbs and spices for him to drink. With no way to look inside his abdomen, the doctors had no way of being sure what was

wrong. Medicine in the large Greek and Roman cities was much advanced over that in Nazareth or even Jerusalem for that matter. And calling in someone from afar was just not within the realm of possibility. Finding enough money to keep ordinary herbs on hand for emergencies was all a poor family could manage. There was certainly no way to get hold of enough money to call in a physician from miles away.

Joses' condition grew worse. The pain spread. At night he would call out in pain, drawing up his knees and rolling on the mat. Abby, wringing her trembling hands, was beside herself with grief and worry. Jesus tried to console her, but this was her man, the father of little Miriam. God dare not let him die!

Nothing Jesus or any of the family could say helped very much. Even though she knew Jesus was right when He pointed out that there would be no trouble she might face but that Jehovah would be with her.

He kept reminding her that she must not be angry with God for making Joses sick. God does not do that. Disease and death are never his will. They are rather the result of living in a world gone bad from disobedience and sin. All of us suffer because we are part and parcel of a fallen race.

Her scream was heard far beyond the walls of the house where Joses and Abby lived with Miriam. The neighbors rushed into the streets in their nightshirts for they were awakened by the blood curdling noise during the third watch of the night, around two-thirty. It was

Abby. Joses had died in his sleep and she had opened her eyes to the noise of silence. The groaning and heavy breathing had stopped. Her scream had startled little Miriam who was now crying hysterically.

Mary and the boys arrived within minutes all out of breath. Fear, mingled with a tinge of hope, filled the tiny room. Jesus moved to the mat, leaned down, and gently closed Joses' eyes. Mary and Abby stood wide-eyed in disbelief although they had known for many days that only a miracle could save their son and husband.

"It's all right to cry, Abby," explained Jesus. "Tears are God's way of cleansing your soul. Come, look. Look how relieved he is. His pain is gone. Death is so much like sleep after a hard day."

"What will I do?" wept Abby. "And what will happen to my Miriam? Joses is gone and I know not where. How can I ever raise my little girl without him? I loved him so."

With a twinkle in his eye, as if He knew something which she didn't, Jesus began to recite words from the Hebrew scroll He had learned in school. "I know that my Redeemer liveth, and that he shall stand at the latter day upon the earth: and though after my skin worms destroy this body, yet in my flesh shall I see God: whom I shall see for myself, and mine eyes shall behold, and not another."

The words sounded familiar to Abby, but she confessed that she had no idea what they meant.

"Abby," said Jesus softly, "they mean that death is not the end of anything. They mean that the day will come when Joses will live again, not just as a disembodied spirit, but as a real bodily person. Someday you and I will join him and we will *know* him. Together we will look upon the face of God. They mean that you and Miriam will be all right. Just wait. You will see. I know you believe in God . . . believe me!"

The words from scripture seemed to bring such assurance to her brother-in-law, who knew so much scripture by heart, that the twinkle in his eye brought renewed hope. Abigail, tears gushing down her already stained face, embraced her brother-in-law, words giving place to sobbing.

This was the second death in the family. Mary had lost a son, the most painful experience any mother could go through. Abby had lost a husband, a grief almost impossible to bear for one so young. Miriam was too little to join in their sadness, but the day would come when she would feel this terrible loss.

In a small town like Nazareth, news spread quickly. Concerned neighbors came from all over to comfort and console Mary and Abby. There was a lot of hugging as people tried to feel the pain with the grieving family. And little Miriam? By the end of the day, she was worn out from having been picked up by every woman, cooing and kissing her pink cheeks.

The funeral and burial were almost a carbon copy of that of Joseph, Joses being buried beside his father. Many of the same people came. The local priest read some of the same encouraging ritual which Zacharias had

251

used at the burial of Joseph. Though some did not notice it, the absence of John, the son of old Zacharias, was not overlooked by Jesus. When Old Joe had died, cousin John had been there and his presence had been a great help to Jesus.

And He missed him.

CHAPTER FIFTEEN

Tolmai was an old widower living in the tiny village of Cana in Galilee. While never considered one of the wealthier citizens of the area, he was of ample means and lived in a neat house with an upper level reached by a stairway on the outer wall. His trade was that of a potter and, for years, he had enjoyed being known almost everywhere as the best in the business. There was a kind of God-given talent which he had and it was noticeable at once when a customer looked over his wares.

"Stop the wheel," he cried, "stop the wheel!" One of the novices learning the trade had allowed a tiny pebble, no bigger than a mustard seed, to remain in the clay mud of a pot he was turning. No one would ever have seen it, that is, no one but Tolmai.

"We cannot sell that!" exclaimed the old potter, as he slapped both sides of his head with his hands.

"Sorry, sir. But what have I done?" inquired the young boy, slowing down the wheel.

"See that? See that speck?"

Obed, the apprentice, leaned toward the pot, squinting his eyes.

"I can hardly see it, sir."

"When that vessel is baked and cured in the ovens, that which you can hardly see will shine like a silver shekel! I do not put my name on anything with the slightest defect. Would ruin my business."

Obed dug out the speck and started the wheel again. Within minutes the spot was healed over and Tolmai smiled his approval.

The graceful lines and the firm texture of his work were characteristics which identified Tolmai's pieces wherever they were sold. In addition to that, his natural ability at mixing bright colors and imposing a mellow glaze was a quality admired by the world's most discriminating buyers. And his work was found far beyond Cana, even in distant places like India, and Persia, and Rome where foreign traders had carried it.

At some inconspicuous place on each bowl, pitcher, vase, and dozens of other practical and ornamental pieces, the potter left his trademark. It was simple, the letter T inside a larger C, which apparently meant *Tolmai of Cana*. When a person saw one of these pieces of pottery, there was no question as to who made it or what it was worth. It was very valuable.

The potter was advanced in years and, although slowed to the point of a snail's pace, he continued to work in his little shop behind his home. As he grew older, his work was even more coveted because of its scarcity. At his age, he was doing well to produce a third of what he used to do. People who knew his work wondered who would replace him when he died.

His son had worked at times with Tolmai, but he never measured up to the skill of the older man. Furthermore, the son was never much interested in the trade of turning pottery. It was a messy job, with all the wet clay, and it was back-breaking to sit at the wheel all day every day.

The old potter never insisted that his son follow him in the business. Had he done so, it would have pleased him, but he knew that his boy had to find his own way. He did expect the elder son to engage himself in some kind of labor, hopefully creative and artistic.

Tolmai's heart felt like it had a big hole in it because a younger son, named Isaac, had died from an unknown disease when he was seven years old. Never a day passed but that the potter thought of the little boy who might have followed him in the family business. Even the elder boy, whom everyone called Nat, felt the loss keenly and wished for a brother.

One afternoon in late summer, Amon and his wife, Tamar, a couple near Bethsaida, had gotten into a small boat to cross the lake. The sky was blue and the day was calm as the little craft left the shore. Several people were aboard and all were laughing and talking, simply enjoying a perfect afternoon.

Suddenly, as the boat neared the half-way point, a wild rush of wind slapped the sea and the boat capsized. Such occurrences were not rare since the cool air from the surrounding mountains, under certain conditions, coming in contact with the balmy air over the water, often produced violent squalls.

The storm, fierce as it was, lasted only a few minutes, but those who survived the experience never

255

forgot how afraid they were. Of those who drowned, there were only three, two were Amon and Tamar. The news of the tragedy spread rapidly across Galilee. And the community did not soon recover from the loss of two of their esteemed citizens.

"What will become of Flip?"

That was the question on everybody's mind. Flip was the ten year old son of the Amons and there were no relatives to be found anywhere.

Some of the neighbors considered passing him around from family to family, but they were aware that such a situation was not healthy for the boy or the families.

There were two problems. Nearly all the households were poor and blessed with several children. One more child to feed and clothe was not an easy choice to consider. The other problem was that Flip, while being a likeable child, was slower than the other boys and girls in the neighborhood. He was not retarded, just slow. Some of the boys his age had named him *Dopey*. It was not the kindest thing to do, but Flip never seemed to mind and the boys meant no harm. Before long, most of the people in Bethsaida were affectionately referring to him by his new nickname.

When Tolmai's son, Nat, heard about the problem in Bethsaida, he mentioned it to his father. "Why don't we take this boy and make a home for him?"

At first, it was a shock to the old potter, who found it hard to conceive of the idea of taking in, at his advanced age, a ten year old homeless boy. Nat could see the surprise in his father's eyes.

"You and I miss Isaac so much, dad. I could take this boy under my wing and care for him. It would be good to have a brother again. And the boy would probably help fill the void in your own life. Who knows, he might even like pottering! And you know of my dislike for it. Maybe he could learn the trade and keep the business going."

The discussion got a little heated before it ended and the old potter wondered why his son seemed so bent on doing this thing.

Nat had not shown much interest in any of the boys and girls in Cana, not even so much as to speak to them. After his younger brother died, he had become somewhat withdrawn. Tolmai refused to think too much about it because Nat's nature was contemplative and studious. He would rather sit under the fig tree in the courtyard and think than fool away his time with that sticky clay. And people? He didn't dislike anybody. He just found some things more to his interest than socializing.

Every day or so, he would slip off down to the synagogue school and slowly print on his papyrus scroll a scripture as the teacher read it aloud. By this time, his writings had grown into several sizeable rolls of sacred text. Hours were spent under that fig tree, by himself, thinking deeply about these scriptures.

Nobody in Cana condoned the fact that he was of

257

little help to his old father. But, no one thought of him as being lazy or shiftless either, because he stayed busy with his own private little library, a kind of non-professional student.

The scriptures which he copied were, without exception, those which had to do with the coming kingdom. With all his heart, Nat believed that prophecies about the coming Messiah were about to be fulfilled. Of all the devout men in Cana, including the teachers at the synagogue, he probably knew more about the works of the prophets than anyone else. And that made him cautious. Yes, he was looking for the Messiah, but he had known more than one pretender to that title and he was not about to be fooled by some self-appointed revolutionary.

For some reason, unreal as it seemed, Nat had taken a special interest in this little boy whom he had never seen. Tolmai did not think he was up to the trip at his age, so it was agreed that the decision and the journey would be left to his son.

When Nat arrived in Bethsaida and inquired as to the whereabouts of the lad, it was discovered that Flip had been given shelter by a farmer in one of his sheds. He was literally eating with the animals, eating from the barley troughs with the donkeys.

"Don't be afraid," exclaimed Nat, as he approached the ragged and frightened child crouched in the corner of the shed. "I am your friend. My name is Nat and I live in Cana. Do you know where that is?"

With eyes filled with wonder, the little boy sat motionless and said nothing.

Moving cautiously closer, Nat, knowing how alone and suspicious the abandoned child must feel, leaned down and looked into his eyes.

"Please don't be afraid of me. I know what happened. I did not know your daddy, but you must miss him very much. Nobody can ever replace him. But you cannot live like this. I don't have a little brother and it would be great if you and I could be friends."

Flip batted his wondering eyes and smiled At that point, Nat reached out his hand and touched him on the shoulder. Flip did not resist.

The potter's son, who had enjoyed being pampered by his parents as a child, could not believe that anyone should have to live like this sad, little boy. Since no one wanted the responsibility of the child, and since no legal arrangements were necessary, Nat just gathered up the dirty boy in his arms, and returned with him to Cana.

Nat liked him at once. Flip seemed so much younger than ten, more like five or six. And that touched a tender spot in the heart of the potter's son. Isaac was about that age when he died. And Flip? Well, what kid wouldn't like a strong, kind, deep-voiced man who would take a boy in, feed and clothe him, and protect him from the loneliness of being an orphan?

Their trip from Bethsaida, around the north end of the lake, passed through the cosmopolitan town of Capernaum. There they stopped at the local inn for refreshment.   From Capernaum, the two of them journeyed through the Plain of Gennesaret, a beautiful valley where the flowers bloomed in abundance. This was the first time Flip had been so far west and he ran and played in the lush fields. Nat thoroughly enjoyed watching the antics of the little boy and thinking of his little brother, how he used to sit for hours watching Isaac frolic in the tall grass.

Only a few days had passed since the lad from Bethsaida was welcomed by the old potter to his new home in Cana of Galilee. It was good therapy for Tolmai who, as the years wore him down, had about given in to decrepitude and death. To watch Flip play, to hear him laugh, to watch the growing friendship between big Nat and little Flip – it was like a tonic for the old man. He walked a little straighter now and smiled a lot more since the wonderful child had come to his empty house. And he mentioned it to the boy.

Flip was having fun with the little dog which, as if something had predestined it, showed up at the house in Cana on the very day the boy arrived.

Old Tolmai was watching from under the leaves of the fig tree where he was relaxing in Nat's favorite chair.

"Flippy," he shouted, using the affectionate name by which he always referred to the child, "come here a minute."

The lad jumped to his feet and came running, the dog at his heels.

"Yes, daddy Tolmai, can get you something?"
"No, my son," answered the old man. "Since you have come here, there is nothing I need!"

Flip looked a little blank, as if he did not understand what daddy Tolmai meant.

"You can never know, Flippy, how you have changed my life!" With that, he reached out his wrinkled hands and took the boy's face between them. Then, with great emotion, Tolmai said, "Before you came, I was ready to die. My steps were slow and my breath was short. I had no appetite. Nothing interested me anymore."

"You feel better now?" interrupted Flip.

"Much, much better! You are like sunshine. Your energy is contagious. Everything is full of wonder and adventure for you. Your young life has been hard on you, but everything you do says that you have learned to accept what has been handed you and move on. That has been so hard for me to do. I don't like being old. My spirit still wants to run and jump like you, but my bones say no."

"Then I'll run and jump for you, daddy Tolmai," said Flip, reassuringly.

"That you will," replied Tolmai, "that you will."

As soon as it could be arranged, the boy was enrolled in school. Other children were invariably a step or two ahead of him in their studies, but Flip was a lot of fun. Even the teachers had a warm spot for him. Being a little slow mentally, but never embarrassed by it, he was forever saying something so hilariously silly or doing

261

something so ridiculously crazy that the whole class split apart with laughter. Everyone liked Flip. On those days when he was sick and unable to come to the synagogue school, it was not the same. The day was a drag without Flip.

At night, Nat would help the growing boy with his memory work. It was all so easy for big brother that it didn't seem possible that this lad had such a hard time with his lessons. Eventually, the boy would arrive at some measure of achievement, but he was far from the top of his class!

The relationship between the man and the boy ultimately made them inseparable. The bond of mutual respect was like an unbreakable cement which nothing on earth could weaken. In later years, the people who met them thought they were blood brothers. Some were surprised to learn that they were not related at all, because everyone insisted that they looked alike.

After the death of Tolmai, the potter's shed was rented out to a young apprentice from near-by Chabulon. The wheel and all the tools were sold to the new tenant because, though Nat and Flip helped out some in the shop, neither had any interest in continuing the business.

Tolmai had saved enough that Nat did not have to do much about making a living. He could spend most of his time pursuing his search for the kingdom. And Flip, now in his early twenties, had gotten a good job with a wheat farmer in the country. Hardly a day passed, however, when they did not see one another, at least for

263

Leslie H. Woodson

a few minutes.

It was a hot night in early autumn. The chores were done and two young farmers came into town with Flip. The evening had been planned for several weeks. Nat had invited a couple of his friends, men of a similar studious nature, to drop in for a while. So the six men sat in the coolest spot they could find in the courtyard and talked into the night about the latest happenings in and around Cana.

"Send that bowl of almonds over this way, Bart," said one of Nat's friends.

Flip, turning to Nat, said, "What did he call you?"

"Oh, that? A lot people around here call me Bart since father died. Some of them call me Bartholomew out of respect for dad."

"How come I call you Nat?"

Nat chuckled as he crunched an almond between his teeth.

"It just kind of stuck, I guess. You see, my mother gave me my name. My name is Nathaniel, but nobody ever wanted to use that mouthful, so they began calling me Nat. Dad always called me that, too. Except when he was angry with something I had done. Then he growled out the whole thing, *Nathaniel Bartholomew,* emphasizing every sound in it."

Everybody laughed, especially Flip.

"You think you're pretty smart, don't you? All these years I never heard anyone call you Nathaniel. And

264

now I find out that you've got *two* names."

The air was rent with the raucous laughter of five men enjoying the joke on Flip. It was great just being together like this and enjoying one another's company.

"Well, you're not as smart as you think, Bart!" shouted Flip, pointing his finger at the man he respected more than anyone on earth.

"You don't know my name either. How about that?" continued Flip. "We have known each other over twelve years and you don't know *my* name!"

The young man stopped and waited for someone to say something. No one did.

"Batholomew!" he shouted with a friendly snarl. "My real name is Philip. Mother was from Macedonia and she told me that I was named for the father of Alexander the Great. Everybody just calls me Flip for short."

Several years passed and one day Philip came running up under the fig tree all out of breath. Nathaniel raised his eyes from the scroll he was studying. "Hey, what's wrong with you? You look like you've seen a ghost."

"No, no, Nat . . . Not a ghost. I have found the Messiah! He is from Nazareth and his name is Jesus."

"Philip," he said, "you're so dopey you wouldn't know the Messiah if he had a halo around his head!"

"You've got to see him. Come with me and I will show you!" insisted Philip, as he tugged at Nathaniel's arm like an anxious child who had just made a great discovery.

  "All right," said Nathaniel, "but nothing good could can ever come out of Nazareth!"

CHAPTER SIXTEEN

When Archelaus died Jesus was approaching his eleventh birthday, much too young to know much about the world of politics even though his thoughts were advanced beyond most of his peers. He was maturing on schedule and, by the time He reached his late teens, had begun to grow more interested in the affairs of the nation.

Joseph had talked a lot about the occupation of Palestine by Rome and the underground movement bent on driving out the foreign soldiers. Jesus remembered some of those conversations with his father when He was yet quite young. And He was interested then, but nothing like the interest which He nourished at this later time in his life.

The elder carpenter gave the impression that he was a bit ashamed of the rabid fanatics who carried curved blade sicas in their girdles, with which to stab anyone friendly with Rome. The common people were confused by the extremes in political viewpoints which ran all the way from working for the Roman government to a pledge to destroy it.

It was not easy for the ordinary folks to get passionately incensed against Rome since the empire had allowed the Jews more freedom than any other captive people.

Joseph was never overly upset with Rome itself. He was thankful that his people were allowed to continue their worship of Jehovah when other conquered countries were forced to serve the gods of the empire.

Regardless as to who controlled the political scene, the boy Jesus was growing up with an inner sense of personal freedom which was not to be conditioned by any king. All his life, He was to continue his search for the truth wherever it might be found – Nazareth, Jerusalem, or even Rome – in the conviction that the truth makes men free.

There was much corruption in the House of Israel. One did not have to be a man, much less a prophet, to see that. Rome was in power because the Hebrew leadership had lost its divine right to rule through sheer, godless, political chicanery. Israel had been destined from her beginning to be a theocracy, a nation ruled by priests. Ultimately, God had meant the entire populace to become priests to one another and the world.

Somewhere the original glory had faded and the nation lay in the shades of apostasy. The young son of Mary had heard his father talk a great deal about the family aristocracy of the high priest and the tendencies toward nepotism within the higher echelons of the state religion.

It did not seem to Jesus, as He grew up in Nazareth, that it made a great deal of difference who ruled in a nation. A man had to determine for himself if he would be free or slave. That was true whether the ruling king were a Jew, an Assyrian, a Chaldean, or a Roman.

By the time He had reached the age of twenty,

Jesus had decided that He would be unfettered by the control of outside forces. Some of the people complained about high taxes, but they were always folks who were unhappy about something. That is human nature. Everybody likes to make others think he is having a hard time. It makes good conversation and feeds the martyr complex.

Nobody enjoys paying taxes. Not even Joseph had liked it, but his family never heard him say much about it. Joseph was like that. He just worked a little harder at tax time and saved for the day when the tax collector would come around.

Jesus knew that He had been born at the end of a journey to Bethlehem where Joseph's taxes were to be assessed by Quirinius, governor of Syria. Regardless of the galling taxation, the father of Jesus had always appeared glad just to be alive. It was worth a great deal to live in a land where he could take care of his family without being molested by anything worse than tax collectors. There could have been secret police.

No one ever heard Jesus rebel against Roman authority. And He definitely cautioned others against it. All of this Jesus had learned from his father who had taken pride in being a good citizen, though he never achieved that title which could be granted only by the Caesar himself.

The sun was far down in the west, on a workday afternoon, when there was a skirmish in town between a

269

couple of Roman soldiers and a drunk Jew. Just before closing time, one of the shop keepers, from up the street, walked into Joseph's place of business. Jesus remembered the incident as if it were yesterday.

"Well, Joe, I guess you heard about the trouble in town today?"

"Oh, yes, these things we have to expect when someone drinks too much," answered Joseph, as he continued sweeping up the sawdust from the day's work.

"Sure, Joe, everybody knows that! But that isn't the problem. The problem is the way Rome keeps its thumb on us as if they own us body and soul."

"Rube," said the carpenter, using the guest's given name, "Somebody's got to keep order. You know that. For now, it's Rome who has that responsibility."

"I can't believe that you would take the side of the forces of Rome," exclaimed Rube loudly.

"Nobody's taking sides. There is really no one else to keep rowdies in line. You don't want people drunk in the streets."

"Joe, you are missing the point. We are all tired of Gentiles telling us what to do. They control our lives, tell us what to do, and when to do it. And they even take our money which belongs to Jehovah. We have a duty to do something about this."

"Tell me, Rube. What can we do?"

"I don't know, but this kind of thing makes me churn inside."

"You are hurting no one but yourself," said

Joseph, as he stood the broom in the corner. "All we can do right now is obey those who rule over us. If they stop us from our worship of Jehovah, we can't accept that. But obedience in civil matters and paying taxes, that is a part of being allowed to keep our way of life."

Rube wasn't convinced, but he did know that Old Joe was a sensible man and there wasn't much he could argue about when the carpenter had made his point so clearly. For the rest of his life, the son of Joseph remembered that conversation almost word for word.

Jesus loved his country. The hills around Nazareth seemed almost divine. Being well read in the history of the Hebrew people, there was hardly a foot of soil anywhere Jesus walked where He did not recapture the image of some event from the past.

When He had visited Jericho on one of his trips south, He gazed long upon the thirty-six room red, black, and gold palace which had been built by king Herod the Great and his son Archelaus. It was a luxurious winter capital with Roman baths, mosaic floors, and wine cellars. However, it was not the palace which impressed the son of Joseph. It was the memory of Joshua who, in obedience to Jehovah, marched seven times around the city, shouted and blew on the shophar, and watched the walls come tumbling down!

At Megiddo, He envisioned the seventh century battle which Israel lost to the Egyptians as Pharaoh advanced to help the Assyrians. King Josiah, an ancestor and one of the godly kings of Israel, had been killed at that very spot.

And there were the Carmel mountains. He had been there twice and both times He could not help recalling the contest held long ago between Elijah and the prophets of Baal. Jehovah had proved himself there that day as the only God who answers by fire.

God had been good to Israel. Much of what was taking place during Jesus' growing years seemed ominous of bad things to come. The older He grew, the more the spiritual torpor and religious complacency of his land disturbed him. The young student knew what had happened to his own north country just seven hundred years earlier and what the Babylonians had done to Judah in the sixth century. It could happen again.

The political and religious leaders were apparently blind to the approaching judgment. There were days when Jesus wanted to shout out a warning to the people, but something laid a restraining hand on his tongue as though the time were not yet ripe for such things.

Many of the people of the land resented the religious leaders. For some unexplained reason, Jesus felt pity for the Pharisees who spent their days fretting over a multitude of unimportant matters, meticulous details of the oral law. They looked so miserable and unhappy with their sanctimonious fasting, their demonstrative prayers, and their continuous display of piety. So concerned were these men with minuscule legal matters that they often forgot to love and serve their fellows. Actually, the religious professionals had gotten to the place where they bored everybody with their religion. They even bored themselves!

Jesus never refused to pay tribute to duly appointed authorities. Nor did He neglect Sabbath worship. It never occurred to him. Never did He refuse to obey his parents on the assumption that He was free from the Law of Moses. Nor did the thought of failing to make the annual pilgrimage to Jerusalem seem worth considering. Being free did not lessen his obligations. It increased them.

As a young man in the Jewish community, the young carpenter lived by the traditions of the elders, but He never made his faith a thing of formality or minute detail. He was too free for that.

God was as real to him as the wind in the trees. The Spirit of the Lord was vibrantly alive everywhere He looked. While He continued to go to the services of worship and instruction at the synagogue, He did not believe that one had to go there to find God. Often, the most moving visits with God were those spent alone on his knees under the olive trees. He had only to reach out his hand and touch the skirts of the Eternal. But had anyone asked him whether one should go to Sabbath synagogue, He would have said that there is no question about it. The people of God need the comradery and fellowship which worshiping together brings. Jesus knew that and felt pity for people who tried to be religious by themselves.

273

His concern was that there might be some who would give up on the family, abandon the synagogue, and strike out on their own when He promised that God is everywhere and can be found by anyone at any time.

"Everyone," explained Jesus when He talked with his friends, "should have his quiet, personal times with God, but he should never miss a single chance of worshiping together with others."

The common folk of the land were becoming increasingly disenchanted with the established religion and its leadership. Jesus felt that, too, but He knew that no one helps a situation which is going bad by turning it over to the devil! The objective is to try to help the situation by struggling within it in hopes of making it better.

Jesus, from his earliest memory, felt a deep respect for the clergy and teachers in Israel. That was how Joseph and Mary had taught him. It would not be until many years later, after having become weary with their continuing harm to God's people, that He lost that respect. From the day when He detected the difference between truth and error, sincerity and hypocrisy – from that day his esteem for Israel's religious leaders began to dwindle. Ultimately, Jesus was to recognize the blatant hypocrisy of both the political and religious establishments.

There were some who really did not care what the clergy said or did. They were too busy with other things like making a living. Religion was irrelevant to what they were doing. And there were others who cared little for the religious beliefs of the nation, but who were rabidly committed to the defense of Israel as a nation.

One rainy day, one of these zealous advocates of Israel's superiority came into the shop shaking water all over some of the small, unpainted toys which Jesus had just finished. It wasn't hard to see that he didn't care because he was mad about something.

He wasn't a newcomer. In fact, every day or so he would appear. The carpenter's shop was a spot where community meetings took place regularly. Usually the men talked a lot about everything and said nothing! Of course, the craftsman would not allow them inside, but they were free to gather in the courtyard. Often, Jesus would laugh out loud at some of the idle-brained comments made by the men outside his window.

This day it was raining and the men had not appeared, except for this short haired fanatic from a nearby town. Everyone in the whole country side knew Simon. Always hyper and loud, most men got out of the way when they heard that he was in the area.

"Everyday it's the same thing!" shouted Simon as he stormed through the door.

"What's happened this time?" inquired the shop keeper.

"That cursed Roman sentry stopped me up the road again to check my identity. Just because I carry a sica blade in my girdle does not give him the right to

Leslie H. Woodson

invade my privacy!"

The loud-mouth intruder was a member of the underground in Israel, a group who called themselves zealots, extreme patriots bent on restoring the old nationalism which every Hebrew longed for. They were prepared, however, to kill anyone in the employ of Rome or anyone who even collaborated with the enemy. It didn't take much to get the fire going in Simon's soul, just a question about who he was and what he was up to.

"Simon, you are too sensitive, too quick to reach for your sword," said Jesus, trying to calm the red-faced fanatic with thoughts of murder in his heart.

"Rome is not going to go away," continued the carpenter, "because your little band may kill a dozen or two of them. Think how you are wasting your time."

Ready to explode with anger, Simon started to curse, but caught himself when he remembered how the man in the shop felt about that.

"Sit down, friend Simon," said Jesus. "I've got a few minutes."

Digging into his breakfast basket, the carpenter pulled out a couple of crusts of bread which Mary had sent with him for mid-morning break. Handing one of them to his guest, Jesus began quietly. "Let me tell you a story."

"Don't waste my time telling me another of your dumb stories," erupted Simon as he turned toward the door.

"A long time ago," Jesus continued, "there lived a man in this valley whom my grandfather Jacob knew."

276

Simon had stopped in the doorway.

"The man had a family but, other than his immediate kinsfolk, he lived pretty much to himself. To say the least, he was different and was never interested in making friends. Grandfather even said, at first, that he could not tell whether the man could talk, because he never heard him say anything. Because he was so strange, people naturally suspected a lot of bad things about him."

By this time, the man in the doorway had turned around and seated himself on one of the stools. He was cooling off a bit, but he was a little restless because it was not easy to see where Jesus was going with a story which had nothing to do with him. Or, at least, it didn't seem to.

"Where are you going with this?" interrupted the impatient zealot who would rather be out killing some Romans.

The carpenter went on, ignoring the interruption. "A neighbor, who lived near my grandfather, noticed one morning that two of his prized goats were missing. Being a high tempered man, he raged and swore, blaming everyone he could think of for stealing his goats. So, being of a suspicious nature, he immediately thought of his unfriendly neighbor. Picking up the nearest stick, he started for the house where the quiet man lived. As he neared the house, he could see the wife cooking in the little courtyard and he could smell the delicious aroma. He would know that smell anywhere. It was boiled goat!"

Simon crossed and uncrossed his legs as the story, in which he had not the least interest, dragged on.

277

"Get to the point!" he demanded. "I've got things to do as soon as it stops raining."

Jesus wanted to ask him what he was planning to do when the rain stopped . . . kill somebody? But instead, He went on with the story as if no one had tried to break his thought.

"Most people in a small town know everybody's business. The strange man kept no goats and, from all appearances, he was ragged poor. Unless you had money, you certainly did not have goat on a non-special day. Without even asking whether the man was guilty, grandfather's neighbor swung his stick and knocked the boiling pot off into the dirt. Horrified, the wife jumped up and ran."

At about that time, Jesus picked up the plane from the bench and began to turn curly shavings from a piece of sassafras he had been shaping. As he planed, between each long stroke, he continued the story. "Hearing the commotion, the quiet man appeared in the door of the house and stood looking for a moment at his frightened wife and the angry man with the stick."

The plane made a swooshing sound as another sliver was removed from the sassafras board.

"As quick as a flash, grandfather's neighbor . . . Oh, by the way, his name was Manasseh, but grandpa called him Man. Without hesitation, Man was on top of the suspect."

Swooosh went the plane again.

Simon had become more interested and, obviously

more relaxed, he had stopped crossing and uncrossing his legs.

"Who gave you the right to my goat?" Here Jesus reached for a piece of rope which He strangled in his hands, graphically describing how Man tightened his grip around the quiet man's throat. "Who do you think you are? What kind of a man are you? You are no man at all!"

"Loosening his strangle hold so the man's excuse could be heard, Man demanded an answer," continued the carpenter. "But, there was no response except a raspy, gurgling sound which was no answer at all. It was then that grandfather's friend realized that the quiet man was quiet because he was not only deaf; he was dumb. He really could not speak."

Swooosh . . . Swooosh and two slivers curled to perfection fell on the dirt floor.

"Grandfather's neighbor was so mad that he beat the man in the face until he lay unconscious on the ground. The whole time, the wife was screaming through her fingers, standing horrified in the shade of a nearby fig tree. When Man finally got off the pummeled victim, he pointed his forefinger at him and swore that he should have killed him."

Taking a deep breath, the carpenter laid down the heavy plane and, looking into the eyes of Simon, said, "That night the quiet man died and Manasseh was in serious trouble."

"All right," said the young zealot, "so what? Why

are you telling me this story?"

"Upon investigating, it was found out from the frightened wife that her husband had not stolen the goats. The goat, which had been boiling in the pot, had been given to them by a relative who knew that her husband had been unable to get work for a long time and that the children needed something more than bread."

Simon looked back at Jesus as if to say, "Well, what's that got to do with anything?"

Turning back to the bench and picking up the plane, the carpenter said, with great feeling for the poor, misguided patriot, "The point is, Simon, that you hate everybody. You are suspicious of everyone. You hate the Roman sentry who is only doing his job. He doesn't hate you. But you hate even your neighbors if they pay their taxes or if they are kind to a Gentile."

Jesus stopped and looked long at the floor.

"Simon," He then said, displaying his feeling of disappointment with the zealots in general, "We never know what makes another person act as he does. And, in our rash actions, we make many mistakes which hurt innocent people. When evil fights evil, evil always wins."

The young man on the stool looked away but made no reply.

"I love my country, too. And I love the traditions of Israel. But, there is a better way to restore our land than by the use of the sword. Put away that sica blade in your girdle. Stop making yourself so miserable. You just might be totally wrong."

Some of what the carpenter said rang true, but He just didn't live in Simon's world. So reasoned the fiery spirited zealot as he moved toward the door. It had stopped raining and, as the seething visitor stepped outside, Jesus called to him.

"By the way, Simon. Manasseh later found the goats unharmed. They were hiding in the brush several furlongs from the herd. How do you think Man felt when he got that news?"

CHAPTER SEVENTEEN

There have always been boys with soft faces and curvaceous bodies, young men with feminine traits and falsetto voices. Jesus was not one of them.

Later efforts to portray his deity by making him look effeminate were honest mistakes. What that has to do with deity is unclear. One who lived in a peasant home in Nazareth and worked in the carpenter's shop would never have appeared so delicate. He did not display long, tapered, graceful fingers as we have sought to reinvent him. No one knows what He looked like, but He certainly would have been rough-hewn, tough-skinned, horny-handed and possibly somewhat untidy.

At any hour of the day, the people who knew him found him with dirt under his nails and soil on his garments. When He worked, He worked hard. And when He played, He played hard, too. His hands were calloused and full of splinters from working with rough lumber. His knees were usually scabbed and sore from the tough-and-tumble games He played. His masculinity was never in doubt.

From the time Jesus was old enough for the chemical changes which mark adolescence until the day when He left the workbench for a teaching ministry, He was as much attracted by members of the opposite sex as were any of the red-blooded Hebrew boys in Nazareth.

In the spring of 11 A. D., when Jesus was about

fifteen years old, a new family had come to live in Nazareth. Newcomers were not unusual since people had to move where the work was to be found. And it was never much of a problem since one or two ox carts could carry all their simple belongings. In addition to that, the old nomadic life had left lingering traces. There was a time when Joseph had considered moving his own trade to Jerusalem..

The new arrivals had come from Gadara in the Decapolis, east of the Jordan River, to pool their meager resources with a local kinsmen in an effort to provide bread for themselves. Deborah, the oldest of four children, a lovely young woman with a wholesome appearance, graced the evening as she came down to the fountain to draw water.

Jesus had seen her only by accident as He passed in the vicinity en route home after having delivered a plow to a nearby farmer.

When her visage fell across his gaze, his heart skipped a beat and a strange emotion filled his stature with a kind of aching rapture. It was all so new. Girls had never been given much of his time because He was too busy. In fact, the village girls were of no particular concern to him, but then He had not seen Deborah.

The following day He slipped away and hid near a goat stand hoping that He would see her again. Almost an hour passed and there had been no sign of her at all. Suddenly, in the midst of a group of neighborhood girls, she appeared. Again, the same sensation flooded his whole being. Even his face seemed to flush as though He ought to be embarrassed.

It was nearly a week before He was to see her again and this time by the strangest of fates.

In one of the tiny niches which lined the bazaars, He caught sight of her. She was selling cloth garments which her mother had made to help pay for the bread and fresh vegetables they had come to town to buy. No one was near her stall. She was by herself, sorting out her wares, when Jesus startled her at the doorway.

Apologizing for his abruptness, He smiled and introduced himself as the carpenter's apprentice who worked in the little shop of Joseph at the edge of town. Quickly, He explained that He had seen her several days earlier while returning to the shop. Shyly she admitted that she knew who He was. She had already seen him and inquired about his identity.

That night, when the bazaar closed, He helped her carry the unsold garments back to the house where He met her mother.

The next day, while on an errand to make another delivery, Jesus detoured through the market place to speak to Deborah. This time, however, she was noticeably cool toward him as if she were afraid to speak. No matter how hard He tried to get her involved in conversation, she ignored him.

Finally, noting the hurt in his face, she explained, "My parents have forbidden me to talk to you."

Puzzled by the unexpected rebuff, Jesus stood

285

speechless for a moment. "They won't let you or you just don't want to talk to me?"

It was not hard to see that the young girl was torn apart inside. Her eyes were red with unshed tears as she continued. "No, no! I like you very much. I have no choice. If mom and dad forbid me, there's nothing I can do."

The carpenter, with the boyish face, admired her with the heart of a man. Her respect for her parents and her sense of responsibility to them filled him with admiration which made him like Deborah even more.

"Did they give you a reason?" asked Jesus.

"Something about your being the son of Mary."

Talk around town about Mary had died down across the years, gossipy suspicion that Mary had conceived him by a Roman soldier during her engagement to Joseph or maybe even before. There is always someone ready to revive an old tale for the benefit of new-comers in town. And people did like to talk.

Jesus and Deborah did not see each other again except at a distance. While He respected the wishes of her parents, He wondered what could make people so suspicious of one another. Why could people not accept their neighbors on their own merits? And why should one's background or even his past deeds be held against him? It was all baffling to a young man trying to understand his world.

Furthermore, He had never understood what folks in town had against his mother. It was impossible that so

286

holy a woman could ever have disgraced herself! If that was what they were thinking, He would never believe it.

Deborah and her family went their way and He forgot about her except on rare occasions when He was alone with his thoughts under the stars.

Life continued pretty much as it had always been except that the days grew longer with the responsibilities of the shop and his increasing interest in the Law and the Prophets. Often, until far into the night, He would study by the flickering light of the lamp. At times his mind would wander off and He would find himself thinking wistfully about doing something great someday. While He enjoyed the shop, there was a deep down feeling that something entirely different awaited him. And the strange anticipation became stronger as the years passed.

He wished that there were enough money and leisure time to go away to rabbinical school and learn to be a rabbi! He would be a good one – He knew that. There were a lot of things in his heart which He would like to say to the people. Being a rabbi would give him the right to do just that. The thought refused to depart, but it grew dim by the time He realized that He could talk about religion without being a rabbi at all. Of course, He was quite mature by that time – nearly thirty years old.

It was not until He had been talking religion to his own townsfolk for months that the Pharisees, literally dragging a poor woman caught in act of adultery, challenged him to decide her fate. They were all chattering at once as the pitiable wreck of womankind, ashamed to lift her head, was thrown like a pile of garbage at his feet.

"You think you know so much," said one of the clergy, "tell us what to do with her."

In the background, He caught the distinct sound of a voice demanding that she be punished. "Stone her! Moses told us what to do. Stone her!" That was exactly what the law said was to be done with people like her.

Turning abruptly in the direction from which came the voice, Jesus raised his hands. There was silence. Slowly and sternly, he spoke. "You may throw the first stone, sir . . . if you have no sin!"

When the mob began to disperse, Jesus stooped and took the woman, still lying in a heap at his feet, by the hand. "Go and do not this thing again," said Jesus. "There is no one here to condemn you. God loves you."

As she lifted her grateful eyes to thank him, He caught his breath. Disfigured by sin as she was, He saw through the tears streaming down her cheeks the unmistakable face of Deborah. And He remembered.

He remembered with sadness the day her parents had despised him. He remembered how innocent and beautiful she was the first time He saw her drawing water from the village well. He remembered how his mother broke down in sobs when He told her what Deborah had said. A dull ache lodged somewhere deep inside his heart as the broken woman turned away to lose herself in the crowd. And more in thought than in speech, his lips moved to form unspoken words which only God could hear. "Forgive them. Forgive Deborah. Forgive her parents. Forgive these Pharisees. None of them really know what they have done."

From the earliest stirring of his manhood, Jesus had thought a great deal about marriage and family life. Of course, there was nobody with whom He ever became really serious because there was so little time for anything but work. It may be that He did not marry, in the normal pattern of his time, because of the death of Joseph and the heavy obligations of the family. Being fully human, the same hormones stirred in his body as in that of any other man. And so He wondered about his future – whether there would be someone for him. Certainly, Jesus had great respect for women and held marriage in the highest regard.

By the time He was able to get away from the shop and make a life for himself, He had already pledged himself to the life of an itinerant preacher. It is almost a foregone conclusion that entering into his decision not to marry was the heavy pressure of vocation which was upon him. There was little place in such a rugged schedule for a wife.

Though He never completely gave up the idea that He could be a family man if He desired, there were crucial issues so demanding that marriage would have been out of the question. It goes without saying that the psychic often requires freedom from the normal circumstances of society. And it was all a matter of priorities with Jesus.

Marriage was not for everybody and it fell into second place where the kingdom of God was concerned.

Mary was to remember, long after her son had died, that Joseph had told her of an incident in the shop one day when a rabbi, who had come ordering a reading desk for the synagogue, put his holy hand upon the head of the youthful carpenter.

"What are you going to be when you are as big as your father?" asked the rabbi.

The venerable teacher had smiled smugly as though he already anticipated what the answer would be. Jewish boys usually followed their father's trade and the rabbi expected him to say the normal thing: "I will be a carpenter."

But, without a moment's delay, the boy had replied, "I want to be a man as strong and good as Joseph!"

That He was to become without question and the rabbi was so impressed that he made no reply.

Mary had moments when, like any mother, she was a little concerned that there was no sweet, young girl in his life. There was never the slightest hint that Jesus was uninterested. More than once, she had sensed the notice which her eldest son had taken in one of the village daughters. The ladies were always from good families and much admired by Mary. Nothing ever came of any potential relationship, however, and one day she nervously approached the subject.

The room was empty of members of the family except for Jesus, who had stopped by the house on the way back from work in a neighboring village. The relationship between mother and son was warm and affectionate. Mary knew He was special. And Jesus knew Mary was special, too.

So, there was never any embarrassment about showing her concern for his future as a family man. She wanted the best for him, whatever it might be. It was just that He had never talked about it and she was at a loss to know what He was thinking.

"Have you got a little time for your mother?" she asked, as she dried her hands on her apron.

"Sure, mother. You know that I always have time for you. No one in the world is as important to me as you. You surely know that."

Jesus kissed her tenderly on the cheek and prepared to sit down.

"The last thing I want to do," she began apologetically," is pry into your life in places where you deserve privacy. If I am going in the wrong direction, stop me!"

"Mother, I have no secrets from you," He assured her. "What's so important? Are you worried about something?"

"No, not worried," replied Mary, "just a little confused."

She went on.

"My boy, you are such a fine son, so responsible,

291

and so very good. You are handsome and gentle. You are strong and fearless. There is no question but that you would make some good woman a wonderful husband."

Jesus leaned back and smiled broadly.

"I knew that was on your mind. Lately, it has been so noticeable that I just figured you would get around to it soon."

The room grew silent.

"Mother," Jesus finally said, "no one in the world could understand me but you. There are things we share which no one else would ever believe."

Everything was quiet again. Mary waited.

"There is nothing abnormal about me, mother. The same feelings thrash around inside me as in any other man my age. Sometimes I lie awake at night and remember how you and dad used to snuggle up on that old mat, how devoted you were to each other, how mutually dependent you were. And it was so beautiful."

"Your father was an easy man to love, son. I miss him still, and I think of those wonderful moments, too," replied Mary, her big, brown eyes misting over with unshed tears. "The nights now are so lonely. Every woman needs a good husband. And every man needs a loving wife."

A tear dripped down Mary's cheek and Jesus reached out his hand and wiped it away.

"There are times when I think that it would be the greatest thing in the world to have a wife and maybe, someday, children of my own. There's no one in particular out there, but you and I know a lot of wonderful young women who would grace any man's life. It's not that I haven't found the right woman, but it is more as if there is something which I am supposed to do which would make it very hard on any woman who might marry me."

"What could there possibly be that you might have to do where a woman would be disadvantaged? With a husband like you, no woman would ever have to worry about anything."

Mary was trying to make her son feel better, but it wasn't working.

"All I want, son, is for you to be happy. Since your father died, you have had to work so hard. There has been so little time for you to be a child and have fun. Fate has forced you to be an adult all your life. It is time for you to fall in love and settle down with your own family. A man is nobody without children. And I am nobody without more grandchildren."

"Oh, mother, I know so well what you are saying. The years have been rough, but they are rough for almost everybody. These are harsh times. You must know, however, that I never resented having to take dad's place and care for you and the children."

The room once again was quiet.

"Our faith teaches us," suggested Jesus, as He pulled the conversation back into gear, "that a man's immortality lies in his children. If I have no children of my own, then, according to the elders, I will cease to be at my

293

death. No one will remember me. No one will continue my life and work. I will have lived in vain. Do you think that is true, mother?"

By this time, Mary's eyes were over-flowing with tears. Her lips trembled as she tried to speak. Clearing her throat and wiping her eyes, she bubbled over with beautiful thoughts which lay quietly on her mind.

"My son, *you* will never die. Your life will go on forever. God did not give you to me to let you just disappear. You are a miracle child and, whether you have children or not, a life such as yours will go on forever."

Mary moved off the stool where she had been sitting to get a face cloth to dry her eyes.

"Mother," said Jesus, as Mary turned her face back toward him, "I don't want you to be disappointed in me. It is possible that I will never give you grandchildren. So far, it just doesn't seem to be in the plan, whatever that is, that God has for me. Why God might want me to remain a single man when, at the time of creation, He sanctioned marriage and child bearing for all people is still a puzzle for me. Until He shows me something different than what I now feel, it looks like it may be just God and me."

Although Mary longed for a house full of children, what her son had told her was comforting. She would have to be able to live with that. What could be greater than lots of grandchildren she could not begin to imagine. Maybe someday she would know what that might be. For now, patience and prayer were about the only thing Mary could do. Feeling helpless was not any fun.

CHAPTER EIGHTEEN

Until the very last day of his earthly life, Jesus retained the verve, enthusiasm, and excitement which characterized him as a boy in Nazareth. The wonder of God's world, with its beautiful breath-taking sights, joyous sounds, tempting smells, and delicious tastes were enough to fill his young mind and body with rapturous ecstasy.

When later He was called by some of the more rigid clergy of his day, "glutton and wine bibber," it was not a matter of over indulgence, but rather of being young and human enough to enjoy God's world. He had simply learned to love the good things of life as He grew older in Nazareth. Wherever family and friends were enjoying good, clean fun, He was there without waiting for an invitation.

People never thought of him as a somber recluse. Much of his time had to be spent in the workshop, but the carpenter was always present on feast days and holy seasons to participate and enjoy the festivities. His presence was welcomed, some even saying he was the life of the party.

There were other times, however, when He was deeply moved about life, deeply serious about the problems which confronted the nation, thoughtful about the people who always appeared to be sheep without a shepherd. But there were also times when He laughed and sang around the fireside in the evening. And his dry sense of humor was captivating, so much so that his friends would shake their heads in wonder at his fresh way of looking at life.

He was so full of life, so vibrant and exciting to be around. Most of the younger set liked him at once. Jesus joined in their games and, when there was a chance to get away for a day of leisure, enjoyed hiking through the country lanes and across the hills. As the group of boys and girls would climb the mountain paths, they could be heard singing the tunes which were popular with the young people of the time.

For once – it was one of those rare occasions – Jesus had caught up with his chores at the shop and decided to join several of his friends on an outing to Sepphoris, the chief town of the region, which lay about four miles to the northwest of Nazareth. There was never a great deal to see or do in Sepphoris, but at least there was more going on there than in the sleepy little town of Nazareth.

They started early, before sun-up, and returned long after nightfall to the valley where lay the lazy town of their birth. It was a happy day for everyone. Each youth carried a bag of hard bread, dried fish, and figs which had been prepared for the occasion. At intervals, when passing through the vineyards which abounded in the hill country, they stopped and refreshed themselves with the tasty grapes which hung in large clusters on the vines. No one was in any hurry. If they didn't get back when they had planned, they were old enough to take care of themselves and nobody would worry about them.

Everybody knew by now that Jesus had a knack for telling stories. He could make up a good yarn out of just about anything that happened. In fact, he had the uncanny ability for just making up stories right out of his heart. They were, at times, a little different because they usually had an underlying meaning which He did not make exactly clear to them. One had to think the story through so as not to miss the nuances which held the secret. But they were far better than the worn out riddles the older folks told. And when He told stories which put the religious leaders in a bad light, his friends loved them. Nevertheless, they were glad that their stuffy parents were not around to hear them.

That day, as they sucked the delectable juice from clusters of grapes, the young carpenter told them a story about a man who owned a vineyard much like the one from which they were gleaning the tasty morsels.

"This farmer had leased the whole thing to some tenants who refused to honor the claims of the servants when they came for the owner's share," Jesus began. "Some of the servants they beat. Finally, the farmer sent his son to collect and the tenants reasoned that, if they could get rid of the son, they would easily take possession of the vineyard from the old man."

"How would anyone think he could get by with that?" laughed one of the boys. "You'd think even the dumbest guy would know better than to try. There are

297

laws, you know."

With a kind of knowing look in his eyes, Jesus finished the story without pausing to answer the question. Picking up a stick from the ground and scratching the hard soil, the story-teller continued with an unexplainable softness in his voice.

"So they killed the son."

Then, like one who had returned from another world, the young story teller lifted his face and said, "They never gave a thought to the fact that the owner would surely come one day to set the matter straight."

Where the story came from, no one knew. Even Jesus wondered about it. It just seemed to come out of the air. But, while He told it, every boy and girl listened as if his words were golden nuggets dragged from the mountain stream.

The words were smooth and came easily from his lips. And as He spoke, there was something more than plain eloquence about his stories. They appeared to be possessed with the eloquence of a god.

Too soon, the outing came to a close. They had spent the better part of a day just wandering around through the markets looking at the ugly camels and viewing the wide assortment of wares which were for sale in the maze of tiny shops. On the way home from Sepphoris, they ran up and down hills shouting loudly as they came to the bottom all out of breath.

Once, when one of the girls fell and sprained her ankle, Jesus had helped her to her feet. Finding that she could not walk, He carried her in his strong arms until she was able to hobble, holding to his shoulder. He was so strong and gentle with her that she thought it was worth spraining an ankle to be treated so tenderly.

She liked the way she felt and decided that very moment she would try that again. It certainly had worked that time!

When people came into the crude little place where the son of Mary worked, they began to notice what fine features and strong muscles the hard working boy revealed. It was not that He was handsome, though his mother was forever telling him that He was. He was rather ordinary looking, but there was something about the resolute look in his eyes, the firm set of his jaw, and the broadness of his shoulders that made him look the part of an exemplary youth. There was something regal about him.

Some of the women in the village, who had gossiped most in earlier days about his mother, secretly admired him and wished that some of his strong, youthful qualities would rub off on their own sons. Their boys were always offended, of course, when those mothers spoke of Jesus as a role model for young men.

Work days continued to be very much alike. They were busy, but terribly routine. One had to fight the boredom at times. The carpenter had just finished assembling a table He had made for a customer and was rubbing it down to a good finish when he heard excitement on the street near the shop. That was not a usual

299

occurrence in a little town where nothing ever happened out of the ordinary. Walking to the door, He saw a crowd of teens who had gathered around a Roman soldier on a white horse. As it was nearly time to break for his morning snack, Jesus walked down to where the crowd had assembled. There before him was the most beautiful white stallion that He had even seen. This had to be a high ranking military man to be riding such a steed. The saddle and bridle were studded with gems that glistened in the rays of the setting sun. The horse was a picture of conquest with its bulging muscles and nervous stance.

There were not many things that the young Nazarene ever really wanted. Being unable to afford luxuries, He refused to let himself desire them. But, that day He was overwhelmed by a sudden impulse to have a horse like that which the soldier rode. He wondered just how fast it could run, how many miles it could cover, and how quickly.

Of course, the whole thing was out of the question. He had no money and there were all those mouths to feed. That night, as He lay on his sleeping mat, He could not go to sleep for a long while because of the wild dream which kept running through his head, dreams about what fun He could have with a horse and saddle like that.

During the following days, He spent a few minutes before beginning his chores – just a few because there was no time to waste – carving a copy of the white horse from a piece of olive wood. He had become quite adept at carving and the finished product was an exact scaled down replica.

Several people had wanted to purchase it, but it was not for sale. Jesus figured that little carved stallion would be the nearest He would ever come to having his dream come true. He thought of the wonderful rocking horse Joseph had given him on his fourth birthday. He had felt like a king then. It was a wild thought to imagine a day when a carpenter's son might ride on a conquering white horse! But what would ever happen if we could not dream?

Now that Jesus was well into manhood, there were times when He had to fight off the temptation to set aside some wood project He was completing and contemplate just who He really was. Did Jehovah have something for him to do beyond the shop in Nazareth? Mary always thought so. Had He been influenced too much by his mother's ambition? She certainly had big ideas for her son. Or was God himself trying to tell him something?

It is almost certain that by the time He was thirty, Jesus knew himself to be the Messiah, the One anointed to take the seat of David and do something for the dejected people.

The question which He kept pondering was when and how He had come to this decision. Was this knowledge his from the beginning or did it develop as He grew in stature and in wisdom with Jehovah? If it were a

Leslie H. Woodson

progressive revelation, when did He first sense his messianic mission? These were questions which swirled in Jesus' head more and more as He grew older.

Was it after the baptism? From what we see of him in scripture, it would appear that He suspected who He was long before that. If it were prior to his baptism, was He aware of the destiny awaiting him as a growing boy in Nazareth? Such consciousness would have had to be a developing thing if the humanity of Jesus were a reality.

The full force of his regal role probably came late in life, maybe even after the baptism by John. But the gentle stirrings must have been present within his mind and heart quite early. Possibly, by the time He stood seriously discussing the scriptures with the elders in the Temple, at the age of twelve, Jesus had begun to realize who He was, maybe even earlier.

It was certainly within the realm of possibility that the first thoughts of a divine rule arose in the conventional manner. During the long years of waiting for his hour to come, Jesus' fervent dream for Israel commenced its development with a zealous desire to see the nation of Israel free to be its destined self. None of the prophets had envisioned a more expanded dream for Israel's messianic destiny than had He. But it moved on to a vision of a divine reign in which righteousness and peace for all the world would be supreme.

As Jesus grew from childhood into early manhood, the oft-discussed plans to end the occupation of Israel by

Roman soldiers began to appear so futile and devoid of God's will as to disillusion the young prince altogether.

James, who was known to be disenchanted with religion, was committed in his mind to helping get rid of Rome. And he found it hard to understand his older brother's lack of concern for what he himself considered the most important thing in the world .

"Why," James had asked, "do you not understand the importance of freeing our land from Rome? You clearly love Israel as much as I, but there is no fight in you."

"You are right on both counts. I do love my country. And there is no fight in me. At least, not the kind of fight which most people think will bring freedom."

"What other kind of fight is there?" asked the younger brother, showing impatience for such foolish talk.

"Few people realize that swords and spears never accomplish anything but sorrow and defeat for all who engage in such conflict. Nobody wins in war. Everybody loses. The only kind of fight which does any good is love."

James jerked his head back in disgust. "Who ever heard of fighting with love! In the entire history of man, what nation or tribe do you know who fought a war, much more won one, without spears and bows? What kind of weapon is that?"

"That's just it," said Jesus. "Nobody has ever thought of love as a weapon of conquest except God. You see, brother, the only sure way to get rid of your

303

enemies is by loving them to death."

James never brought the subject up again. The whole thing was ludicrous. He had always loved the first born of Joseph and Mary. There had never been any envy in his heart. And they had always been close. But after that conversation, they drifted apart.

The heart of Jesus had been moved and excited that day when He saw the mounted soldier of the Roman guard riding through the village streets. Such sights had always made his heart beat a little faster. There was something about that symbol of power that both frightened and intrigued him. He had imagined how it would feel to wear those colorful uniforms and carry that shield and spear. He was human enough to think of the thrill of being empowered to represent the High Court. But there was something sinister about the blind, ruthless force which characterized these soldiers. Even if they had been in the hands of Israel's own guard, it would have been no different. While still a boy, He had felt that, if everyone would live for God and love his fellows, there would be no need for laws and soldiers with spears. No, that was not for him.

There were times, even when a little boy, when Jesus had felt like a prince, an heir to some great throne. Was it because Mary made him feel that way by her consuming desire to see her son fulfil her dreams? He wondered. The whole idea was so far fetched as to bring his sanity into question. After all, Jesus knew that his family had no real claim to power even though both Joseph and Mary could trace their ancestry all the way back to king David.

For a boy born in poverty and living in despised Nazareth, such a dream was so unreasonable as to be laughable. And dream it was, for He often awoke in the middle of the night from a vivid experience in which He was seated on a golden throne with masses of people prostrate before him.

Never did He share these outrageous dreams with anyone but Mary, who was, at every such moment, filled with elation. Young Jesus, however, felt a sense of pathos in the simple telling of it. You did not have to be very smart to remember what happened to another dreamer who told his brothers of his crazy visions of ruling over them!

The dream was like most dreams in that it was always confused and mixed up when one was awake. It was not all good. Neither was it all bad. At first, Jesus could not understand it at all. But it just kept repeating itself.

When Caesar had removed Archelaus from authority in Judea and exiled him to Gaul, Jesus remembered Joseph's wondering about the use of power to remove power. No ruler was so powerful that he could not be demoted and punished or conquered and executed by another. Not even Caesar was invulnerable to possible overthrow.

There was so much jealousy among men in places of power, so much greed and immorality, that any young man, with the religious principles which had been instilled within the boy Jesus, found the whole political complex rather nauseating.

"Someday," Joseph had often said in his discussions with Mary, "God will put a ruler in the world who will reign over all nations in moral justice and righteousness. There will be no end to his kingdom. The prophets promised us this."

Jesus wistfully longed for the day when such a ruler would appear on the horizon. Strange as it seemed, there was the nagging suggestion that even He himself might figure somewhere in that Day of the Lord.

No one ever guessed that the boy who grew up in Mary's house and worked in Joseph's shop had anything kingly about him. There were a lot of things that people admired about him and several things which they questioned as well. But there was nobody who could have suspected that the day would come when Jesus would be executed on a charge of claiming to be a king.

From the hills surrounding the little city of Nazareth, Jesus could see what seemed to be the ends of the earth.

The town where He lived was a kind of basin whose rim was formed by mountains. As He climbed to the top of those hills, He could look north over the rich plains to snow-capped Mount Hermon where the Jordan River took its rise. Westward, in the distance, He imagined that his eyes could see Mount Carmel and the Bay of Accho on the Mediterranean Sea. When the day was clear, Jesus looked into the east at Tabor's wooded heights and the beautiful Sea of Galilee. And southward, beneath his feet, lay the Plain of Esdraelon which was rich in history as a pass for merchants and warriors.

As the young man looked across the wide spaces, He dreamed of the day when all the earth would be covered with the glory of God as the waters cover the sea. Joseph had taught him to begin every day with faith that such a day would come.

Many times Jesus talked into the night with his mother about these insistent thoughts which kept demanding his attention. Every time Mary would simply say, "Whatever He says to you, do it!"

One evening, Mary asked her son what He would do if He were the king of the Jews. She was a little shocked that she had asked the question. It had just seemed to come out of the air. But the answer came without delay as if He had been thinking about that for a long time.

The first thing He said was enough to make any mother pop her apron strings.

"If I were king of the Jews," began Jesus, "I would get rid of all that needless wealth beneath which Herod and the priests at the Temple are smothering. I would give it to people like our poor friends here in Nazareth who have such difficult times."

Mary smiled in unfathomable joy as her boy

continued, her mother's heart bursting with pride.

"And I would try to lead the nation into a renewal of commitment to love God with all our hearts and our neighbors as ourselves. The whole world would know that there is a king in Israel who rules in justice, mercy, and truth. And I would gather about me men who share my compassion for the weak and sinful and my dedication to the coming kingdom of God!"

Mary wiped away the customary tear from the corner of her eye. Almost in a whisper, she said, "The Messiah Himself could not do more!"

CHAPTER NINETEEN

Once or twice each year Joseph and Jesus made a trip to Accho on the Mediterranean to pick up materials for the carpenter's shop. After the death of Old Joe, Jesus would often bargain with a neighbor to go along and take his ox cart. The trip was too long for a single cart, but two could carry about all that would be needed for six to eight months.

Most of the trees used for lumber by the carpenter were found in the local area, but good cedar had to be shipped from Tyre down the seacoast to Ptolemais. Then, about the only way it could be carried inland was by wooden wheel carts. The trip had to be planned in advance. Such a journey would take three or four full days by the time the cedars were skinned, loaded, and carefully secured. And someone had to be at the shop to take orders and make deliveries.

Jesus always enjoyed the times when the trip became necessary because, like his father before him, He loved the out-of-doors. Therefore, when the morning arrived for departure, the oxen, lent by a village farmer, were hurriedly geared up to the carts which had been checked out thoroughly the day before to make sure that nothing could go wrong. Jesse, his friend in Gaba, was scheduled to meet him on the outskirts of Sepphoris at a pre-arranged time and Jesus did not want to be late.

Jesse had not been waiting long when the

carpenter showed up with his cart.

"Jesse, my friend! Great to see you again," said Jesus, as the two men embraced. "Has life been good to you since we were together last?"

"I suppose I could say it has. My family is well and business is good enough to keep us fed. That's about all one could expect," replied Jesse in jovial fashion.

"Have you been here long?"

"Oh no. Arrived about an hour ago. Spent the time putting extra fat in my wheel hubs. What's going on in Nazareth?"

"Nazareth is exactly like it was a hundred years ago," laughed the carpenter. "Nothing ever changes where nothing ever happens!"

Jesse joined in the laughter.

Their trip from Sepphoris to Accho was uneventful except that it gave the two men a chance to catch up on things which had happened since they last saw one another. These trips were hard work, but they were fun.

It was nearly noon of the second day before they got to Accho. The boat had been unloaded three days earlier and the cedar for Nazareth was piled by itself and tied with ropes. Jesus paid the ship captain who handled the transaction and began to untie the wraps. Jesse joined in as the logs rolled apart.

One by one the aromatic bark was shaved off the logs and piled in a basket which would be emptied in the large wooden container provided by the shipyard. By removing the bark, there was more room on the carts for the logs themselves. Jesse, not being a carpenter, handled the rough timber, placing and holding it while Jesus dressed it down with the adz.

About half the pile had been shaved by nightfall of the second day when the two men called it quits. They were exhausted and, finding an out-of-the-way spot away from the wharf, stretched out on the ground and slept soundly until daybreak. Early the next morning they were back at the shipyard.

"Looks like some pretty good cedar this time. I remember that there were some shoddy looking logs in the pile last time," observed Jesse.

"You're right. I was badly disappointed with the shipment last year. Had to work around the bad pieces. So much waste my profit was cut way back. Most of the time, however, the logs are select grade and I can use every inch for something."

The bigger part of the morning was spent shaving the rest of the pile of logs. While the oxen spent the time munching on barley which had been brought in the carts, Jesus and Jesse loaded the wet, sticky poles of cedar. When the entire pile had been transferred to the carts, heavy ropes were wrapped across the logs and passed under the carts where they were pulled tight and secured at the side. It had taken about four hours and they were ready to return to Nazareth. If they did not run into any trouble, the afternoon would get them well on their way.

As the men prepared to leave, Jesse called

attention to two large, wooden figures leaning against a railing on the wharf.

"Yes, I know," said Jesus. "Those are carved idols of Baal and Astarte, objects of Canaanite worship from before the time of Joshua. I suppose they are being shipped to some town where they will be enshrined in a place of worship."

Jesse was Jewish, but in a nominal sort of way. Although he never went to synagogue, he would never think of bowing before such an idol. But on the other hand, there wasn't much about it that upset him too much.

"Well, everybody to his own thing is what I say," remarked the carpenter's friend. "Can't worry too much about what the other guy does with his religion."

"You are right, Jesse. Everybody must be free to worship as he wants, but doesn't it strike you as empty-headed to worship a piece of carved wood?"

"I guess so, but then how can we know? I mean, how do we know that we are right and these idol worshipers are wrong? Too big a puzzle for me."

"Look, Jesse. Suppose I should take one of these beautiful cedar logs and make a field post out of one end and carve a god out of the other. Would you worship it?"

"Of course not. Not me. But maybe it's important to them. Must be. I don't guess they would do it if it were not important, would they?"

"But why? The answer is that it is all they have been taught. We know whom we worship. Our God is not a thing. Our God is He who *made* all these things.

Jews know this. And yet, we sit back and ignore the darkness in the world when Jehovah God has chosen us to enlighten our neighbors."

"But that seems like an invasion of their privacy to me," reasoned Jesse.

"We are never to impose anything on others. Everyone must make his own choices. But if I saw my neighbor about to drink poison, it wouldn't be an invasion of his privacy to warn him of what he is doing! We are called to be witnesses, Jesse. And the reason our land is about to collapse is because we have been unfaithful to guide our neighbor into the light."

Jesse felt deeply convicted hearing the words of his friend. He knew that Jesus was right, and he also knew that he had never said anything to anyone about God. Frankly, God had never been very real to Jesse anyway. And how does one go about bragging on someone he doesn't know? It was all a blur to the man from Gaba.

"This whole religious thing has always been puzzling to me," said Jesse, shrugging his shoulders as he checked the cart one last time. "How do we know we are right? We Jews have never seen Jehovah. How do we know these images are false gods?"

"These idols are not *false* gods," Jesus continued. "They are *no* gods. Look at those two images. They are two chunks of wood. Somebody has made himself a god. Man doesn't make God. God makes man!"

"Well, you know a lot more about this than I do," replied the man from Gaba, shaking his head in total

313

confusion. It was abundantly clear that Jesse didn't understand and wanted to drop the subject.

"Check that rear rope on your cart one more time," cautioned the carpenter, as He pointed to what looked like a loose knot. "Be sure that it will not come loose. Once it does, your logs will never stop rolling on these mountain slopes."

The men had traveled about a mile on their return trip without saying much. Jesse was thinking and Jesus was letting him. They had stopped to check the ropes, a thing which had to be done regularly with the jolting of the wooden wheels on the rocky road.

"These cedar trees go back a long way with us Hebrews," said the carpenter, as He groaned under the strain of tightening the load.

"A thousand years ago," He continued," David built him a palace in Jerusalem and he got his cedar logs from Lebanon. Probably the grand-daddies of these very logs. And when his son, Solomon, built the Temple, he turned to Hiram, king of Tyre, to provide him with hundreds of these beautiful, strong cedar trees. After a thousand years, here I am still using the same noble cedars in my shop."

"But you are not building a temple," remarked Jesse, with a touch of humor.

"In a sense, we are all building temples. Each one of us is a temple of God's Spirit. God doesn't live in earthen temples like those graven idols in the pagan groves, but in our hearts. But I know what you mean. No, I am building pillars and beams and fence posts. And that is important, too."

"What are you going to do with these two long logs?" asked Jesse, pointing to the cedars which had given him so much trouble because they hung so far over either end of his cart.

"Those will become masts for sailing vessels. They are special orders. I will have to shave and taper them until they are just right to hold the rigging of the ship. Those masts will be a challenge for me. Almost as big a hassle as they have been for you in getting them this far on our trip!"

Jesse knitted his brow and nodded his head in agreement, wiping the sweat from his face.

As the travelers came to the junction of the pass where the road turned right to Jesse's house in Gaba, Jesus commented on the rich history of the surrounding area. Every Israelite in the whole area knew of the unbelievable things which had happened long ago around Gaba.

"It's holy ground, I guess," said Jesse, looking wistfully across the fields and into the hills beyond.

Pointing to their left, the carpenter, who knew as much about the region as did Jesse, explained, "A number of Israel's greatest battles were fought a stone's throw from where you live. I have never been to your town, but you probably have some monuments to those big conflicts."

"You're right. There's one right near my house which was raised hundreds of years ago as a memorial to king Josiah. It's just a big pile of stones, but it is holy ground for the people of Gaba."

Each night the two men slept on the ground beside their carts. Sleep was not easy to come by, however, due to the brigands and cut-throats who came out of the hills after nightfall. No one knew about the frequency of such attacks better than Jesse. He had been in a fight with a cut-throat, in the broad open daylight, when making a journey to a relative's house a number of years earlier. He still carried the scars from that encounter. And he never wanted to face such a thing again.

During the last night of the return trip, Jesus was shaken awake by the very thing which Jesse had feared. Two masked men were standing over him and one of them was carrying a blade which he made certain the sleeping man saw.

"Don't try to rise," demanded one of the robbers. "Stay where you are. Just hand over your money pouch. Do it now!"

By this time, Jesse was awake. As he started to get up, the other bandit put his big foot on the alarmed man's hand. Jesse screamed from the pain.

"Ben, get the other bag!" shouted the man with the knife.

When the little pouches were pulled open, the one belonging to Jesse had one shekel in it and the one handed over by Jesus was empty. The last bit of money, other than Jesse's shekel, had been spent in Sepphoris for bread for the two of them and a little barley for the oxen.

"We ought to kill you for wasting our time!" yelled the muscular giant of a robber, the one who carried no knife because, with his robust size, he didn't need it.

The nearly empty barley bags, hanging lazily on the side of the carts, were turned inside out for signs of hidden money. None was found. Looking at one another in disappointment and growing anger, the robbers left no doubt in Jesse's mind that he would not live to see the light of another day.

"Please do not kill us," begged Jesse, trembling with fear. "Please take the shekel and let us go. That's all we have."

The robber, with the knife, grabbed Jesus by his beard and jerked him off the ground.

"Your friend over there is scared," growled the thief as he rubbed his nose in the carpenter's face. "What have you got to say?"

Lying beneath one of the carts, Flax was watching the intruder's every move. With taut muscles, he was waiting for the right moment to attack, his eyes darting back and forth at the assailants.

Jesus said nothing. He just looked back at the man with pity in his eyes. The robber, who was twisting his victim's beard, was too close to focus, but Ben saw the pity in the eyes of the carpenter and he felt ashamed.

"Let him go," shouted his partner. "Come on, let's

get out of here."

When the disappointed thieves were out of hearing range, the man from Gaba looked at Jesus. "Were you not afraid?" he asked, trying to swallow the lump in his throat.

"Of course," admitted the carpenter. "But the most dangerous thing in the world is to let your attacker know you are afraid."

"How do you manage *that*?"

"For one thing, you do not resist or return violence for violence. When we resist, it is obvious that we are threatened. And second, you don't try to talk yourself out of your predicament. Never beg. Keep your composure. Stand tall. Take what they do to you. And keep quiet."

"That brute was about to knife you in your heart!" objected Jesse, still in shock from the attack.

"No, Jesse. Had I reacted as you did, we would both be dead. You are still alive because one of us refused to beg or argue."

"I can't believe that you just stood there and took it on the chin."

"Believe me. The world will not be a better place until we stop being cowards and quit trying to prove that we are not by acting tough."

The man from Gaba brushed himself off as he complained about the pain in his hand. Jesus rearranged his tunic and the oxen groaned as the two men put the carts back in motion. It was still dark, but there was no sleep left in either man.

"You see, friend Jesse," said Jesus sadly, as the

two of them continued their journey toward Nazareth, "the world is a difficult place. Man is either threatened and, as a result, he is afraid or he is afraid and, as a result, he is threatened. Cowards are always going to be in trouble and so are bullies."

"How then are we to go about living in this kind of, as you say, difficult place?"

"The way most of us think is that we should defend ourselves. Granted, we must never fail to defend others, even if we have to sacrifice our own lives. But we should not engage in any kind of aggressive defense of ourselves. To do so is to invite trouble you do not need. There is an old proverb handed down from ancient times."

After a moment's pause, he quoted the proverb. "Whatever you would that men not do unto you, do not that unto them."

"That's nice talk," complained Jesse, "but nobody can live like that! How can you get ahead in this world if you are forever worried about the other guy? For me, it's hard enough just to take care of myself."

"It's the other way around," sighed Jesus. "The world itself will not long survive unless we all learn to live by that ancient rule. It has worked for centuries for the few men and women who have tried it."

For the rest of the trip home, Jesse was uneasy, paying more attention to what might be around the next bend in the roadway than to his business of delivering the load of logs. Jesus sensed his jitters but said nothing.

There was no way to know what the thieves may

Leslie H. Woodson

have said to one another as they went on their way. Nor was there any means for learning how their behavior may have been influenced by the composure of their victim. But it was safe to assume that they never forgot that day on the road between Sepphoris and Nazareth. And neither did Jesse.

CHAPTER TWENTY

Never could Mary recall a Saturday morning when her oldest son had to be dragged out of bed against his will to go to synagogue. James, whose interests lay elsewhere, dreaded the day like the plague. It was the one day when he could rest after the grueling six days of hard work. After all, he would insist, isn't that what the day is for? Why should such a sacred day be disturbed with repetitious and monotonous traditions which had been created just to annoy him?

The other children were like most of the boys and girls in Nazareth. They could take it or leave it, but they always made the trek at dawn to synagogue. There was really no choice. Living in Joseph's house meant you had to keep the Sabbath.

Actually, the Sabbath began at sundown the night before and lasted until sunset on Saturday. For Jesus, the whole thing was exciting. Every Friday He would get all tingly inside thinking about it.

It would all commence each Friday with three blasts on the shophar blown by the hazzan, the official who was in charge of getting the service started and stopping it at the proper time as well. There would be some who would arrive earlier and get the better places to sit or stand and others who would come straggling in late and remain in the shadows at the rear. At the household of Joseph, however, there was never a chance of being late. Young Jesus saw to that as He pushed and yelled and helped the younger ones on with their Saturday best.

Because they were on time, the family of Joseph and Mary normally found bench seats along the front wall. Seldom, however, did the children sit for long. Older people with bent backs, walking with sticks or leaning on the arm of someone else, would appear and the children would immediately rise and offer their seats. They had been carefully instructed that disrespect for their elders was not acceptable. Folks noticed and commented to one another about the good job their parents had done in rearing them.

Facing Jerusalem, at the front of the synagogue, a menorah with its seven tapers of light mesmerized the congregation. The shimmering light from the lamps held the attention of the people even more than the words which would later be spoken. Jesus could have sat for hours just gazing at the bright flame and thinking about all sorts of things. Like one looking at the clouds and imagining animal shapes, even faces, young Jesus envisioned the hands of God in the orange-red tapers before him.

The service began precisely on time with a prayer offered by one of the men who had been selected for participation that day. It was always a layman. Only a few men felt uneasy about such participation; most considered it an honor.

Jesus remembered the time when Joseph stood up there by the menorah and, with the lights flickering on his face, led in prayer. The boy felt real pride that day, pride in seeing his own father recognized.

And he remembered how priestly Joseph looked as he prayed. Although the prayer was not necessarily a formal liturgy, the contents were always similar. The prayer would extol Jehovah for his faithfulness to Israel, for entering into covenant with Abraham, Isaac, and Jacob and promising a Messiah who would bring his people peace.

The people would shout "Amen!" Then, everyone would respond in unison with Israel's most sacred verse of scripture: "Hear, O Israel: the Lord our God is one Lord." Jesus could feel his flesh crawl as the mighty chorus resounded through the room.

No one recited the statement of faith with more gusto than Jesus. Of course, there was no way anybody would outdo Joseph. The Sabbath was the crown jewel of the week for him and he lived every day in anticipation of the time of worship.

As the hazzan removed the scroll of the Torah, unwrapped it, rolled it open, and held it aloft, the assembly hall was deadly quite. He had seen it done dozens of times, but every time the up-lifted scroll was lowered and laid to rest on the reading desk, to his eyes there was an unearthly glow which encircled the sacred scriptures.

When the hazzan finished the prayer of thanksgiving for the Torah, three or four men would be called to the front to read portions from the scroll and, if they wished, offer a blessing. The Torah was then neatly wrapped and replaced in its holy niche and someone from the congregation would walk to the front and give his interpretation of the scripture which had been read. The men would then recite the Kiddush, a blessing said over the wine.

The final act of worship and instruction was on Saturday morning when the haftarah, a reading from the prophets, climaxed the Sabbath ritual. Once again the hazzan would blow a blast on the shophar and the time of rest and fellowship would continue in the homes.

Of all the families in Nazareth, none would have been considered more devout and loyal to the tradition of the elders than that of Joseph and Mary. There was absolutely no work done from sundown on Friday to sunset on Saturday. Once in a while, one of the children would be seen by a neighbor doing some little mischief prohibited on the holy day, but it was never serious and was usually overlooked. But Joseph, especially Joseph, had been extremely strict about the many little laws surrounding the day. For example, he would never have thought of traveling more than two thousand cubits on the Sabbath. To do so would be a sin. So the family did not go anywhere much on Saturday since a Sabbath day's journey was slightly over a half mile.

There was one Sabbath which Jesus could never forget. He had been on an errand to deliver some wooden items He and the boys had made in the shop. They were being taken in an ox cart to a wealthy trader in the Holy

City. It was the middle of the afternoon on Friday when He passed near the hill of execution outside the walls of Jerusalem. It was still early enough for him to get into the city, make his delivery, and find a place to stay before sunset.

While He was familiar with crucifixion, the young carpenter had never witnessed the deliberate taking of a human life by anyone, state or individual. His own religious tradition prescribed stoning for capital crimes, but the Romans put their criminals on crosses and left them under guard to die. No one could be put to death by the Jews anymore without the consent of Rome unless it was a purely religious matter of no concern to the Imperial City.

Crucifixion was a horrible way to die. Sometimes the victims were simply strapped to the crossbeam and left to die of exhaustion and starvation. At other times, the victims were nailed to the cross and died from asphyxiation and loss of blood. Either way, it was a horrendous sight for anyone to witness, especially for the first time.

As He came on the scene, Jesus caught his breath. It was a dark, foreboding day and what He was seeing made it even more ominous. The sufferer had apparently just expired and the guard was checking all vital signs to be sure. Representatives from the Temple were present to make sure the body was not on the cross after sunset. Such desecration of the Sabbath was against Jewish law.

A half dozen strong bodied men were with the

Temple clergy, probably shiftless men hired on the spot to get the body down and help with the burial. And there were, as would be expected, a number of Roman soldiers. Already the birds were gathering overhead in anticipation.

A few people had come out to the bloody hill as spectators. There had always been some who made a sport out of watching violence of any kind.

"Who was he?" Jesus asked of a grinning, dirty, half nude bystander.

"They call him Beera," answered the offensive man, showing his rotting teeth. Then, with an insensitive laugh, he added, "But, I guess now he's nobody!"

Jesus was not amused. "What did he do? Must have been awful?"

"Says on that sign over his head that he raped a young virgin," grinned the man. "Doesn't seem like such a bad thing to me! That's what women are for!" To the disgust of Jesus, the filthy bystander then threw back his head and guffawed with merriment.

By that time, the strong armed men were untying the hands of the dead man and lowering him from the cross. It was not hard to see that there was nobody there to care for his entombment, no family or friends, so he would be carried off and dumped in a pauper's grave.

As the sun set over the hill of execution, just a stone's throw from the city of David, Jesus tried to clear his head. If God were watching this, what would He think, wondered the carpenter. What brutality could be worse than what He had seen that afternoon? A man had brutalized a woman whose life now would never be the same. The Romans had brutalized the Jews, even dictating how a Jew could die. And the Jews had brutalized a man accused of a horrible crime by hanging him naked before public gaze upon a cross. And there was the grimy bystander, a kind of typical human being who brutalized everyone by his insensitivity to another's pain.

What disturbed Jesus most was that no one seemed to care. No one!

"What has happened to us?" He cried aloud in the darkness.

The sound of his voice startled him. Pulling the gear of the ox until it was off the main road, He fell in a heap on the ground in the loneliness of a Sabbath afternoon. Tears ran down his face as He sobbed aloud. For what seemed later to have been hours, the weeping continued. At last, getting control of himself, He dropped his hurt into the lap of God.

"Heavenly Father, God of Abraham, Isaac, and Jacob, we never meant for our people to get into this kind of mess. We made them to be righteous, to be just, to be full of mercy. Our dreams for man were so beautiful. What has happened to our people?"

Suddenly, it dawned on him that He was saying *we* rather than *you*. The thought of blasphemy rushed to his brain, but Jesus knew that there was no such thing as that in his prayer. His eyes stared into the roadside darkness.

It was like a vision which swam before his

327

enhanced sight. As clear as day, there was Adam, still wet from creation. And there was the heavenly choir singing in the tropical garden. And, too, there was the Father leaning over the battlements of heaven and Jesus himself right there with him.

Gradually, as if returning from a trance, He found himself again in the gloom of the roadside at the foot of the empty cross. He was still praying.

"Forgive them, my Father. Let love and justice roll down like streams of living water. I must do something. I must. I *know* I must. What am I to do? Show me the way. Walk with me. Our people cannot go on like this."

Numbed by the experience which He had just been through, Jesus rose from his knees and, in a daze, pulled at the ox until the cart was back in the ruts of the road. As He passed through the gate into the city, the lamps had been lighted in the windows and the street torches filled the air with the stench of burning oil. Staring at the city which lay before him, it was hard to focus on anything in particular. The holiest place on earth was a spread-out blur, slithers of light from a thousand lamps dancing in his head.

This was the city of David, the holy mount where the father of the nation had offered to sacrifice his own son to Jehovah God. That was a long time ago. Here was to be the light of the Gentiles which would one day illumine the whole world to the reign of the Lord on high. Teeming with life as the city was, except for this night which was now welcoming the Sabbath, Jesus detected the smell of death all around him. Not just the death of one man on a cross, but the dying gasps of an entire race, the putrescence of a nation rotting away in apathy.

The town would be quiet and asleep within a couple of hours only to arise in the morning without bothering to wake up. The people would go through their ritual like walking zombies. And come Saturday night, the people of Jerusalem would go about their bargaining, buying and selling whatever could be traded, without ever thinking what life in their city was supposed to be.

Wrapping his tunic tightly about him, He folded himself into the corner of the cart, pulling the ragged blanket his mother had made over his feet. There He would try to sleep. But, the night was fitful. The words of Jeremiah, which had so impressed him in school, kept pounding in his head: "Many nations shall pass by this city, and they shall say every man to his neighbor, Why hath the Lord done this to this great city? Then they shall answer, Because they have forsaken the covenant of the Lord, their God, and worshiped other gods, and served them."

When the lazy morning sun peeped over the majestic Jordan hills, Jesus roused himself and walked to the Temple where Sabbath worship was in progress. After the service was over, He returned to his faithful little ox and spent the remainder of the day watching the beast munch at the grass beside the road. No one traveled on the Sabbath. That was strictly forbidden. He would have

329

to wait for evening. All afternoon, his mind was filled with thoughts of the awful scene of death which He had witnessed the night before.

The delivery of the goods, which He had brought from Nazareth to the wealthy merchant, were delivered after sundown. That night, the merchant was gracious enough to let the carpenter sleep in his courtyard until the morning.

It would be a long trip taking three or four days, but the plan was to stop in Sabaste for a visit with a friend of the family. The usual route would have been to bypass Samaria and travel east of the Jordan due to the hatred which the Jews felt toward their mixed-blooded cousins in central Palestine. But Joseph had taught his sons quite early that such racist prejudice was not becoming to the people of Jehovah. And the young carpenter could not help remembering the story grandpa Heli had told him about the Samaritan who helped dig out his mud-stuck cart.

Traveling alone gave Jesus time to think about a lot of things. The crucifixion! That colored his every waking moment with an inextinguishable sadness. And the strange feelings He had as the city rose up before him in the night vision . . . it must have been a vision because it was so much more than He had ever seen before.

While in Sabaste, the host family took Jesus up on Mount Gerizim to see the sacred temple which the Samaritans had built in competition with the Temple at

Jerusalem. It was certainly not an elaborate edifice and it was a known fact that, since the time of Jeroboam, the worship on Gerizim was a mixture of Judaism and paganism. Jesus did not make comments while the host explained what He was seeing, but his heart hurt more and more as the long journey progressed.

Mahali, his friend at Sabaste, was a descendant of one named Nadab, a Hebrew who had married a woman imported by Ashurbanipal from Elam in the seventh century. Although Mahali had become much more Hebrew across the years in his customs, the pagan influence of ancestral marriage still tinged his religious traditions. Jesus knew that and longed for the time when the Samaritans would be loved back into the fold and helped to rediscover their ancient heritage. There were nine children in Mahali's family. Jesus wished there were time to talk to each one since, if any improvement were ever to be made with the Samaritans, it would be with the much more impressionable younger generation.

On the morning of his departure, the young carpenter from Nazareth prayed aloud with his friends. And they listened with great respect. "God of our fathers, Abraham, Isaac, and Jacob, our hearts are filled with praise that we have been blessed in this line of holy descent. Lest we take pride in our ancestry, make us to remember that we could have been brought into the world outside the family of the patriarchs. We are children of Abraham, not by accident, but because you decided for us."

331

Leslie H. Woodson

Here in the prayer, Jesus paused, waiting a moment for Mahali to soak in what He was saying. Then He went on. "Our fathers have not always been faithful to this heritage and, as a nation, we have drifted far from our beginnings. Yet, I know that you love and care for all of us alike. And you long for the day when your people will be one. Let the blessing of Abraham abide upon this household, upon these nine sparkling-eyed jewels, which are so filled with hope, that each of them will watch for the kingdom of God, the kingdom for which we yearn and believe is about to dawn. Let us all be prepared to enter it. This is my request, O Lord, this is my dream. Jehovah be praised."

Cordial farewells were exchanged and Jesus was on his way for the last leg of the journey home, fully aware of the difficulties awaiting him from brigands and beasts. With him was a basket filled with bread, grapes and nuts which the lady of the house had insisted that He take with him. "This will tide you over until you reach the first inn," she assured him, placing the lunch in his hands. Not wishing to be too obvious, He waited till out of sight of the house to begin munching on the fresh nuts.

The land through which He traveled was pretty much hill country. For this reason, it was necessary to pick and choose carefully the valley through which to pass. But Jesus knew this country like the back of his hand. Carpenter and ox could have made the trip with their eyes shut.

The following afternoon, leading the ox cart slowly down the descent into the village of Ginaea, which was about six or seven miles from the border of Galilee, He saw in the distance a group of men approaching slowly from the northwest. Not until they were within shouting range did Jesus realize that this was a colony of lepers who, because of their dreaded disease, were not permitted inside the walls of the city.

Leprosy was a loathsome disease which, in its advanced form, ate away large chunks of flesh leaving gapping holes in the face, especially around the nose, mouth, and eyes. Even in its milder form, the white patches and nodules on the skin were cause for humiliation and shame. No one was permitted to touch them lest he be rendered unclean and thus not allowed in the Temple or the synagogues. So the lepers kept their distance, calling in unison, *Unclean! Unclean!* at the first sight of an approaching stranger. They were further instructed to announce their presence by wearing mourning clothes with their hair disheveled and their beards covered. Such was the scene materializing in the distance.

The sight of a group of lepers was not at all an unexpected thing. There were many of them and most towns and villages had a group near enough to the city walls to beg for food. So, the pathetic sight of misshapen humanity was not new to this young, teaching carpenter. Jesus halted the ox and waited for the colony to reach him. As they drew nearer, hoping for food, they continued to cry in one terrible voice, "Unclean! Unclean!"

333

Shaking his head vigorously and putting his fingers to his lips to quiet them, the man with the cart said, " You do not need to say that to me. You are not unclean to me. Come, let us sit here on the rocks together. Do not be afraid. No one will hurt you."

"We are not afraid. Nothing could happen to us that is worse than what has already devastated us, but we cannot touch you," they said. "Are you a stranger in these parts? Do you not know that contact with a leper makes you unacceptable? If we get near you, you cannot go home to your family."

"I am sorry but I think you are afraid. I am not afraid of you and I do not want you to be afraid of me," the stranger assured them.

Reaching into the basket which the mother in Sebaste had prepared for his journey, Jesus pulled out large chunks of hard bread and handed a portion to each of the men. It was more bread than they had seen for a fortnight and they ate like they were starved.

During the conversation, which lasted into the night, the young carpenter learned a great deal about his new friends. One of them had been a carpenter like himself. Under more normal circumstances, it would have been good to discuss the work which they both loved. But for a man who had not been near his family in over two years, nothing was of any interest any more. Another was a prosperous farmer from an out-of-the way place in the Plain of Sharon. How he longed for the green fields of home, the warmth of the hearth, and the touch of his children. A third was a Levite who was no longer permitted anywhere near the Temple.

Of all the sufferers in the group, the Levite was the most bitter. Deep down inside there churned and boiled a hatred for any god who would let one of his own servants have leprosy. It was not only unfair. It was downright malicious and, if he should ever get rid of his disease, he had promised himself that he would have nothing to do with the Temple or the God whom he had worshiped. Every man in the colony had his own story and one was as heart-wrenching as the other.

While the men related their sad tales of woe, often with loud laments and weeping bitterly, Jesus had emptied the basket of nuts on a flat rock where the men were devouring them as they rattled on in their despair.

Only occasionally did the carpenter from Nazareth break into the conversation. He just listened intently and the men knew they had found someone who cared. Their tales of woe went on and on, each one participating in the sad story.

"You have given us food to eat. Without it, we would have not survived much longer," said one of the younger lepers. "But I really wish I *could* die. Our bodies are revived now, but only that we may suffer our heartbreak another day. There is no life among us lepers. Only three years ago my childhood sweetheart and I were married. This leprosy appeared only a few days after my little boy was born. I have not seen him now for over a year and my heart hurts because I am away from the two

335

people I love."

Jesus looked at the young man with compassion. He wanted to say, "You are clean! Go on home." But knowing how ridiculous that would sound to them, He remained silent.

After what seemed like hours, the stranger from Nazareth reached out his hand and laid it on the shoulder of the one nearest him. The gesture was like a bolt out of the blue. The lepers, called to attention by the touch of a human hand, straightened their stooped backs and looked full into the eyes of the man with the kind face.

With his hand moving from the leper's shoulder to the top of his disheveled head, Jesus began to speak. "How my heart breaks to see you suffering this awful curse. I can only imagine how lonely you are for your wives and children. Right now, you feel helpless and hopeless. You must think that there is nobody to love you, that no one cares what happens to you."

The distraught men were nodding their heads as the young traveler described their innermost feelings. He went on. "It has to be the most devastating life in the world. You go to sleep every night hoping for the morning. And every morning you wish the day would end.

"This is not something which God has done to you. He never sends disease and He never wills death. God wants the very best life in the world, abundant life, for all his creation. Leprosy is not the will of God. What has happened to you is the result of Adam's sin. We are like one big family and we suffer individually because of the brokenness of the race. It's not your fault. It's not God's fault."

The men were absorbed by what He was saying. All they had ever heard from the rabbis was that they were lepers because they had sinned. They felt so guilty and so angry. Of course, they had sinned. Didn't everybody? Even the rabbis? But there were people all around them who had sinned far more grievously than themselves. Why did they not all have leprosy?

"Do not let yourself be angry with God. And do not be so outdone with yourself. You did not do this to yourself and you cannot cleanse yourself. But I know Someone who cares and will help you."

"Who? Who could care about us? Who would want to help us? Nobody will even touch us. Tell us! We will find him," they cried out in one cacophony of gurgling hope.

"You are not hearing me. It isn't what has happened to your decaying flesh that is your biggest problem. We can handle anything that comes our way if our hearts are not sick."

"But our hearts are sick.! We are sick all over," broke in the Levite. "There is no sickness like this. It is hard enough to be ill when your family cares for you, but to be sick and rejected by the whole community is more than we can bear. Why doesn't God let us die?"

"You have a dis-ease in your flesh which has colored your whole life," explained the stranger. "The

337

crucial thing is not what happens to us; the crucial thing is how we react to it!"

Glancing toward the Levite, Jesus went on. "You must not let this drive you away. Now is when you and God can be the best of friends."

The frailest looking one among the colony was weeping aloud now. "But it is so lonely out here in these barren hills. We are so foul to ourselves. We do not want to touch each other. The uncleanness, the stench is terrible. Nobody will come near us. You are the only person who has talked to us in years. We are not living anymore. We are all dead men."

"No, you are wrong. You are absolutely wrong. You have been listening to the wrong voices. You are not dead. You are still very much alive. And you are not unclean!"

With that, the men moaned loudly in unbelief, shaking their heads to emphasize their rejection of such foolish talk. Their new friend was very kind, but He just didn't understand. Until a person walked in a leper's sandals, there was absolutely no way to see what the leper faced. Nice talk, probably the nicest they had heard in a long time, but it missed the whole point. The groaning and sobbing was growing.

Sensing their despair, the stranger softly said, "Jehovah never looks at your flesh. He looks at your heart. If the priest declared you clean, you would still be dirty in God's sight until your heart is right. And if your heart is right, it matters not what the priest says! I tell you, if you will turn your thoughts toward Jehovah, confess your attitudes of anger, feelings inside which He already knows, and trust his love, you will be clean!"

Every man looked at his hands. They peered into the rotting sockets of the faces around them. Nothing looked any different. They did not understand. What could this kind but mad stranger be thinking?

Jesus so much wanted to speak a word of cleansing, to send them on their way to the priest. It seemed almost presumptuous, the very thought as if He could do something here, but it also felt so right. If the lepers did not understand, they were not alone in their confusion. There was much which He was struggling with, too.

When the dawn broke, Jesus hugged each of the smelly lepers and blessed him with a word of hope. Reaching into his girdle, He lifted out a small leather pouch, untied it, and poured its contents on the ground. It was the money He had received from the wealthy merchant in Jerusalem as payment for the delivery of a cartload of wood products He had brought from the little shop in Nazareth. Carefully dividing it into as many little heaps as there were lepers, Jesus then placed the money in their hands.

Taking the hand of the leper whose appearance was the most pitiable, the kind stranger tenderly kissed him on his pustulant face, and said, "Go now, my good friends. Go now and may God cleanse your hearts until you are every whit clean."

339

Soon the man with the oxcart was only a pinpoint in the distance. The lepers stood spellbound in the morning light until not a trace of their new friend could be seen. Then, softly someone spoke.

"Who was that man?" he said wonderingly, as he rubbed his white hand across the pustules on his face where the stranger had kissed him.

CHAPTER TWENTY ONE

One of the most difficult things for mother Mary to cope with was the fact that James had not bothered to keep in touch. By the time he had reached the age of twenty-three, James had pretty well established himself as a reputable merchant with his own shop in the bazaar at Jerusalem. Five years earlier, his schooling done, the next to the oldest son of Mary had apologized to his mother for his total disinterest in his father's trade. The carpenter's shop was obviously in good hands anyway, with Jesus apparently cut out for the job. His older brother was very good at what He did and James figured that the first-born was the proper one to continue the family business.

There was never any jealousy or envy toward Jesus. In fact, the income from the shop was barely enough to keep the wolf away from the door. That alone was enough to turn James away from the life of a carpenter. His dreams, from the earliest time he could remember, were of the day when he could get out of Nazareth and set up a business in the capital city. There had never been any doubt that he could make lots of money and see the world. Even Mary had sensed, from the tender days of his childhood, that her next-to-the-oldest son would do well in business.

"I am sorry, mother," he had announced one evening in the summer of his eighteenth year, "but every man has to start sometime to make his fortune."

Leslie H. Woodson

"But you are only eighteen," Mary had said. "You are still my little boy."

"I will always be your little boy, mother. In case you haven't noticed, I am a man! I cannot stay here any longer without feeling that I am wasting my life."

"But you do not have to go *now*. There is surely something you can find to do here in Nazareth. I know yu never cared for your father's shop, but there are other jobs. Why, somebody just told me that Amos, the silversmith, is looking for an apprentice. You like working with metals and gems. I know you do."

"There's nothing for me here, mother, nothing that appeals to me and nothing with any future. Don't try to talk me out of it. I refuse to be dirt poor like father. Someday I am going to have a big house with lots of servants. And we are going to have meat *every* night for supper. Then you can come and live with me and we will enjoy the good life together. My dreams take me way beyond this country village."

"James, my boy, your father never made much money, but we were always happy. Being poor never embarrassed me. This little place has always been a palace for me. Your eyes are too full of money, son. You worry me so. What's a mother to do?"

Mary knew that her son's mind was made up and that, come morning, he would be gone. If she had not known it before, she knew it when James explained that he had met a wealthy tradesman from Jerusalem who would be returning with his servants the following day. He had

342

offered James a job and it was too good to turn down. Not everyday did such an opportunity turn up. Only a fool would walk away from it.

For the next five years, James relished the distant places where his work carried him, not just in Palestine, but far beyond to places like Damascus to the north, and enchanting Egypt to the south. And he had come to know such interesting people, not at all like the dreary folks at home.

One by one his dreams were coming true and Chesed, his boss, had found his young employee to be a tireless worker and very dependable. His wages had been gradually increased every year and he had been frugal in handling his money.

He was now twenty-three and, with the money he had saved and a vast knowledge of the world market, he had established himself as a reputable merchant catering to the upper class in the Holy City.

It was not unusual to see his little shop filled with well-heeled men and women looking for household wares, expensive gifts, and trinkets from afar. James marked the price up by two hundred percent on practically everything and everyone knew it, but his customers had plenty of money and enjoyed bragging about how much their purchases cost them.

Mary's second son had the edge on most of his competitors. His travels with his former employer, a world-class international trader, had provided contacts from across the ancient world. While deliveries, by donkey carts or camels, were slow, especially those from great distances, James had standing orders with most of his suppliers and his credit was good.

He had never seen such beautiful eyes. She had been in the store several times and, every time he saw her, his heart skipped a beat. James had carefully guarded his single status. There had been a number of women in his life since leaving home, but there was never time for courtship and the relationships were short-lived. Maybe later, but not yet.

He was already married – to his business – and there was no way anyone would be permitted to interfere with that relationship. So, on this morning, the proud owner had marshaled all his defenses, mustering the courage to smile and ask a dangerous question. "May I help you?"

"I love this little lamp! This is not my first time in the store and . . . ."

"Yes, I know," broke in the flustered shop keeper. "I mean . . . I am honored to have you here."

"I was about to say that this bronze lamp is lovely. The details are superbly done. Where does it come from?"

"It's from Arabia and is one of a kind, made to my personal specifications. I never carry duplicates, only originals."

As James looked at the young woman, he knew she would have no problem with the price tag. Her clothing was of fine silk with much embroidering and exquisite multi-layered lace. She did not need to tell him. It was from India. He had seen the same quality work when he was there and it was more than even he could afford.

"Do you live here?" asked the young shop keeper.

"Oh yes, only a short distance away on Abraham Way. I live in the white house with a portico and many bright flowers around the courtyard."

He knew the place at once. It was one of the largest homes in Jerusalem and the fragrance of the flowers perfumed the entire area.

"May I ask your name?"

"My name is Dinah and my mother is known as Mary of Jerusalem."

"What a coincidence," replied her smitten friend. "My mother's name is Mary, too."

"Where are you from?"

"I was brought up in Nazareth," he answered, almost ashamed of his humble birthplace. "But I have traveled far and wide, so it's hard to say just where I'm from."

"Your shop intrigues me. It's my favorite of all the gift stores in the bazaar. I am going to go right home and rearrange my room to see just how I can make this lamp work. I'll be back. Whom do I ask for, in case you are not here?"

"Oh, I am almost always here. My name is James and I own the business."

The girl left and James wrote Dinah's name on a

Leslie H. Woodson

scrap piece of papyrus and stuck it under the base of the little lamp. And he made it a point not to sell it to anyone else.

That night, the young man, so dedicated to the single life, slept very little. He tried to talk himself out of it, but his heart was gripped with fear that he might be falling in love.

So occupied were his thoughts of Dinah that, when he arrived for work the next morning, he found it hard to take care of business. It was something he never did, but within the first two hours, he had made several mistakes in tallying up the sales tickets. Every minute, he expected to see her come in the door. But she never showed. And he was disappointed.

Then, one afternoon, just before closing time, Dinah appeared in the milling crowd outside the shop. She was pointing at the bronze lamp and speaking to an older woman beside her, probably asking her opinion. Brushing aside his fear of complicating a relationship, James picked up the little lamp, walked into the crowd, and handed it to the young woman.

"And who might this be?" he asked politely, bowing slightly toward the older woman with the same beautiful eyes as Dinah.

"This is my mother, Mary. And mother, this is James from Nazareth. He knows how much I like this lamp."

"Then we should buy it," said Mary, as she started untying her money pouch.

346

"No, no," exclaimed James, as he pushed her hand over the open money bag. "This is my gift to the most beautiful lady in Jerusalem who has already paid me double with her captivating charm."

Mary resisted, but the young shop keeper would have it no other way.

"Then, we would like your company at dinner tonight."

James' bearded face, brown as it was from the desert sun under which he had traveled for five years, showed unmistakable signs of blushing around his eyes.

Mary liked that. For her, it was the sign of a gentleman, a sensitive man like her late husband.

"We will expect you tonight. Sometime around sundown. Dress casually."

With that, Dinah and her mother took the lamp and moved away from the crowd in the direction of their home. And James returned into the shop wishing that the afternoon would quickly pass.

James had been in a number of wealthy homes while traveling with Chesed in Syria and Arabia, but none had impressed him more than Mary's house on Abraham Way. Not only was it lovely to look at, but there were several spacious rooms, one a luxurious guest room on the second level.

A very old woman, dressed in the traditional garb of a servant, opened the door and escorted him into the gathering area where he waited for Dinah to appear. Soon she stood in the doorway, glowing and radiant as a goddess. James gulped, swallowed hard, and grinned awkwardly.

"Hi James," she said, "I am so happy that you were able to get away from the store. Mom has prepared my favorite meal of antelope, lentils, squash, and cheese. Hope you like it."

The nervous, young guest was certain that the meal didn't matter as long as Dinah was there. Just then, a second servant appeared with a selection of honey-dipped dates and nuts plus a cruse of the most exquisite wine produced in all of Palestine.

"If the family could see me now!" thought James to himself, as he tried hard not to show his uneasiness.

A basin of fresh water was brought, in which the young shop owner washed his hands according to the law laid down by the elders. While drying his hands, a second vessel was set before him as a third domestic removed James' sandals and washed his feet.

Time had come for the meal and Dinah led her new friend to the sumptuous feast which had been spread for him. As he was directed to the place of honor, a lad, of about twelve years of age, arrived at the table.

"This is my little brother," said Dinah, "who has just come from his studies."

"Shalom," said the well-mannered boy, "my name is John Mark. And you are . . .?"

"I am James," replied the guest, still numb from everything which was happening so quickly.

The meal was delicious and the entire evening was a night to remember. In the days following, Dinah and James saw each other every day, either at the shop, where she had pitched in to help, or at the home of Mary of Jerusalem. In less that two months, the two inseparable friends found themselves in love.

Never in a thousand years would Jerusalem's youngest and most desirable bachelor have thought marriage to be in his future. But time changes things. And beautiful Dinah had made marriage seem the natural thing to do. There was no way on earth James could resist her charm.

Several months before Dinah came into the picture, the prosperous young merchant from Nazareth had been so intrigued, by the work of an itinerant goldsmith from Phoenicia, that he had purchased several of his works of art. The goldsmith had set up temporary shop for two days behind James' place of business where he crafted, with his portable furnace, crucible, and stock in trade, jewelry much admired and coveted by women all over the world.

Among the pieces, which had appealed most to James, was a gold ankle bracelet, intricately designed, studded with pink pearls from the pinna found in the coral of the Red Sea. He did not know why, but the piece had been hidden away from the greedy eyes of his patrons as if there were some reason he was not supposed to sell it. At last, he knew why he had kept it.

"It is the most beautiful thing I have ever seen," cried Dinah, as she gazed at the betrothal gift. Tears sparkled on her olive cheeks like stars in an Arabian night.

"*You* are the most beautiful thing *this* Jewish boy has ever laid eyes upon," replied James. "The gold fades in comparison to my beloved's face."

The following day, the espousal contract was drawn, another feast was held at Mary of Jerusalem's house, and a fellow merchant witnessed the signing of the nuptial agreement.

"A whole year!" sighed the husband-to-be. "That will never pass!" But it did. And finally James and Dinah were married in a lavish ceremony. Friends, whom James had met in other lands, were there. And from the money circles in Jerusalem came a host of well-wishers with expensive gifts. At the end of the week of festivities with families and friends, they moved together into their newly-constructed house at the intersection of Isaac and Rebecca Roads.

Mary of Jerusalem had made it clear that she expected her son-in-law to respect the Sabbath and go to Synagogue of the Date Tree, the place of worship nearest to the couple's home, every week. From the beginning, Dinah's mother knew of the inclination of her son-in-law to ignore the faith of Abraham.

"Dinah was brought up that way and her tradition must be respected," insisted Mary. "You are now a role model for John Mark, too. Since the death of his father, he has lacked the moral and spiritual guidance which he knew before."

One evening, shortly after the marriage week was over, the family became embroiled in a heated discussion about James' cynicism. It all started when Mary of Jerusalem asked how her son-in-law got so turned off by the faith of Abraham when his family seemed so devout.

"Your mother is very worried about you. She and I had a long talk during the festivities and I really felt sorry for her. Her heart is broken. You ought not do this to your mother! How long has it been since you went to synagogue? For that matter, how long ago did you visit your mother in Nazareth?"

"She is a good mom and I love her, but I cannot be religious when it doesn't interest me. I guess my god is my business," answered James, trying desperately to defend himself.

"But what about Jesus? Your older brother appears to be *very* religious."

"My older brother and I had always been very close. We drifted apart, however, several years ago and I haven't seen him for a long time."

"Why did you?" asked John Mark, who had always begged for a brother.

"Why did I what?"

"Why did you drift apart?"

"It's not that I don't still love him," answered James, disturbed at the thought that little John was upset. "We just never had anything in common. He likes one

351

kind of life and I like another."

"What do you mean?" asked Dinah.

"All He ever thought about was religion."

"What did you think about?" asked the boy, wide-eyed with wonder.

"Business! Making my fortune. Good stuff like that. And see what happened! I have made it – my own shop and lots of money and . . ." James looked with ravishing eyes at Dinah, "and my wonderful wife."

Mary, Dinah, and John Mark looked at him in disbelief. No one spoke a word. The words coming out of his mouth did not sound good, not good at all.

"What's wrong?" shrugged James, throwing his hands in the air in desperation. "Look where that religious stuff got Jesus. Still in that dirty carpenter's shop piddling with small paying jobs, no money, no wife – and still talking religion! Some guys never learn. I still love him, but I feel sorry for him. After all, we *are* brothers."

The silent stares from the rest of the family stabbed him like a rapier. Everyone was clearly disappointed, even his new bride, Dinah. Finally, Mary of Jerusalem broke the silence.

"You are a good man, James, and I am proud to have you as my son-in-law, but you have a big hole in your head. And your money will never fill it."

"I don't dislike God . . . if there really is one. All I'm saying is that religion was crammed down my throat morning, noon, and night by Old Joe, mom, and my older brother. Why can't a person be allowed to live his own life without being forced to believe in something he can't swallow? Maybe someday, when I am too old for anything else, I will think about God. Too busy now. Anyway, religion is for old folks, not people with ambition and dreams for success."

It had not been a good evening. No one was mad, but everybody was uncomfortable as the newlyweds left. Mary was irritated by the unreasonable things her son-in-law had said. In her heart, she knew that he was not as far from God as he thought. And John Mark? The boy was confused and hurt. Dinah's biggest worry was that there might be a rift in her family and she knew she would never be able to handle that. James sensed the hurt in Dinah's beautiful, sad eyes and, for some reason, he felt embarrassed.

Early the following morning, Dinah cautiously suggested that her husband find Jesus and restore the relationship which, in his heart, she knew he would like to do.

"I will think about it," said James, kissing his wife on the forehead. But he really had no intention to follow through on his promise and Dinah knew it.

"We never talked about it," said Dinah reflectively, "but there is something about your elder brother that is different,"

"Oh, He's different all right," James quickly retorted.

"No, not that way. He just seemed to me, when

353

we talked together at the wedding, like an honest, down-to-earth, sincere, compassionate man. I liked him at once."

"Did I say I don't like him?"

"I will pray that the day will come when the two of you will be friendly again. I will pray that someday He will be able to make you see that there is a God and that religion is really good for you."

"Well," said James, "we probably will see each other again someday. If not before, when mom dies. But if this religion thing is true, He will have to prove it to me!"

"Maybe He will," replied Dinah, with a smile that brightened her beautiful, sad eyes. "Maybe He will."

CHAPTER TWENTY TWO

Someone was pulling at the hem of his tunic and it startled him.

"You look so strong, so full of health! I never saw a god before. Are you Asklepios? Yes, that's it, a Greek God!"

Jesus turned to face the man who had spoken to him. "What did you say?" asked the carpenter.

The man in the pool repeated what he had said and added, "I knew at once that you have to be a god!"

"I am not Asklepios. I am Jesus, son of Joseph, and I live in Nazareth."

"It's been a long time, but I was once strong and healthy, too." The most conspicuous thing about the man standing in the cool water was his sad eyes. "Those days are past and gone forever. I come here to Hammath as often as someone can bring me. These waters are supposed to make me well, but they mock me. I have been here year after year. So far nothing has happened. And I am angry."

"What do you suffer from?" asked the carpenter from Nazareth.

"The physicians don't know. The only thing I know is that my body hurts from my head to my feet. When I am in these waters, the pain is less, but the moment I leave it all comes back. I have been here a dozen times and only the gods know why I keep coming."

While He never went there during his public ministry, Jesus had this one time been in Tiberias when He was twenty-four years old.

Located on the southwest shore of the lake, the city of fifteen thousand had been built recently by Herod Antipas in honor of Tiberius Caesar. Known for its hot-water baths, the town quickly became a resort, lending itself to a lax style of living. For this reason, plus the fact that the inhabitants were predominantly Greek and Roman, the stricter Jews felt a great distaste for the new city. To make matters worse, Tiberias was situated over the ancient cemetery of Hammath. And that rendered the town taboo.

The atmosphere was wet and hot, as would be expected from the steaming sulphur springs. However, the springs being famous for their healing powers, there was never a shortage of people from surrounding areas, especially Gentiles.

Not in his twenty-four years had the carpenter from Nazareth seen so many sick people at one time. Some were obviously suffering from terminal diseases. There were men and women whose bodies were twisted and misshapen by muscle and bone disorders. Some cried in awful pain while others sat limp in the water with hollow stares. And they were not all old. Many of them were very young.

The big heart of Mary's son was breaking as He looked at this sea of misery. For a moment, He wished that He *were* God. He knew what He would do. He

357

would empty that pool of its suffering and send every one of those poor people home with their health restored.

Unable to resist the urge, Jesus moved closer to the steaming pool. The anxious throngs were pushing and shoving and He found himself struggling to avoid falling into the water. It may have been because the pain in his heart could be seen on his face, but someone in the pool was tugging again at his tunic. If the face of Jesus betrayed the compassion in his heart, no less did the face of the man in the water convey his unbearable pain.

"No," answered Jesus, "I am not Asklepios. Do you ever try to talk to Jehovah about your hurt?"

"There are so many gods that I never know which one to ask. It all seems useless anyway."

"Prayer is never useless," replied the carpenter, "and you don't have to pick and choose the correct god. There is only one God. Where are you from?"

"I live here now, but I am a Greek from Cyprus. We have many gods."

"There are many idols," replied Jesus sadly, "but only one God."

"Who is this one God? What is his name? How do you know about him?"

"Jehovah is his name. He has revealed himself to our father Abraham. He is the God of the Jews," explained Jesus, speaking very slowly so as not to force too much on him at once.

"Would I see him if I came to Jerusalem? Does He live in the Temple?"

"No, we do not have idols. Jehovah is the true Spirit of all creation. He made the world. And He made you."

"Do you know this Jehovah?"

"Yes, I do."

"Tell me about him. What's He like?"

"The God of Abraham is the God of righteousness and love. He wants us to do right and disciplines us when we don't. But He is, above all, forgiving. If one word were all I would be given to define him, that word would be love. We Jews serve him in return for the compassion and love shown to us."

"We don't have any gods of love in our religion. That is, none except the fertility gods."

"That is very sad," said the stranger at the edge of the pool.

"Then, if this Jehovah, as you call him, is love and compassion, He will stop my pain?" he asked, wrinkling his brow with the hopeful anticipation of a child.

"I cannot promise that He will stop your suffering, but I know that He will help you see what has happened to you in a new light. And He will empower you to handle it. The most important thing is not what happens to us, but how we respond to it. Some people react in bitterness as if life has been unfair to them. Others accept whatever life throws at them in the belief that, with God's help, adversity cultivates growth."

"But that makes me angry. If this Jehovah loves us so much, why would He let this happen to us in the first place?"

"That's a puzzle for many people. We are like children growing up with skinned knees and broken arms. Each experience teaches us something about life. Don't waste your pain. Learn from it. And you will have less pain because you will be stronger to bear it."

"It's more than a puzzle. It doesn't make any sense at all. If Jehovah is really a God of love, He would take this pain away in a moment," said the man in the water, as he turned loose of Jesus' tunic.

"You do not understand it now, but the pain may be doing you more good than freedom from it. Someday Jehovah will send us a Savior who will deliver us from what seems to be an injustice which life has dealt us. Until then, we all wait in faith together for the day when the whole world will be made whole."

"I wish I could believe what you are saying, but it all sounds like fairy tales to me."

"This is brand new to you, I know," admitted Jesus. "You can't know how much I would like to take your suffering away. I would bear it for you, but I'm not sure just how to do that."

Jesus, breathing heavily, looked wistfully across the water. Then, under his breath, as if talking to himself, He said, "At least not yet."

The grimacing lines of pain were still visible on his face as the carpenter from Nazareth prepared to leave. In a real way, the pain which Jesus felt for the suffering man was far greater than that experienced by the man himself.

But the poor man in the pool had no way of knowing that.

"You need to learn more about Jehovah. Once you do, you will love him even as I," Jesus assured him. "You have said that you don't get to this pool often because you have to find someone to bring you. So I know it would be difficult to get to synagogue, too. But if you could arrange it, the Sabbath worship and instruction at the synagogue would greatly enlarge your understanding of Jehovah."

"It sounds like it would be good to know this Jehovah God of yours," said the miserable man at the edge of the healing waters.

"You have to start somewhere. Remember, you do not have to know him to call upon him. He knows you! And He will be listening for your voice now that you have been introduced. With all this pain, there is little you can do, so there is a lot of idle time. Talk with God. Think only of him. Ask for what you need. Believe in your heart that Jehovah cares, because He really does. The difference in your life will be unbelievable."

Jesus had not walked far beyond the city limits when He came upon a girl beside the path who was lying face down on the ground. He immediately reached down to help the fallen child. But when He rolled her over, it was easy to see that she was either dead or unconscious.

At first, Jesus thought the woman had been murdered and left at the scene of the crime. As He paid closer attention, however, He saw the white foam around

361

her mouth and the wild look in her open eyes. She was not moving, but she was breathing spasmodically.

Sensing that someone was standing behind him, He asked, without looking around, "Are you with this woman?"

"Yes," came the reply, "she is my daughter and I spend most of my time following her around."

"What do you mean?"

"We never know what she may do or where she might go. Her father and I once tied her to a tree in the courtyard, but we felt so badly about it that we had to loose her. She has spells like this, gets caught up in a frenzied fit and then just passes out."

"Do you know what is wrong with her," asked the carpenter.

"No. That's the hardest part. Sometimes she seems all right, but there are these times when she becomes rigid and makes animal like noises and falls on the ground."

This time she had already been through the frenzied stage and the mother was waiting for her to come to. "When she comes to herself again," explained the mother, "she probably will not remember a thing that happened in this horrible struggle."

The girl on the ground began to move her arms and legs. Slowly, she regained enough strength to sit up when, with a sudden burst of energy, the girl sprang to her feet. Her eyes were still filled with fear. It was almost as if she recognized Jesus and did not like him.

The young carpenter was sure that He did not know her, but there was something hauntingly familiar about her expression.

"I hate you! Leave me alone! I hate you!" growled the girl. "I hate you! I hate you! I hate you!"

"She never sounds like herself when this happens. Her voice is not hers. And we dare not touch her at such a time because she is so strong. We are afraid she will choke us," sobbed the mother. Wiping her eyes, she continued to speak. "But I have never known her to come to after a seizure as angry as this. She is almost like two different people. I am so frightened all the time."

"How did she happen to be here? I suppose you live in Tiberias?"

"This is our home now. Latti, my daughter, comes out here often. Especially when she is having one of her spells."

Latti's mother pointed to a grove of trees several hundred cubits beyond the roadside. A score or more people were beneath the trees, some sitting, others standing or jumping and leaping into the air. From a distance, most of them looked disheveled like they had been in a windstorm.

"See those people? They congregate here just about every day. Latti was on her way to the grove when this seizure over-powered her. Those people among the trees act much like my Latti."

Jesus had already noticed the strange looking men and women in the distance. He had seen people like these

363

before, but never so many in one place.

"The people in town say they are ghosts from the past, people who once lived in Hammath and who now come from their graves in the old cemetery," said Latti's mother. "It is said that they refuse to give up their old home to us strangers."

The carpenter smiled.

"I am sure that is not so," He consoled her. "You don't think of your daughter as a ghost, do you?"

"Oh, no! That's just what everybody in town seems to think about those others in the trees."

The daughter, who was now down on all fours like a wild beast, was growling and barking, slobbering and spitting huge globs of white foam on the ground.

"Leave me alone!" she again cried. And it was more like a command than a plea.

The carpenter from Nazareth did not attempt to explain what was happening other than to reassure the mother that the people in the grove were not ghosts.

Not being Jewish, the poor woman would have been unfamiliar with the views of Israel about demons. In fact, there were some in Israel, like the priestly Sadducees, who did not believe in the existence of demons at all. And outside the borders of Palestine, there existed all kinds of superstitious beliefs about what could not be easily explained.

Somehow, although He was not sure why, Jesus knew exactly what the problem with Latti was. The evil spirit in control of her life was as real to him as was the

364

girl herself. It was not that He could see the demon. It was rather that He actually recognized the personality which others did not know. It was as if He had struggled before with this evil spirit, a fallen angel who had been cast down in prehistoric times.

"The day is coming," said the carpenter, "when we will know how to handle things like this. Our darkness will be taken away and we will understand. God will show us what can be done to give back to your daughter the control of her life."

"Sir, I do not understand. You talk like Latti really is two people."

"Not exactly. She is only one girl, but someone else has moved in and taken over her mind and body. She is living as a slave of an unseen but destructive master."

"Where do you get this knowledge, Sir?"

"I am not sure that you would know what I was talking about if I should try to explain. It's a long story. Started when I was just a child. Actually, started before I was born. There has always been this unexplainable closeness which I feel with another world than this. God speaks to me. He has told me that the day will come when people like Latti can be freed from the evil powers which control her."

"Why must we have to wait if that is true? Why doesn't your God do something now?"

"In my heart, I am sure that He is doing something now. Precisely what, I cannot say. But He has started his redemption of the world. Maybe the hour has not yet come, but it will."

"What am I to do? Just sit and wait? We don't have that much time. We need help now!"

"We all need help now! Sometimes I wonder, too, why God delays. We Jews have been waiting for a thousand years for the promise to be fulfilled. For reasons which no one understands, there is a growing certainty that the time is now."

"When your God does whatever it is that you are talking about, will He care about us Romans?"

"God is no respecter of persons or nations. Wherever men and women do his will and seek his kingdom of righteousness, there his promise will be fulfilled."

The woman was puzzled, but it sounded like there might be some hope. Even if she and her daughter had to wait, and that was something she did not want to do, waiting is always better tolerated if there is a chance that things might get better.

"If I could do what I want right now," said Jesus, "I would throw the demons out of your daughter. But this is not what is to be. My hour is not yet come."

The more Jesus talked, the better the woman felt, but the more confused she became.

By this time, three or four of the people from under the trees, had wandered over to the roadside where Latti was still crouched, still making animal sounds. They would scream out or utter unintelligible noises, make vulgar moves with their bodies, and spit at Jesus. Strange as it must have seemed to Latti's mother, all of them exhibited hostility and hatred for the man with whom she spoke.

As the carpenter from Nazareth looked at the pitiable sight before him, He was tempted to demand the demons to come out, but some higher power would not give him permission. The inner voice was constantly saying to him, "Not yet! Not yet!"

The conversation broke off rather quickly when one of the possessed men standing nearby jumped astride Latti and began tearing off his clothes. His intentions were obvious. Flax, instinctively sensing that the girl was in trouble, lunged and embedded his teeth in the man's ankle. With the help of the dog, Jesus and Latti's mother managed to pull him off her daughter.

There was nothing more that Jesus could do and both He and the woman knew it. As He prepared to leave, she pulled at his arm to detain him a moment longer. "Sir, I have an older sister who lives near the city of Sidon. She has a daughter who acts just like Latti. Just talking to you has helped so much. If you are ever in Sidon and come across her, please tell her what you have told me."

Jesus assured her that He would remember her request. If they should ever meet, He would do what He could. His heart was telling him that it would be so. Latti's mother felt it, too.

It was not until eight years later, after the death of

367

John the Baptist, that Jesus traveled to the coast of Tyre and Sidon where He unexpectedly met Latti's aunt. When the Syro-Phoenician woman came asking that her vexed daughter be healed of her demonic plague, He knew at once that this was the woman for whom He had made a promise long ago in Tiberias.

To the distraught woman He said, "O woman, great is thy faith: be it unto thee even as thou wilt." And her daughter was made whole. God's hour had come and the power of Satan had met its match.

CHAPTER TWENTY THREE

In the twenty-eighth year of his life, in the latter part of the month of September, or Tishri, the mature son of Mary decided to make a pilgrimage to Jerusalem. Not until now had He been able to do what was being planned due to the heavy work season at the wood shop. He had always wanted to be in the Holy City at Yom Kippur. No day in the year was more solemn than the Day of Atonement. Every holy time was sacrosanct, but without Yom Kippur, nothing else would matter. No one was expected to attend, but thousands of devout Jews were always there.

The family donkey had been laden with the bare essentials needed for the pilgrimage and the day had arrived for departure. The trip would be a tiring ordeal, being more than seventy-five miles from Nazareth across mountains and through both dry and wet ravines. However, people traveled these routes all the time and thought little about the rigors of such a journey. Jesus himself had been this way numerous times.

He would probably meet a number of travelers and most usually, when this happened, both parties would welcome the opportunity to rest a bit and pass the time of day. The whole thing was pretty clear in his mind and He knew what to expect, including the possibility of highway robbers along the way.

Yom Kippur was the day when the high priest, and

only the high priest, performed at every service including going before the Lord God to seek forgiveness for another year of national sin. Great care was paid to every detail as the priest prepared himself, with the assistance of other less holy men, for the awesome task which was his. The evening before the actual sacrifice, the priest would remain awake all night listening to appropriate scriptures read by his aides.

Carefully designed and cleansed apparel would be worn by the officiating priest and it would be changed more than once as the priest bathed five times and washed his hands and feet twice for each bath. Two goats would be readied for the ritual of sacrifice and, by casting lots, the priest would select one goat to be burnt and the other to become the scapegoat driven into the wilderness.

Before sacrificing for the people, the priest would slay a young bull as an atonement for his own sins and those of the other priests.

The people present for the occasion would be standing shoulder to shoulder in their prescribed courts – the women in the distant area, then the men a bit closer, and the priests nearer still.

The sanctuary, however, was always off limits to everyone except the high priest, and even he could enter only once a year at Yom Kippur. Fear, that the nation might incur the wrath of God rather than forgiveness, gripped the people's minds and hearts like a vise.

As the priest, with trembling fingers, pulled aside the veil of the Holy of Holies, the people would wait with bated breath. Would the priest be struck dead? Would the people be consumed?

Three times the high priest would pull back the veil and tiptoe barefoot into the hallowed room. The first time, he would pile incense on the coals which he carried with him and the room would fill with smoke, symbolic of the prayers of the people. Then, still behind the curtain, he would pray, but not for long lest the people outside faint away in terror. As he finally appeared again outside the curtain, the people could be heard breathing a sigh of relief.

During his second visit, he would sprinkle blood from the bull he had sacrificed for himself at an earlier part of the ritual. Once again, he would emerge from the curtain and the people would recover their breath.

Outside the Holy of Holies, the priest would then sacrifice, in the sight of the masses, the goat which had been selected. The blood of the goat was sprinkled before God in the chamber, a symbol of giving back to God the life which had been given to them.

Each time the priest emerged from the sanctuary, the people would listen for the sound of the tinkling bells and pomegranates on the priest's robe, a welcome assurance that God had not consumed the priest and they would be forgiven.

As the priest appeared the last time at the altar, Jesus watched from the court of the men. With great solemnity, the priest confessed the sins of the nation, hands placed on the scapegoat. This transferred the sins

371

of the people to the goat. As the people made way for the removal of the goat, one of the attending priests led the goat toward the desert to a precipice over which the goat was thrown to its death. By that act, the nation's sins were gone.

When Jesus arrived at the Temple for Yom Kippur, He knew exactly what to expect. Although He had never seen the ritual performed, the procedure had been explained and described often during his years in synagogue school.

As He watched, He also participated in each step through which the priest led the people. The solemn events of the day left him with an over-powering sense of the presence of God. This was the way God had instructed Moses and Aaron from the beginning. Yet, the ritual seemed so perfunctory as if there were something magic about it. And He knew there was no magic here.

Following the driving away of the scapegoat, the people were in a festive mood as they prepared to return to their abodes with a clean slate, a slate which they would invariably defile again.

"What will the end of all this be?" asked Jesus of himself. "How can Israel go on with this total disregard for the seriousness of the covenant? When will the patience of the Lord wear down?"

The word of God had become second nature to the mature carpenter. Everything in the Hebrew scriptures was more and more like an indelible etching which was easy to bring to the surface. Today, as He watched the priest and contemplated the attitude of the people, there was something carnival about the manner in which the solemn festival was being handled.

He seemed not only to remember the scripture, but to recall the event when the first king of Israel was rejected by God. He remembered hearing Jehovah speak to Saul, who had disobeyed the command of God, then sacrificing to make up for it. Samuel had written down the words: "Hath the Lord as great delight in burnt offerings and sacrifices, as in obeying the voice of the Lord? Behold, to obey is better than sacrifice, and to hearken than the fat of rams."

Waiting until the crowds had drifted from the outer courts of the Temple, Jesus sought out one of the priests. Men of Israel had the right to do this even though it did not happen often because the common folks were intimidated by holy men. Soon it was discerned that this young man, with whom the priest was speaking, was no ordinary peasant.

"Could you help me with some troubling questions which I have confronted during the sacrifices today?" asked Jesus politely.

"I'm terribly busy, young man," replied the old priest, "but if it doesn't take too long, I will try to help you."

Jesus began by reciting the word of the Lord, words spoken by the prophet Samuel to Saul at his dethronement, words which had stuck in his mind like a burr.

"Does anything strike you as being inconsistent when we keep coming back every year to sacrifice, having ignored the will of Jehovah since the last time? Are we being presumptuous in expecting God to overlook our failure as a nation, a failure which has come to be a way of life for us?"

"Well, ah, let me see. How would be the best way for me to answer? You have asked a good question, a very good one. Indeed, we are supposed to be consistent. I think we would all agree on that point. Young man, I am really pressed for time today. Could you come to see me later, maybe in a month or two?"

The carpenter smiled graciously, but the priest detected something in the smile which made him know that the young man saw right thorough his thin disguise. Not ready to be put aside, Jesus encountered a second priest, one much younger, and presented the same concern to him.

With the agility of a quick-thinking mind, the boy-faced priest explained that he was a novice and not permitted to speak for the ruling body of elder priests.

"Why don't you wait around until you see a white beard, and ask him," he laughed.

"It would appear that the priests do not know what they are about," Jesus thought to himself. "If our priests are so blinded by their traditions, how can the people avoid being blind also?"

374

When the third clergy came into view, the carpenter thought He would try once more.

"What do you think?" Jesus asked him, after having confronted him with the enigma.

The third cleric waited a moment before attempting to answer, then sat down on one of the huge flat rocks in the wall.

"Why are you interested in this?" he asked.

"I mean no irreverence. But the ritual today, although it was done with precise correctness, came across as an endorsement of some kind of superstition instead of the redemption of Israel by Jehovah."

"Young man, you are wise, far wiser than your years would suggest. I have been debating this with the elders for a long time. True, we can never set aside Yom Kippur. It is our only hope and Jehovah has told us to do it. I have been through it for nearly thirty-two years until sometimes I get the feeling that hardly anybody thinks much about what is really happening."

"It's encouraging," interrupted the young carpenter from Nazareth, "to find a holy man who sees his role as more than a job."

"Never! Not in a thousand years could I ever think lightly of what God has called me to do. I am a servant of the people in his stead."

"What have you done to try to get the covenanted people back on track with Jehovah? Maybe I do not have the right to ask," Jesus apologized, "but this is so important to me personally. I must know where I am

375

going. Although the aging Pharisee did not comprehend the last words of the carpenter, he let them slide and continued.

"You ask what I am doing?"

"Yes, if I may," nodded Jesus.

"It's a fair question. I am afraid that a lot of our scribes, elders, priests, and rabbis are drifting with the tide. There are times when it looks to me like they don't believe in *anything* they are doing. Sometimes even the people themselves, the men and women who are dependent upon us for their salvation, leave the impression that they are not sure of us. Of course, when I mention it to my fellow-priests, they are horrified and refuse to believe that they might give that impression."

The carpenter was a good listener. What the old Pharisee was saying struck Jesus as being right on target. And He was much in agreement with his explanation. The holy man went on, pulling at his white beard in somber thought.

"From the perspective of the Law, which is what I work with all the time, I keep insisting that there is more to being the people of God than being lawfully correct and killing sheep and bullocks. None of that do I discount, but it cannot be a substitute for obedience in the day-to-day life of the Hebrew nation. If we are to be the people of God, there must be something distinctive about us. Other nations have laws. Other nations sacrifice. Some even sacrifice their own children!"

"Then what could we be doing that we are not

377

doing which would make us, as you say, different?" Jesus asked with growing interest.

"In addition to our holy days and devotion to the Law, it seems to me that righteousness has to be considered. We have become experts, or nearly so, at side-stepping the whole matter of righteousness."

"How do you mean?"

"The prophet Micah said it for us," replied the wise Pharisee, rising from the rock wall and pacing across the stone floor. Leaning forward and squinting at the carpenter, the old cleric repeated with emphasis, "The prophet Micah said it for us!"

Jesus knew immediately what he was going to recite. As so often before, it was as if the carpenter knew Micah first hand. The feeling was almost eerie, but these moments came often, and they were beginning to seem so right.

The holy man, face turned upward in holy reverence, began to quote the prophet: "With what shall I come before the Lord, and bow myself before the High God? Shall I come before him with burnt offerings, with calves of a year old? Will the Lord be pleased with thousands of rams, or with ten thousands of rivers of oil? Shall I give my first-born for my transgression, the fruit of my body for the sin of my soul?"

The aging Pharisee paused. "You see, that is not enough! Something is lacking in all this. So Micah shocks us with the simplicity of being a servant nation. The prophets insisted, even though we hear very little about it anymore, that the nation must get rid of its pompous pride, its self-centered worship. God has called us to serve others, not to hide in our sanctuaries and bask in our special favored place with the Lord." The little man, still tugging at his beard, continued with the words of Micah: "He hath shown thee, O man, what is good, and what doth the Lord require of thee, but to do justly, and to love mercy, and to walk humbly with thy God?"

"So, if we believe in the sacrificial system by which Jehovah God forgives our sins, then we ought to be new people and prove it by the way we live our lives in service," suggested Jesus, waiting for the old clergy to agree.

"Not even Moses could have said it better!" replied the Pharisee. "That's where we are in our history and we must not fail again."

Putting his arm around the shoulders of the young man before him, the old cleric prepared to be on his way, apologizing for his duties which demanded his attention. "This has been a refreshing conversation we have had. It is so encouraging for me, so very rare, to find a young man like yourself so visibly concerned about our nation."

Turning to leave, he suddenly stopped and turned back. With unabashed interest in the inquisitive boy before him, he asked, "By the way, what is your name?"

"My name is Jesus. I am the son of Joseph, a carpenter in Nazareth.

The old man nodded and smiled. He explained that he did not believe he knew Joseph, but it was a joy to

379

talk with Joseph's son.

"You have been a great help to me," said Jesus. "It would be an honor for me to know who you are."

"Oh," said the old Pharisee, bowing graciously, "everybody knows me as Nicodemus."

CHAPTER TWENTY FOUR

Jesus was spending less and less time in the shop now. He was walking more in the hills and spending more time with the people. The shop was in good hands with Simon becoming experienced as an artisan in his own right. At last there was a little time for the things which interested him most – like long walks among the flowers and wonderful conversations with the small animals. During these times of contemplation, Jesus always felt that Jehovah God was walking with him. It was really a time of prayer as He discovered that praying is not talking at all, but *walking* with God.

Everything that happened during these days had the imprint of the heavenly Father on it. In fact, even when nothing happened at all, the sensation was the same. He heard the voice and saw his hand in the sun and the rain. All of nature seemed to be in tune with him who created the whole world.

Jesus enjoyed saying, "Good morning, anemones! How do you do, woodchuck? What's new, little goat? Where are we going today, sparrow?" And the comradery between man and nature was as pure as it had been on the morning of creation when the stars sang together and the hills clapped their hands for joy.

Gradually, people were encountered with whom the carpenter, turning teacher, exchanged greetings and shared thoughts about life. Folks enjoyed hearing him

381

talk. His words were so fresh and they made such good sense. More and more, men and women were asking his opinion about a host of things. Some even asked for his much-coveted advice about family, synagogue, and the nation's future.

On one of those special days, Jesus chanced to run into an old couple, both of whom walked with the aid of a crooked tree limb on which they leaned. They were clean, but their clothes were threadbare, so much so that their skin showed through in spots.

"Shalom, neighbors," said Jesus, as He raised his hand in greeting.

The old man, stooped with age, lifted his reddened eyes and nodded his head in reply.

"Sarah is very ill," he explained, gesturing toward the frail, little wisp of a woman by his side. "My name is Shemiah and we are very sad today."

Sensing the compassion in the stranger's face, the old man told his story. He just had to talk to somebody. It was not a new story at all. Poor people all over Galilee were hurting. The chief tax collector of the area had just handed them their assessment. It was more than Shemiah and Sarah had, including the value of their house. And there was no way they could pay it.

It was a known fact that tax collectors were within their legal rights to assess as much as they wished as long as Rome received its share. The practice was little short of legalized robbery.

The heart of Jesus bled for the old couple as He listened to their painful story.

"I know the tax collector," said the stranger, "not well, but I have seen him. Would you like me to talk to him?"

"Sir," answered Shemiah with a lump in his throat, "He will not change anything. Nobody trusts him. Everybody hates him. Sarah hates him. I hate him more than anyone!"

Later that week, the carpenter walked the long trip to Capernaum where He talked with Matthew who did not recall having ever seen the carpenter.

"Shemiah is a chronic complainer," said Matthew in response to the message brought by Jesus. "He's always whining about something. Can't stand the old man."

"He may well be, but these are poor people about to lose their home. Doesn't this assessment seem extreme to you? You are bound to feel some compassion for the poor. Surely, this assessment could be lowered without hurting you or Rome."

The tax collector jumped to his feet, red-faced with uncontrollable anger. "Compassion has nothing to do with anything. I work for the government. They get what they decide is fair and I have to live, too. If I reduce Shemiah's tax, the news will get out and every person in Galilee will demand the same. Can't do it! And who do you think you are making these claims on me? You have no right to get involved in this matter. Rome is on my

383

side, you know!"

"You cannot serve God and money, Matthew," said Jesus, leaning forward with a telling smile, irritating the tax collector to the marrow of his bones.

"God? Who said anything about God? What's He got to do with it? I don't even believe there *is* a god." If there is a God, why hasn't He done something about the poverty of people like this old man?"

"But what if you are wrong? What if there *is* a God and you are accountable to him? Would that make you feel differently about Shemiah? Do you think that believing in God would change anything?" continued the carpenter.

Matthew, finding it hard to believe what he was hearing, dropped his head and muttered something under his breath. Even through his beard, Jesus could see that his face was more and more flushed with emotion. The self-centered old man was at a breaking point.

"I don't know who you are nor do I understand why you care what happens to a nobody like old Shemiah. But I don't like the way this conversation is going and I want you to leave. People like you are always interfering with the affairs of others, forever sticking your noses into somebody else's life where you have no business!" Pointing his finger at the door, he demanded, "Out! Get out of my house!"

With that, Jesus quietly arose and departed from the lavish quarters of the chief of the publicans. Clenching his teeth and beating his fists against the wall, the tax man, whirling around, kicked at a stool and broke his toe.

It was nearly two years later when the carpenter, already having gathered a sizeable number of followers, was teaching at the edge of the Sea of Galilee. The custom's office had been officially set up in the marketplace at Capernaum and the unhappy masses were pouring into the city. People were waiting in line before the little quisling Jew whom Rome had authorized to collect taxes for the Imperial House. Some were leading donkeys, carrying sheep on their shoulders, or driving oxen with a cart. Many had sacks of grain with which they hoped their taxes might be paid. Some were just wearing everything they owned. Nonetheless, even they knew there would be a tax just for being alive.

"Declare your possessions!" cried the collector without lifting his head from the scroll on which he was entering the figures. "Axles on your cart? What are you carrying? Where are you going? Where have you been? Have you sold anything in the last . . . .?"

The inquisitor was suddenly struck dumb. A strange light danced about his ledger. Glancing up from the scrolls, he was staring into the penetrating eyes of Jesus. For once, he could think of nothing to say. And he was embarrassed.

Softly, the traveling carpenter said, with all the confidence in the world, "Matthew, come. . . Follow me!" And the tax man rose to his feet, knocking one of the scrolls to the ground. Ignoring the long line of people, men and women straining to see and hear what the commotion was all about, Matthew followed Jesus out of the marketplace.

Among the encounters with all kinds of people, on those country paths through the hills, none ever compared with those mighty confrontations He had with Jehovah. It had been happening for a long time, but lately the meetings were almost daily.

The rabbis of his people insisted that no one could see God. The bright light of holiness would consume the body, soul, and spirit of anyone looking at the face of God. That was the way they read their scriptures. Yet, this son of Mary was mystified because it seemed as if He saw God every day. God the Father is a Spirit. There was no question about that. But He still knew what that Spirit looks like. No one understood when He talked about such things.

When the townspeople heard about the things which He was doing, they were confused. After all, they knew him well – knew his mother and all his brothers and sisters. They had never expected anything like this out of their young neighbor. Good lad, but mystifying in so many ways. Maybe he was mad. Some were saying so. His brother, James, was pretty confidant that Jesus had lost his way. He was surely not acting like the normal boy he had known in the past.

The passage of time dulls the memory of most of us. That is why Jesus' old friends at Nazareth could threaten to throw him off the mountain when He, much later in his mystifying travels, returned as, what they called a self-acclaimed prophet. They had forgotten how kind and good He had been with them in earlier days.

But there were a few who came to his defense. The woman, whose household furnishings were burned, shamed her friends for their conduct. She remembered. And one of those men, who had found new plow handles in his stable, argued with his neighbors. "I don't care what He claims to be or whether He is crazy or not! You people are wrong in what you are trying to do. Dead wrong! Jesus befriended me when I was down on my luck and I am here to stand up for him. You should be ashamed. To treat one of our own as you are doing is an indecent thing." The farmer was among the few who had not forgotten.

When He began to get serious about religion, the brothers did not object, not even James, because they were all brought up in a pious home. But when the older brother started talking about God as though He were personally acquainted with him, when He started spending more time studying the Torah and praying than He spent in the carpenter's shop, they resented his absence. They even poked fun at him, calling him rabbi.

It was easy for them to discount all the years which the older brother had put into Joseph's shop. He had seen to it that all of the children had enough to eat, clothes to

387

wear, and a place to shield them from the weather. They had a good thing going and they knew it.

From all indications available to him, the time had come to break ties with his formative years and assume the role of an itinerant preacher of righteousness. John the Baptist had appeared again after all these years in the monastery at Engedi. He was now preaching the coming of the kingdom in judgment. As he urged the people to repent, the masses detected the serious nature of the message and waited to see what would happen next. And crowds of men and women were coming to him to be baptized in the Jordan as a sign that they were prepared for the much desired dawn of a new Israel.

John looked the part of a prophet but, since there had not been one for four centuries, the people did not know what a prophet looked like. They knew, however, the moment they saw him, that the rugged fare he ate, the austere garments he wore, and the wildly unkempt hair were signs of who he was. Some laughed. Most felt a strange awe when in his presence.

Jesus remembered the afternoon when young John came with his parents to Joseph's funeral. That was a long time ago. He remembered the long talk they had about John's inner struggle and what the future held for him. And He recalled that everything the son of Zacharias had said that day pointed to this very moment.

When Jesus came to the Jordan to be baptized, He may have been throwing in his lot with John, ready to become a disciple of the Baptist. As yet, the exact nature of his mission was uncertain as was the positive identification of his person. Through the intervening years, there had been a growing consciousness about these two facets of his life but, at the Jordan, Jesus was still searching, still waiting.

The Baptist either had a sudden burst of insight, or he had decided long before that his cousin was the Messiah. More than likely the latter attitude is the correct one. The only thing, about which John was more certain, was that he himself was *not* the Messiah. And he was prepared to get out of the way to let the Kingdom of God become a reality. The Baptist knew that he had been commissioned to declare the Anointed of Jehovah and he was ready to do it when the time came.

Jesus was probably looking for the Messiah, too. That explains his request for baptism. As the son of Mary arrived at the edge of the river, the Baptist turned toward the penitents waiting in the shallow water. "Behold!" he cried, pointing at the figure standing on the banks, "I baptize you with water unto repentance. But He, whose shoes I am not worthy to tie, will baptize you with the fire of the Holy Spirit!"

Concentrating more on exactly what this act of consecration meant to him than on anything his cousin was saying, Jesus ignored the remark and waited his turn.

His concentration was broken, however, when the baptizer shouted at the top of his lungs, "Attention! The Lamb of God who takes away the sin of the world!"

Jesus looked behind him to see whom the wiry

389

prophet was talking about. John could not avoid noting the modesty and humility which graced his cousin. Not until He stepped into the river Jordan, where John lifted him from the water, did the carpenter from Nazareth recognize the ominous thing which was happening.

From the heavens came the voice which Jesus had heard in Joseph's shop the night after his father died. That was the first time He had heard it. Since that time, He had heard it again and again. He would recognize it anywhere. "This is my beloved Son, in whom I am well pleased."

Now He knew. Knew who He was. And knew what He had to do.

CHAPTER TWENTY FIVE

About fifteen miles northeast of Beersheeba, in the mountains of Judah, lived a man named Simon. Simon was so commonplace a name that anyone so-called had to identify himself by either a patronymic – the name of the father – or the place where he lived. Simon lived at Kerioth and had come to be known as Simon from Kerioth.

Kerioth was an out-of-the-way village where nobody of importance lived and nothing of significance had ever happened since the conquest under Joshua. Since the village was not on any trade route which might bring in commodities from the world beyond, families who lived there simply helped one another survive as best they could. The nearest bazaar of any size was ten miles away at Hebron.

So Simon and his family of twelve children – three daughters and nine sons – lived pretty much to themselves and did their best to keep from starving. Life was hard for this big family, but they took it in stride because everybody in Kerioth had it hard. By the time Judah, the youngest of the children, was eight years old, three of his brothers and two of his sisters had died. Being the youngest of seven surviving children, his clothing was always ragged and worn out by the time it was outgrown by the older brothers.

Judah had been named for the fourth son of Jacob

and Leah, the father of the tribe which bore his name. Simon was proud to be a descendant of the patriarch who prevailed above his brethren and finally assumed leadership for the entire family. And he had taught his youngest son to hold his shoulders back and never forget for whom he had been named.

No matter how firmly a father seeks to instill family pride in his children, a thousand and one things can happen to disillusion them with the significance of being who they are. Of all the children, young Judah was the most disenchanted. He never had decent clothing to wear. He never had quite enough to eat. And he never had a day when the situation did not get worse.

At night he dreamed about what the world outside Kerioth might be like. One day he would find out for himself. He would just leave and never return. Now fourteen years old, there was every reason to believe that whatever was out there had to be better than what was going on in Kerioth.

Judah knew better than to mention his thoughts to anyone at home. But he had been planning for months that, when the spring rains were over, he was going to leave.

So before daybreak one morning in early Iyyar, or the month of April, Judah crawled from beneath the comforter, grabbed the few chunks of bread he had hidden under his mat, and sneaked out the door.

The morning was beautiful as the sun rose above the mountains of his youth. Amaranthine flowers of every color and size stretched their faces toward the sun, little plants so hardy that they thrived even in the rock crevices where nothing else grew. Wild life scampered to and fro as if all was right with the world. For a moment, the boy's eyes focused on a little web-footed Hyraxes clinging tenaciously to the side of a towering rock wall. The dirty little town where he lived was so drab, compared with the glory of the hills where God's world had not been tampered with, that Judah felt as if he had journeyed where no mortal had ever gone before.

The higher into the mountains he went, the lighter and fresher the air. At times he would stop to rest and clear away the light-headed feeling before going on toward Hebron.

Judah had roamed in the hills as a child, but he had never gotten this far from his home. This was unchartered territory and it was possible that he could get lost in the mountains and never be heard from again. Simon had taught him how to follow the stars, however, and he did some of his walking in the late evenings. When he did stop for the night, he simply found a shelter in the rocks and curled up with his thoughts under the warmth of the Judean sky. Not knowing exactly the best choice of valley openings, there were times when he had to retrace his steps and find a better way. The trip took the better part of three days.

The bread which he had brought with him lasted into the early part of the second day when he began to feel the pinch of hunger. There were wild berries here and there which helped, but Judah knew he would have to do something soon about food. It was a problem. The problem was not that he had forgotten to bring money with him. There was just no money to get his hands on. Being flat broke in the wilderness with no food was beginning to worry him.

By day three, he knew he was getting close to the outskirts of Hebron. Although it was only about ten miles from Kerioth to Hebron as the crow flies, he had probably traveled nearly twenty up and down the mountains. The feeling of desperation had set in. What was he going to do?

Now that the tired boy was nearing the city, a thin scattering of people could be seen coming and going on the mountain paths. The thought was not long in coming. Those people would have money in their girdles. When, a few minutes later, he reached the activity, Judah talked to himself to build his confidence.

"Sir," he said to an old man walking alone, "I have been walking from the south country for three days and I am hungry. Would you . . . ?"

Before he could finish the question, the old man brushed him aside, shaking his head vigorously.

It wasn't going to be as easy as he thought. As the man moved on, Judah reached down and picked up a loose rock and, without hesitation, struck the back of the old man's head. He fell face down on the ground, the red blood running from the hole in his skull.

Hurriedly, the boy rolled him over on his back and

ran his hand into the girdle around the old man's waist. When he removed his fist, there were two shekels in it. Looking around to be sure that he had not been seen, Judah lifted his tunic and ran, with the speed of the wind, all the way to the city.

With the money, Judah was able to buy something to eat and have a little left over for the next day. He didn't mind sleeping in the fields as long as the weather remained favorable.

During the days, he would offer his unskilled labor to anyone who could use him. A few times during that first month, someone paid him enough to buy bread in exchange for his running an errand or helping in the fields. The pay was never enough. It was not fair and Judah had already found an easier way to get more.

There were dozens of places along the road outside the city where he could hide and ambush someone coming into Hebron. Judah made it a point to attack only those coming into town because he knew that most of them who were leaving had spent all their money. The boy soon became quite adept at this new way of life. At first, he felt a pang of remorse when he took money by force, sometimes having injured the victim physically, but he soon became hardened to it.

Everyday Judah would practice running. If he were going to steal, he would have to be quick on the getaway. It wasn't long until he could run with the gazelles. And, as would be expected, there were soon other young boys of like persuasion who took in the new-

395

comer. Their group was soon to become a sort of criminal family, each one bragging to the others about what he had done.

Since Judah was a new recruit, he was expected to prove himself, so the clan determined what he would have to do. Anyone could knock someone in the head out on the mountain paths where nobody would be apt to see it. But it required some real expertise to steal on the busy streets of the bazaar. So that was what young Judah would have to do if he were to be initiated into the hoodlum gang.

The day was set for the young boy from Kerioth to prove his metal. It was mid-afternoon and the market place was over-flowing with people and pack animals. Judah knew that his adept fingers could easily slide money from the money baskets. The hitch would be in getting away through the maze of people without being caught.

A little, chubby woman was talking with a customer as she carefully filled his food basket with barley cakes and almond cookies. She knew the man who was buying fresh wares and the conversation was loud. People around them were enjoying their banter as they listened to their light-hearted chatter.

Judah had edged his way to the display table where the basket holding the currency sat with a cloth cover. While the woman chatted, the boy quickly jerked the cloth and ran his hand into the basket, making a fist. No sooner had his fist closed than he darted deliberately into the throng, not away from it, knowing that it would be easier to lose himself in the crowd.

"Stop that boy!" cried the baker woman. "Stop that thief! He has taken my money!"

On the contrary, no one tried to stop him. Rather, the crowd moved aside to let the boy through. No one wanted to get hurt and it was not important enough to get involved anyway.

When they met in their hideaway at the edge of town, the boys congratulated him. They had been watching from a distance and he had done his job well. When they counted the coins, there was not actually a lot of money. But it had probably not been a good day for the baker and Judah had proved himself. That was the important thing.

Over the coming years, the group grew to more than a dozen. And they got so good at what they did that they became the talk of the town. The Hebrew authorities were unable to do a thing and the Romans had more important matters to deal with, so the merchants and the pilgrims just had to take it on the chin. Nobody liked it, but it was a lost cause.

The situation worsened as the group of boys, now grown to be men, formed themselves into an organization of mercenaries for hire. In the event a wealthy merchant or a corrupt politician wanted to gain an advantage, these cut-throats were available. It was not just stealing anymore, though that continued, but much more serious crimes were being reported.

It was slave day near Bethlehem. The Roman sentries were at their posts and men and women from all across the area were being bought and sold like animals. On this particular day, which was held somewhere in the vicinity every three months, the mercenaries were always present. Crime never takes a day off, especially if a lot of money is being exchanged.

As always, the Romans were in charge. They were in charge of everything. Judah had come to hate anything Roman because it represented power which the son of Simon from Kerioth had come to despise. Power belonged to the people of Judea, not to the hated forces of Rome. He had killed before, and he only itched for the chance to kill a Roman soldier.

At least fifty slaves had been bought and sold by the time the day ended. Not every slave brought the same amount of money. The stronger looking men brought more than the others. And the beautiful women brought the highest price of all. The last sale was that of a small, dark-skinned man who did not understand anything said or done. It was later explained that he was from Ethiopia.

The curtain was drawn on the auction block and the last of the people prepared to leave. The Roman sentries, having had no trouble during the entire day, were well on their way back to the barracks.

Judah was watching the grinning owner, who had just collected his money for the Ethiopian, as he pulled the draw string on his leather pouch. The man suspected nothing as the smiling stranger from Kerioth approached with a quick chop across his chest. With the speed of a hawk swooping in on its prey, Judah snatched up the money pouch and fled into the hills.

Once safe in his mountain hideaway, he opened the bag and dumped its contents on the ground. There were thirty shiny pieces of silver, exactly the price of a very ordinary slave.

Judah was now thirty-two years old. Five of the members of the aging crime family had been caught by the Romans. They had been accused of crimes against the state and put to death by crucifixion. Two of the group had been killed, one by a robbery victim, who was more efficient with a knife than he, and another in an accident when he fell from his death off one of the mountain cliffs. The rest had scattered, probably still at large in the craggy wilderness plying their trade.

Simon's son had been more successful in crime than any of the others. Some of southern Palestine's biggest robberies had been master-minded and carried out by this one wiley stranger. His clever disguises had protected his identity and, even though he was a wanted man, there was little chance he would ever be found and brought to trial.

More than likely, Judah's avaricious spirit was not something he was born with, but rather a temperament which had grown out of his impoverished childhood. This, coupled with the early discovery that it was easier to take money than it was to earn it, made him the way he was.

Lately, Judah was finding himself a little bored. Anytime he wanted money, he just went out and took it from someone. The challenge was gone. What turn his life might take, there was no way to guess, but there had to be something out there more exciting than knocking people around and taking their money.

And then it grabbed him.

The moon was full, so bright that it wasn't necessary to carry a lamp to see where one was going. It was one of those beautiful Judean days when the afternoon lasts all night long.

Judah was returning to his hideaway in the hills from Hebron, where he had purchased some supplies, when he met a stranger coming into the city. They had barely passed one another when, suddenly, they both stopped. Without turning around, Judah said, "Is that you, Asher?"

At that, both men turned facing each other and, in full recognition, embraced like two brothers.

"Judas, you rascal!" exclaimed Asher. "It's been three, no four years. Where have you been?"

Asher, you see, was one of the group during those days before the nefarious crooks had parted company. And it was Asher who first called Judah *Judas*. The name had just stuck and, by the time the gang disbanded, all the guys were using that name.

"Am I glad to see you," said Judas. "I need to talk to somebody. Got a lot on my mind."

"What are you doing with yourself these days?" asked Asher, punching Judas playfully on the arm. "Made any grand hauls?"

"Not much. That's why I need to talk. I'm not a kid anymore and I am bored stiff with myself. Don't know what to do with myself. Need to find a new line! Got any ideas from where you've been these four years?"

"Not really. I still make a hit on somebody now and then, just enough to keep my body and soul together. I guess you'd say I have retired. Driftin' along. Goin' nowhere."

Judas, even without the moonlight, would have looked melancholy, very distressed. The depression was like an aura around him. Something Asher could feel. And he didn't like it. Sure not like Judas.

Both men waited for the other to speak.

"You got anything in mind?" Asher asked, mainly because the silence was awkward and he couldn't think of anything better to say.

Having broken the ice, he continued, "By the way, do you know anything about this guy who has been preaching in the wilderness near Engedi? Isn't that close to Kerioth, your hometown? Hear a lot of people talking about him."

"Not very far. Don't know anything about him though. In fact, I don't talk to many people. Can't afford to with my past. As I get older I find myself trying to avoid being seen or heard by anybody. Losing some of my old brashness, I guess."

"Well, Judas, seems like he is some kind of prophet, kind of a recent thing. He just appeared one day out of nowhere. I had not heard anything about him until a week or so ago. Since then I have heard his name several times. They say that he is calling on people to repent. Even predicting that the kingdom is about to be reborn."

"That'll be the day!" laughed Judas. "Used to hear my dad talk about the day when the Messiah would come and rule over the whole world. Dad used to get awfully excited when the kingdom was mentioned. Never quite understood it myself. Far out."

"Yeah," Asher butted in, "my old man believed that stuff, too. I never put much stock in this religion thing either. Got enough of it when I lived at home. Haven't heard anything from the folks in years. Sometimes wonder if dad still believes that stuff."

"But, what if our dads were right? And what if this guy is the Messiah? Stranger things have happened, you know."

None of this sounded like the Judas he had known. Asher made no answer and Judas rambled on.

"We're not doing anything," chuckled Judas. "Why don't we go down there and check this fellow out? I haven't been back in the area since I left home eighteen years ago. What do you say?"

Before they parted, they agreed to meet three days hence, at the spot where they were standing, and look up the preaching prophet. That would be the morning after the next Sabbath.

The journey took almost a week. Judas remarked that it was taking a long time and insisted that it was because he was getting older. Asher knew better. Judas had to stop every hundred cubits or so to reminisce about something he recalled from his earlier trip from Kerioth. He had gotten to be like an old maid. But it was all right. What the heck. They were in no hurry anyway.

The day had worn away by the time they arrived at the river, but twenty or so people were still milling around. The banks were soaking wet from the many feet which had dragged water out of the river. Some of the remaining people were wet themselves, evidence that they had been baptized, while others, their tunics still dry, were not yet convinced. The wild, hairy man dressed in a camel skin was not what they were expecting.

Staring at the spectacle before him, Judas said to Asher, "This guy is no politician. He's a pop-eyed fanatic."

The more they heard, however, the less demented the fiery preacher appeared to be. John was making sense. If the kingdom were coming, then everybody ought to be getting ready for it. And all the preacher was insisting on was that a man repent of his past and come clean with God. Hard to argue with that.

"Come on Asher, let's get in the water," shouted Judas, pulling on his old friend's tunic. "Nothing I would like to see more than a few broken Roman necks. How I hate those soldiers! They're everywhere you look. And

John's got the Pharisees' number, too. I despise those religious nuts." ▾

Asher pulled back. He would need to think about it. They could be in for big trouble.

Ignoring Asher's hesitancy, Judas walked right out into the water and waited his turn to be put under.

Splash went the sound of the water. One by one, John the Baptist dipped the penitents. *Splash . . . . Splash . . . . Splash . . . .*

It was Judas' turn. John looked into the eyes of the hardened looking man before him and asked, "Are you repenting of your past? Do you want to be ready for the kingdom?"

"Yes," said Judas, "let's get on with it!" *Splash* went the water.

Waiting in the crowd to see what would take place next, Asher watched as Judas emerged from the waters. When the Baptist finally came to shore, the two crooks collared him. Judas did most of the talking. "What do you have to do to be ready for this kingdom you are promising? Have to have a ticket? Who do we pay? This is new to us."

The wild looking prophet replied, "Simple. Bring forth fruits of repentance."

"What's that mean?" asked Judas, uncertain as to what such talk was all about.

"It means that you must change your ways. You have to stop lying. You have to stop stealing. And you have to stop hating."

Both men felt the sting in the prophet's words, for they were guilty at every point.

"Are you the Messiah?" Asher asked, with a large dose of obvious skepticism.

"Absolutely not!" responded the baptizer, as if such a question made him angry. "I am only a voice crying in the wilderness, a voice reminding the nation that we must make our paths straight if the Messiah is to come."

"You seem to have gathered a lot of disciples. Is just anyone welcome to sit at your feet and learn?" asked Judas. "I mean, could we walk with you? What is there to learn?"

"My message is simple. There isn't much to learn. But One is coming after me. He will teach you all things. He is the Messiah and we will all learn a lot from him."

The two men looked at each other. They had no idea who this other fellow might be, but what they had seen in John, they liked. He was a man's man – strong, muscular, and fearless.

"I would like to make my life count for something," said Judas, momentarily recalling the folly and uselessness of his past years. "Count me in. I'll be your body guard or your hit man – whatever you need."

"Don't have a need for anything like that, but I am honored that you want to hear more. I'll be back at this spot tomorrow." The baptizer took leave of them and disappeared into the wilderness.

"This guy makes me nervous," said Asher to

Leslie H. Woodson

Judas. "Do you realize what the Romans will do with anyone who goes around talking about a kingdom other than the empire? I'll hang around a while, but don't expect me to sign up as you have done. I don't think I am ready for this. Not ready to get my head chopped off."

The conversation slowed and the minutes seemed like hours as the men found themselves in deep thought about the future of Israel and their own destinies as well. It was a lot to think about, an awful lot.

"I have a gut feeling about this John guy. He says he is not the Messiah, but maybe we can change his mind," remarked Judas. I would give my life for any man who can clean out this Roman scum and the detestable religious clowns of our land. We could become a powerful empire again and you and I could be in on the ground floor. Think where that would put us! Right at the top, that's where!"

A relationship developed between John the baptizer and Judas Iscariot. Together they laid their plans for Israel's rebirth, a coming to life again of the reign of King David. John kept preaching repentance and righteousness while Judas talked without stop about the politics of power. John was suspicious of any politics and wasn't sure where Judas was going with his ambitions. The thing the man from Kerioth could not understand, about the baptizer from Engedi, was why he would not lay claim to the kingdom and get on with the bloody fight. That was where the glory would be! Nevertheless, the more insistent he was that John be the Messiah, the more irritated the baptizer became.

This went on for several months and, while the crowds anxious for baptism continued to grow, John seemed to be making no progress as Judas analyzed the situation. He even kept talking about someone else who was going to be the new king. The questions grew bigger and bigger.

Finally, disillusioned with the dreams he had for John – or were they for himself? – the day came when the man from Kerioth broke his ties and abandoned the loser from Engedi. When the baptizer talked about the coming of the Messiah, he would always say, "He must increase and I must decrease." Why did he have to put himself down like that?

A couple of days later, Judas – who had lost all interest in John and had not seen his friend Asher for some time – decided to go up to Jerusalem and find out what this other guy was up to, the young man from Nazareth who, some folks were saying, was doing some powerful things. He wasn't preaching anywhere, but the men who had talked to him were captivated by him.

When he saw the man from Nazareth, as people referred to him, he was impressed. There was no preaching going on at all. Jesus was talking with a bunch of children; one little boy was sitting in his lap while others sat at his feet. The man was radiant with charisma. One look was all it took. Judas was pretty convinced that he had found the new king of Israel.

With an inner compulsion, which was driving him

407

Leslie H. Woodson

with excitement about the possibilities of a political coup, Judas swore to himself that he would be in on this new world empire. He would encourage this man from Nazareth to be the bright new leader of the people of Israel. And he would convince the nation that this was their king. Perish the thought, but if Jesus should reject his role in the kingdom as had John, by the grace of Jehovah God, he himself would *force* him to become king!

CHAPTER TWENTY SIX

Not far from the palace of the king, Herod had constructed a royal prison in honor of Mark Antony. Situated northwest of the Temple area, it served as a royal fortress insuring protection of the holy precincts. Garrisoned by Roman soldiers and partly surrounded by a deep ditch nearly two hundred feet wide, it was a prime example of ancient maximum security. The last place anyone would want to be taken was the pretorium of Herod at Caesarea or the prison at Antonia.

The Roman emperor used Antonia to incarcerate anyone defying the rules of the empire. And Herod used it as a lock-up for those under his immediate jurisdiction who created needless unrest for the nation. Persons imprisoned there, by direct command of or in cooperation with the Imperial throne, were customarily chained to a soldier or had their feet placed in the stocks. Not a very happy place to spend an evening.

In the autumn of the year 25 A. D., a local skirmish developed to the north of Jerusalem. A number of irrate Jews had gathered around a self-proclaimed patriot and were calling for the people to rise up against Rome. They had no official support from any religious or political body nor were they members of the Zealots. This kind of thing was far from rare in the time of Jesus. Hardly a month passed but that somewhere in the land, there were visible signs of unrest.

A tall, full-bearded man in his thirties was brandishing a short sword over his head and shouting to those who had gathered.

"Down with the pagans! Down with Herod! Down with Rome!."

Some were annoyed by him. Others felt deep sympathy because they shared his hatred for a foreign government. And others laughed in total disinterest as they found the performance a break from the dull day.

"How long will we allow this foreign pig to rule over us? Are you just going to lie down and take it without a fight? Herod is destroying our great land. He is a slave of Caesar. He is not one of us!"

"You are really a silly pig yourself," shouted someone from the small crowd, not in the least impressed.

"Let the man speak," cried another, attempting to disguise his own hostility.

"How do you think we could ever muster enough support to drive these foreigners out?" yelled a woman, sympathetic to the cause, but skeptical that anything could ever change.

"Tell your children what is going on. They are still too young to know what we have lost," insisted the man with the big beard. "Tell them the story. Do not be afraid of this monster from the pits! Join ranks. We can do it. We must do it!"

"You are going to get us into trouble. Leave us alone. Go! Get out of here. Who are you anyway?"

"Makes no difference who I am. Somebody has to

lead. I will be your leader. Follow me and we will whip these mongrel dogs."

"Oh, so now they are dogs. I thought they were pigs," shouted one of the irritated people in the crowd.

With the last rebuff, the man grew angry and aimlessly swung his short sword, striking an innocent bystander. The cut was not severe, but it was clear that the man with the sword was out of control.

"You are mad," screamed an old woman standing at the edge of the crowd, now growing in size.

By this time, the police from the nearest town had arrived and, after a brief scuffle, had the man in custody. The crowd broke apart and the struggling, cursing man was carried away bodily, thrown astride a horse, and delivered to the police barracks.

By nightfall, the misguided patriot was in the stocks at Antonia. The authorities accused him of disturbing the peace, insurrection, open revolt against civil power, and rebellion against Herod and Caesar. These were serious charges which made him liable to both Roman and Jewish law. In short, he was a double criminal. His chances of ever being free again were few.

After a few days of confinement, he admitted that he was from a little place near Jericho and was the son of a man known as Abba. Checking into his background led to further information about the identity of this man whom no one around Jerusalem knew. He had been arrested numerous times by the Jericho police for robbery but, with the financial assistance of his father, had been able to bribe

411

his way out of trouble.

It was also discovered that he had murdered a man in Emmaus for which no specific charges had been made. From the time of his childhood, he had been in constant trouble. It was one of those cases which left the village people of Jericho completely bewildered.

There was little question about what should happen to this criminally inclined insurgent. When interrogated about his seditious activities, he was belligerent and unrepentant. Should he be let out on the streets again, he made it clear that he would form a gang and go to war against Herod. Furthermore, he would kill every Roman sympathizer he could find.

It was agreed that the tall, full-bearded man would stand trial for robbery, murder, and sedition. And the chances of avoiding crucifixion were slim to none. To put him to death at once would be inadequate punishment, so the judges decided to keep him in the stocks until a later date. This would be a more severe punishment and it would also serve as an example to those who might try anything like this in the future.

There would be no release from the stocks except for toilet privileges and a short jog in the courtyard once a day. Then he would be chained to a Roman soldier. Visitors would be permitted only under strict supervision with a soldier always present to monitor the conversation.

Jesus heard about the imprisoned man and, being in Jerusalem in the autumn of 25 A. D., felt inclined to seek an audience with him. Inquiry was made of the sentry's at the entrance of Antonia prison and, after a short wait, permission was granted.

Using a large iron key, which was attached by a chain to a soldier's waist, the guard opened a heavy wooden gate and Jesus was led into a dark corridor. Except for the lamp carried by the soldier, there was no light. Both the guard and the visitor were forced to feel their way through the blackness. Passing at least five cells, where occupants were awaiting judgment day, they arrived at the little, damp room where the murderer from Jericho sat with his feet in the stocks.

The smell of body sweat and human excrement was nauseating. Jesus stood in front of the caged man while the soldier remained on guard just inside the doorway. Scowling at the soldier, clad in the military uniform of the Herodian guard, the prisoner cursed his captors.

"I am Jesus of Nazareth," said the visitor, "son of Joseph."

The dirty man in the stocks made no reply. He refused to take his eyes off the soldier who, under different circumstances, would be dead, done in by the patriot's sword.

"I have come to tell you that someone cares about you."

"Ha! What a laugh!" shouted the prisoner, turning suddenly in the direction of the stranger in the shadows. "I tried to inspire the people to throw off this cursed presence of Rome and kick this Idumean pig out of the palace and this is what I got. Does this look like anyone cares? Get out!"

The man in the stocks cursed, leaning his head back to gather some force, and spat at his guest. No one said anything and he spat again.

"I know why you are here," replied Jesus softly. "I know that you want to overthrow the government. And I know that you think this is a patriotic and God-serving thing to do."

"Hrumpf," grunted the prisoner, as he rubbed the cramp in his leg.

"I also know that you have been an unhappy person all your life, that you have been a thief, even once killed a man. But, look at yourself today. Has any of this made your life any better?"

The man turned his face away, jaw set like an attack dog, and uttered unintelligible sounds suspiciously like a growl. Jesus went on.

"You simply must understand the seriousness of your situation. There is no way you are going to be allowed out of here and life is going to become unbearable for you. If you clench your teeth and hate those who put you here, they win, not you. You will have to relax your tight muscles, calm your taut nerves, and forgive."

With that the prisoner spat again at Jesus. "Forgive! How dare you. I never forgive! And neither do I ever ask forgiveness. Forgiveness is a coward's way out. That's not for me. Never! If you have nothing other than this silly talk, then leave. Nobody asked you to come here. Go and leave me alone."

The guest from Nazareth sat down on the damp floor and drew his legs up in front of him. Leaning forward, he looked into the eyes of the poor man trapped in the stocks.

"I can leave. In a few minutes, the guard will force me to, otherwise I would stay as long as it might take to stop you from hating yourself so much. What are you going to do with the rest of your life? It will likely be spent in this room, but you still have control over *how* you will spend the time you have left."

"Easy for you to say," the prisoner exploded. "Looks to me like there's nothing I can do about anything. I'm tied up like an animal. That's the way these foreign pigs treat us Jews. They act like they are the chosen people instead of us!"

"God has chosen us all," Jesus said, slowly emphasizing each word. "The only people who are special with Jehovah are those who do his will. That can be Gentiles as well as Jews. He loves us all. And He will forgive us all no matter what we have done."

"Who believes in God anymore?" moaned the prisoner in anguish. "What has He done for Israel? All those promises that He made to Abraham . . . where are they now? Gone with the Roman wind!"

No one spoke. The room was quiet except for the sounds outside in the prison yard. The silence continued so long that the soldier guarding the prisoner pushed back

415

his helmet to see exactly what had happened.

At last, the prisoner went on with his complaints against God.

"Look at us! We are the slaves of Rome. As if the Babylonians were not enough – now it's the Romans. Where is God in any of this? While He sits aloof in his heaven out there, we suffer like caged beasts! Where is his promise of a deliverer for his people? If things ever change, we have got to do it ourselves."

"You are half right. What we have got to do is change our attitudes toward others. We must learn to love and forgive even those who we think are our enemies if we are entitled to be kings."

The carpenter from Nazareth could see that the man before him was thinking.

"Anyone can rule with force, but only the real people of God can rule by love. And God? He's not just out there? Take it from me, He's not only out there . . . He is right here!"

"What does all this have to do with me?" asked the prisoner, now a little more in control of himself.

"Everything," replied Jesus. "Only God can get you out of here. Only God can set you free."

The dirty man in the stocks had been listening with his eyes partly shut. Suddenly, as if surprised, he opened his eyes widely and exclaimed, "God can get me out of here?"

"Do not misunderstand," continued Jesus. "This room is not important. We all have our dark rooms. It is not how dark the room is that determines anything; it is how light our hearts are. That's the secret. It is not these walls which imprison you. You built a wall around yourself long ago. God wants to forgive you and fill your heart with love so that where you are makes no difference at all. Yes, only God can get you out of here; only God can set you free. Only He can get this hate out of your heart. And only He can fill your heart with peace, unspeakable peace."

By this time, the hardened criminal was not as belligerent nor as calloused as when his visitor entered the cell. Jesus could not see the soldier behind him at the door, but the man in the stocks could. Even the soldier himself had been touched by the words of this stranger. Something was happening inside that cell and, whatever it was, the prisoner and soldier both liked it.

"What did you say your name is?"

"My name is Jesus."

"How about that? My name is Jesus, too. Jesus Barabbas. Everyone knows me as Jesus, son of the father."

"Me, too," said the man from Nazareth.

As the soldier stepped aside for Jesus to leave, the visitor paused, turned again to Barabbas, and smilingly said, "I hope we will meet again."

With that, the Son of the Father walked silently down the corridor and Barabbas sat quietly in his cell with his thoughts. For the moment, he forgot the discomfort of the stocks on his hands and feet, muttering to himself again and again, "Only God can get me out of here . . . Only God can get me out of here? . . . Only God can get me out of here!"

In the spring of 29 A. D., the prison Antonia was filled with captives as was always the case. It was spring time and the prisoner from Jericho was still in the stocks awaiting his fate. Pilate had met with his political and judicial advisors in preparation for the forthcoming Jewish Passover. Every year, special precautions were taken lest the rabid Hebrew nationalists get out of hand in their religious frenzy, for a restoration of what they called the Kingdom of David.

The small ruckuses which regularly erupted during times of Hebrew festivals were usually managed with little difficulty, but every year the tensions mounted higher and higher. Pilate could not afford any more trouble with his superiors in Rome. One more mistake and he knew he was gone.

When he heard that the priests and elders were conducting an ecclesiastical trial for a young teacher, a peasant from Galilee who claimed to be the Messiah, he was not particularly interested. This was a religious matter and Rome had given the Jews freedom of religion as long as it did not interfere with Roman law and order. It was much ado about nothing anyway, and it would pass.

When, on Friday morning before Passover on Saturday, the priests and elders from the Temple showed up at Pilate's place, the governor feared that things were getting out of hand. They had brought the young teacher, whom they had charged with blasphemy for claiming to be the Messiah, and set him before Pilate.

It mattered little to the governor whether Jesus were or were not some kind of blasphemous clown who said He was a god. What did matter was that the Jewish concept of Messiah included that of being a king. The claim to be a king was far more serious to Pilate and Caesar than the claim to be a god! Any such pretension was a direct threat to the Roman throne. This is why Pilate was far more concentrated on whether Jesus claimed to be a king than whether he thought of himself as God.

The Romans had, for several years, a custom for ingratiating themselves with the rowdy Hebrews at Passover by releasing one of the Jewish prisoners. This was in exchange for peace and quiet in Jerusalem. Pilate seized upon the opportunity to settle the issue and get Jesus, who he thought was innocent, off the hook.

So he had the guards bring the notable prisoner, Barabbas, into the courtyard beside the teacher from Galilee. All Israel despised this self-acclaimed deliverer of the Jews who had robbed and pillaged and murdered their own people. Congratulating himself on his brilliant maneuver, Pilate pointed first to the prisoner from Antonia.

"Whom do you want me to release for you? This man, Jesus Barabbas?" Then, pointing to the prisoner from Nazareth, the governor continued with a knowing

419

smile, "Or this man, Jesus Barabbas?"

It was clever, using a play on their names, but it was an even shrewder ploy than it was clever. He was confident that no one would want the criminal Barabbas running loose again. They would be forced, by their own sanity, to choose the benign teacher over the criminal from Jericho. This would get Pilate off the political hook. But he was wrong. The elders and priests persuaded the crowd to choose their despised enemy over their esteemed friend.

The prisoner, Barabbas, still chained by one hand to the soldier, raised his other fist in triumph. As the soldier unlocked the chain and set him free, the criminal from Jericho looked into the face of Jesus and remembered.

He remembered the conversation that day in the cell when Jesus from Nazareth had come to see him. And he remembered his words.

"Only God can get you out of here. Only God can set you free." And Barabbas wondered.

EPILOGUE

Life was never to be the same after the death and resurrection of Jesus.

It was not the same for Jesus himself. No longer was He to be bound by the limits of mortality. Never again would He feel the nerve shattering blows of the Roman hammer as the crude nails pinned him to the cross. Nor would He face the agony and humiliation which robbed him of mankind's last remaining dignity, the right to die a natural death surrounded by those He loved.

The terrible loneliness of being the Son of God among the sons of men was over. He was done with the ache of being misunderstood and rejected by the very people He had come to reclaim. There would never be another day like that moment when He was betrayed, denied, and forsaken by his closest friends. No one would ever spit on him again. He would never again wear a crown of thorns on his head nor would anyone need to lend him a tomb for his broken body.

Everything was different now for Jesus of Nazareth. His old mortal frame had been exchanged for an incorruptible and immortal body, a body recognized by his friends, but splendidly improved. No longer was He to be bound by the restraints of space or time. Now He had been glorified, his mission accomplished, his royalty assured.

The thorns had been replaced with a crown of

421

everlasting rule. And the humble donkey had been left behind forever. Now he rides astride a white charger followed by a heavenly host, an army of angelic beings crying, "King of kings and Lord of lords."

Life was never the same again for mother Mary. Can any among us even vaguely imagine what confusion and heartbreak must have flooded the soul of sweet Mary as she watched her son die on that cross? The angel Gabriel had promised her that the child she had conceived without a man would rule over the house of Jacob forever. There was no question about the identity of her son. She had not known any man and no one could convince her that the birth of Jesus was anything less than a miracle.

What strange twist of fate had brought him to that black day in history? Why had God allowed this to happen? And where was He at this moment when Mary needed his word of assurance more than at any time in her life? The silence was so loud that she covered her ears.

With the loss of Joseph and Joses, the departure of young Mary, and now the death of Jesus, Mary felt and looked much older than her years. She was not yet fifty, yet she felt in her heart that she was old enough to die.

Jesus knew that. At the cross, He had made sure that she would be properly cared for by publicly appointing the only apostle present to be a son to Mary. For a while she wanted to stay in her little house in Nazareth. There were so many wonderful memories there. All the children had been born in that house except Jesus.

Every nook and cranny reminded her of some happy event. She did not want to leave and, in fact, with the help of solicitous neighbors, Mary remained in Nazareth for several years.

John kept track of her and, when he became bishop of the church at Ephesus, accepted the role only on the condition that the mother of Jesus be willing to live with him in Asia.

Mary, who was now bent with age and in declining health, listened as John explained the situation. "Mother Mary," said the apostle, using the affectionate name by which he always had referred to her, "the time has come for us to make a big decision. You remember that Jesus insisted that I take his place and care for you. All these years, I have tried to do that."

"No one could I ever love more than you, my dear boy," interrupted Mary. "You have been a son to me and I have never needed anything that you did not provide."

"Mother Mary," said John, reaching out and patting her wrinkled hand, "the church at Ephesus has asked me to be their pastor, but there is no way that I can leave you here."

The mother of Jesus made no comment other than with her eyes. They looked so sad. Tears ran down her cheeks. It was clear to John that she could not bear the thought of leaving Nazareth, but Mary was an intelligent woman and she knew that there was no way she could stay there without John.

The children who were still around the hometown

had wanted to do more for their mother, but she invariably thanked them and explained that Jesus had assigned that job to John and she would not want it any other way.

"My son, John," she said, choking back the tears, "Jesus would want you to pastor those people at Ephesus. Other than himself, no one can lead them to believe as well as you. Yes, son. When do we have to leave?"

Three days later John had arranged for the move. Mary gave the house to her son, Simon, who had been living in the shop where he continued the business as best he could. Since the death of Jesus, the carpenter's shop had lost its valued reputation. Work was slow, but there was enough to sustain this lonely bachelor. He never talked much about Jesus because the authorities did not look favorably on members of his family.

Mary was never happy in Asia. It just wasn't the same. She lived only a few months after the move and was tenderly laid to rest in John's own burial cave outside the city. Although she never fully understood exactly what had happened in her life, or why she was so early convinced that her son was the Messiah, she died with her faith resting securely upon what He had done on the cross for her and the rest of the world.

Life was never the same again for Jesus' family. Joses had died while quite young, several years before the crucifixion of his elder brother. Abigail, his wife, never remarried as far as Mary knew. She and little Miriam moved away in an effort to get away from the things which fueled their grief. The family never heard from them again.

James, who had never been very religious before, became a devoted disciple of his older brother following a private appearance of the resurrected Lord. He was convinced of the deity of Jesus, and became the bishop of the church in Jerusalem. It was this former cynic who presided over the first council of the early church in 50 A. D. and officially recognized the right of Gentiles into the fellowship without circumcision. And it was this strong willed believer who penned the beautiful letter which bears his name in which he insists that faith in the Messiah alters our behavior. His peers surnamed him "James the Just" because of his great piety.

Elizabeth continued with her own ministry to the poor and downtrodden in Galilee. She remained a Nazarite and looked in on her mother at least once a month until Mary moved to Ephesus. Beth, as everybody in Galilee knew her, was loved and respected by all. When asked what she thought about her older brother's crucifixion, which was often, she consistently defended him against the charges which had been brought against him by the elders in Israel. She never fully comprehended what his Messiahship meant, but remained faithful to the traditions of the Hebrew community.

Young Judas, the brother and not the apostle, became a committed disciple of the risen Jesus and a much-loved part of the congregation in Jerusalem where James was pastor. Late in life, around 75 A. D., he wrote a short letter in which he contended for the faith, warning the saints against false teachers. When his body was found beaten and mutilated in the Kidron Valley, it was suspected that the nation's elders had ordered his death.

Life was never the same for the Twelve.

Simon Peter, leader of the apostles, repented of his denial of Jesus and kept the disciples together following the resurrection. He became a flaming evangelist, preaching the risen Christ throughout his homeland and finally traveling to Rome where he was condemned and crucified by the emperor Nero. Being unworthy of dying as had his Lord, by his own request, he was crucified with his head down and buried in the catacombs of Saint Sebastian on the Appian Way. The church in the Imperial City grew up on the teachings of Peter and his friend, the Apostle Paul.

Andrew carried the gospel to Greece where the wife of the proconsul Aegeas, Maximilla, was converted. Aegeas was so enraged that he demanded Andrew's crucifixion. On November 30, 69 A.D., the brother of Peter was put to death on an X shaped cross. As he was led to his execution, he leaned and kissed the cross exclaiming, "Hail, thou blessed cross! Thou hast been consecrated by the body of my beloved master!"

Constantius I removed Andrew's remains from Greece to Constantinople and interred his bones under the Church of Saint Sophia. In the year 369, the Abbot Regulus unearthed parts of the skeleton and carried them with him to Scotland where they were again interred. The spot was named Saint Andrews. In the eighth century, when Scotland was at war with England, the king saw, in a vision, the white cross of Saint Andrew against the blue sky of Scotland. Believing that this was a sign that the saint would fight for Scotland, the white cross became the national symbol for the nation.

James, the son of Zebedee, carried the gospel to Spain. Until this day there is an image of the virgin Mary in Saragossa with a hundred lamps burning before it because she is reported to have appeared to James on this spot. Later, returning to Jerusalem, James was chosen as an example by Herod who had him killed with the sword.

John, the youngest of the Twelve, lived to be almost a hundred years old. During his long life, he preached to the Parthians, was miraculously delivered from a cauldron of boiling oil, was saved from a cup of hemlock, and was banished to the island of Patmos. Eventually, he returned to Ephesus, where he had pastored, and died a natural death from old age. A prolific writer, this beloved disciple wrote an account of the life of Christ, three epistles, and the book of Revelation.

When John was too old to come to church in his own strength, men would carry him and set him on a chair in front of the Ephesian congregation where, when asked, "What is the greatest thing in the world?" he would say, "My little children, love one another." Then the congregation would ask, "What is the second greatest thing in the world?" And John, with feeble voice, would

Leslie H. Woodson

reply, "My little children, love one another." Finally, the people would ask a third time, "John, what is the third greatest thing in the world?" And he would answer, "My little children, love one another . . . for there isn't anything else."

Philip and Nathaniel, or Bartholomew as he is also called, worked together for a while as partners in mission. When they separated, Philip was responsible for the conversion of Lady Nicanoia and was crucified in Hierapolis, requesting that his body not be wrapped in linen as was his Lord's, but in the plainest of papyrus.

Nathaniel became a daring gospel preacher to the scholars carrying the gospel to far away India. With his brilliant mind, he was recognized as an apologist for the faith. He was finally flayed by king Astyages in Armenia, a death possibly more torturous than even crucifixion.

Matthew, also called Levi, wrote the story of Jesus in a book which would later be placed first in order in the New Testament. After a period, during which time he witnessed to his Hebrew peers, he labored in Ethiopia, Persia, and Syria. He never questioned who Jesus was. Even when tied to a stake where he was burned alive, he maintained his unshaken conviction that Jesus was the Messiah.

Thomas, known as Didymus, was invited by king Gondaforas, who provided a sizeable amount of money to build a palace. Unethical as it may seem, the funds were used by Thomas to get the gospel into the nation of India. The Mar Thoma Church of India is a monument to the work of this great man.

Before his journey to India, this apostle, unfairly remembered as "Doubting Thomas," left a lasting impression on the people of Syria where, after two thousand years, there is still a Syrian Church of Mar Thoma.

One of the most intriguing facets of Thomas' work was his search for the wise men. When found, he told them the whole story and baptized them. His reward for these deeds was a martyr's death. Pierced with a lance, he died on a mountain – today called Thomas – near Madras.

Simon Zelotes was as devoted to continuing the life and teaching of Jesus as he had earlier been devoted to the party of the Zealots. The raging fire in his soul was brought under control, but it was never damped out. Far from it. This man, who shared the name of a more illustrious apostle, was excited about Jesus. The remainder of his years, after the resurrection of his Lord, were spent proclaiming the good news in Persia. On his shield, which symbolizes the martyrdom of Simon, was placed the battle-ax or the saw. As was Isaiah, the prophet before him, he was brutally sawed in half.

Thaddeus, sometimes known as Lebbaeus, spent his life spreading the gospel in northeast Turkey, southern Russia, and Persia. It was Thaddeus who responded to the call of king Abgar of Edessa who, by the word of this little known apostle, was healed of his leprosy. As a result, the entire court was converted to belief in Jesus as the world's Savior. His life came to an end in Turkey when struck by arrows from a hostile mob. He died in Ararat, a city at the foot of the mountain range where the ark rested after the flood.

James the Less was condemned to death by Annas, the high priest, being accused of breaking the Law. The authorities informed him that he could save his life by renouncing Christ. Instead, he cried out, "Jesus Christ is the Son of God and is at the right hand of the Father and will come again to judge the quick and the dead." With that, he was thrown from the top of the Temple where enemies of the cause of Jesus threw stones at him and a fuller struck him on the head with a club, thus ending his life.

Judas Iscariot could have been a saint. With a kiss, he had betrayed his master into the hands of the Temple police. He meant well, intending to force Jesus to declare himself a political Messiah and destroy his enemies, but the plan back-fired. Had he returned to his Lord in repentance, he would have been forgiven. Instead, realizing what he had done, he returned the thirty pieces of silver and hanged himself.

Through the relentless missionary travels of the Eleven, the story of Jesus was carried all over the ancient world. From places like Spain, Scotland, Turkey, Syria, Persia and India, the disciples of the Disciples spread the joyous news as far as man could go. Nathaniel had cynically asked, "Can any good thing come out of Nazareth?" His question was finally answered.

But there were others whose lives would never be the same. There was the chief officer of Candace, the Ethiopian queen, who was converted to Christianity by Philip the evangelist and carried the gospel back to his countrymen. And the three thousand converted on the day of Pentecost, who had come to Israel from all parts of the ancient world, went back to their homes transformed by the power of the gospel. The centurion, who participated in the crucifixion of Jesus, was so convinced by what he saw that he shared his new faith among the Roman soldiers.

And Simon of Cyrene, who helped Jesus bear his cross, was so moved by the experience that he became a believer. Retiring to his home on the northern coast of Africa, he told his incredible story to his sons, Rufus and Alexander. Later, Paul found Rufus in Rome as a dedicated Christian in the church there.

Then, too, there was Pontius Pilate. Following his abusive treatment of the Samaritans, he was recalled to Rome by Caligula. Unable to deal with his misfortune, he was committed to an asylum for the mentally ill where he spent the bigger part of every day just washing his hands.

And Rachel? What about young Rachel, the younger sister of Jesus, who had so disappointed the family and friends? She had early abandoned her upbringing for the dissolute life of the streets. That was the question mother Mary was asked a hundred times before she left Nazareth for Ephesus.

Rachel, the older daughter of Joseph and Mary, was now in her mid-twenties and had not bothered to contact her mother since the death of Joseph. During that time, she had lived from hand to mouth wherever she could – and that was everywhere.

For the first five or six years, it was one man after another. Rachel was very pretty and very out-going, so it was never difficult to hook a man for the evening. With the money she earned at three shekels per trick, she managed to buy food and keep her clothing clean. Anything more than that was paid to the brothel owner where she maintained her quarters.

For a while she plied her trade around Japhita, a village near Nazareth. When business slowed, she settled first in Chesulleth and finally in Sepphoris where business was usually very good. When her customers were dirty and smelly – and some of them who came in right from the fields were! – she hated herself. But she was adept at using her wiles to hurry her customer along and get rid of him as soon as possible.

It was not unusual, however, for wealthy men to frequent the brothels. When they did, they were most often clean, well dressed, and perfumed. Among them were political figures, rich traders from far away lands, local priests, and other men of culture and class. Rachel particularly liked these men because they did not offend her and because they were loaded with shekels. For them she played hard to get since all the girls knew that such men would pay well and that they all preferred women who had to be persuaded to those who were easy.

After a half dozen years of this, she had managed to get her own place and be more selective in her clients. No more did she entertain filthy scum from the streets. They were not allowed in her little but charming house. She had moved again when the religious authorities in Galilee began to crack down on women who broke the Law.

This time Rachel moved as far away as she could and still be in her beloved Galilee. She and two other high class women moved north to the small town of Gischela, near the border of Phoenicia. Being only about twenty miles from both Ptolemais and Tyre, seaport cities on the Mediterranean, wealthy merchants were a sure thing.

For the next several years, Rachel remained much the same except that she was getting older and, even though she was still under thirty years of age, her life style had worn her down. Life had mellowed Rachel and she spoke more softly now. The lines in her face were getting deeper and she had begun to think about where she would be ten years down the road. Except for the vestigial remnants of the life she had lived, she looked much like her mother. That was where the similarity stopped.

Her once sexual activity had slowed down so that she spent most of her time with three or four of her best clients. It was no longer an everyday and every night thing. Rachel had liked a lot of men and there had never been any consideration of what was right and what was wrong until lately.

Thoughts of her childhood and her godly parents filled her mind and she had begun to long for those early days before her life had gotten so messed up. Often she wondered why she had not remained at home and married a good man of Nazareth and had children of her own. But, there was no going back now. It was too late for that.

Rachel had heard about the execution of her older brother in Jerusalem. When growing up at home, Jesus always seemed a little odd to her, talking so much about God and things like that. But He was anything but a bad boy. Now that she looked back, He was really a wonderful brother. Even though Rachel had spurned his concern for the direction her life was taking, she remembered him with fondness.

She had been away from home so long that everything which had happened since her father's death had been of little concern to her. When she heard of the crucifixion of Jesus, she was at a loss to comprehend what had brought it about.

Two months had passed since the reported death of her brother. She was seeing less and less of the few men she had continued to entertain. In fact, she had not seen her favorite since the crucifixion. That was not unusual because he was owner of a large shipping business which operated out of Tyre and he was out of touch for long periods of time.

Epher, her favorite, was an Arabian living in Phoenicia. His wife was dead and he had been left with two young daughters. Having been with Rachel several times, there was little question about her past, but she was so contagious that he could not stay away. He had talked with her seriously the last time they were together three months earlier.

"Rachel," he had said, "I wish that I were the only man in your life. I know that there have been many with whom you have slept, but you have done no worse than I."

"Epher, my dear Epher," replied Rachel. "You cannot know how I regret what I have done. If we had only met years ago . . . but that would have been a different time and it probably would have changed nothing."

"Why can't we just forget the past and start over?" Epher asked, hoping that he would be convincing.

"Nothing would make me happier, but there's no way I can just forget. I was taught to believe that what I have done is displeasing to God. You would never be able to forget what I have been and I know that God will not forget either."

"My sweet Rachel," said Epher, "we cannot undo the past. We must live today. That's all we have."

The evening ended after what seemed to be hours of emotional conflict. Nothing was decided, but Epher explained that he would be out of touch for about three months. When he returned, he would expect an answer.

It was a cold mid-winter morning in Gischela and

Rachel was washing clothes. It had been six weeks since she had been with any man. Her mind was made up. She was going to accept Epher's offer. Hopefully, he was thinking of marriage and not just living together.

"That's her! That woman with the wash. That's the one!"

The voice was loud and frightening. As Mary turned to see where the voice was coming from, she saw a half dozen men whose apparel gave them away. They were priests and Levites.

"That's the woman," shouted one of the priests. "I saw her with my own eyes. She was on a mat with a man who was not her husband."

As they came nearer, Rachel could see the stones in their hands and she recognized the priest who was making the charges. He had been with her more than once.

With uncontrollable anger, the men grabbed Rachel and dragged her into the street. A crowd was gathering and the vicious little priest was explaining to the people what Rachel had done.

In the distance, less than a half mile away, appeared three horses with three riders. Seeing the commotion, they proceeded with haste to see what it was all about. As they approached, Rachel realized that one of the men was Epher. The other two were later discovered to be paid mercenaries who traveled with the wealthy merchant to provide protection from the marauding thieves.

When Epher saw Mary on the ground with the angry priests standing over her with their stones, he put the picture together at once.

"Get the woman!" commanded Epher. Before the priests or the people knew what was happening, the two mercenaries had brandished their swords. One of them swiftly reached down and pulled Rachel onto his horse. And, in a flash, the four of them were out of sight in the direction of Tyre.

Not until they had safely crossed the border between Galilee and Phoenicia were the horses allowed to slow their pace.

"Rachel," my love, are you all right?" asked Epher.

It was not surprising that she said nothing. Rachel was so frightened that she was in a state of shock.

That night they camped in the hills mid-way between Gischela and Tyre.

When the horses were secured and a fire had been kindled, the two mercenaries moved a short distance away so Epher and Rachel could be alone. By now, Rachel had regained her composure and began to speak.

"Epher," she said softly and unbelievingly, "Where did you come from? I was not expecting you yet. At the very moment when I needed help, there you were!"

"It was the hand of God," said Epher, "the hand of God. Could be nothing else."

"Epher, Oh Epher, the answer is yes!"

"May God be praised," he replied, as he raised both arms and clenched his fists in happiness. "We will be

437

married in Tyre tomorrow!"

"Yes, Epher. We must praise God. Only He could have worked our lives together like this."

"Rachel, I have been waiting for four whole weeks to tell you this. I am a new man!" With that he slapped his hands together with excitement.

"Rachel, my sweet Rachel, how can I tell you this? It is so incredible. One month ago, I was on a business trip which took me to Jerusalem. The city was in an uproar. Mobs of people lined the streets and people were crying everywhere. In the middle of the street was a bunch of Roman soldiers and a mob of your religious clergy. And in the middle of that throng was a man stripped to his loin cloth and carrying a cross."

The woman by the fire shuddered and shivered as he continued.

"I found out that the man was some kind of religious teacher and that he was going to be crucified. Since I had never seen a crucifixion, I went along with the crowds.

"It must have been horrible," said Rachel, her teeth chattering, not so much from the cold as from her nerves.

"Yes and no," replied Epher. "Indeed, it was horrible to watch them drive nails through the man's hands. But when I asked for more information, a young man, standing near the cross with a cluster of women, told me that the dying man's name was Jesus and that He was the Messiah."

Rachel's body shook with emotion.

"Well, I am not Jewish, but we all know about the Hebrew promise of One anointed by God to rule the world. Seemed strange to me that a world ruler would be dying on a cross. But I watched everything.

"The man, this Jesus, He died with such composure, such dignity. The thieves on the other crosses were cursing the soldiers and screaming with pain, but Jesus was very quiet. Suddenly, the sky grew black and lightning flashed and most of the people ran for cover. I was so spellbound by this man that I ignored the storm."

"What happened after that?" asked Rachel, tears streaming down her face.

"That's the great part, Rachel, my love. One of the thieves spat on a soldier and cursed him for what was being done to him. But Jesus . . . . Jesus said softly, "Father, forgive them for they know not what they do."

Now Rachel was weeping loudly. Epher continued.

"That is the way I felt, too. And I fell down on my face and wet the ground with sobbing. When I raised my eyes, I am sure that Jesus looked at me and smiled."

Rachel, between bursts of grief, cried out, "Oh Epher, Jesus was my brother!"

Epher was struck dumb. When he was able to speak, he said, "Rachel, Rachel, I am so sorry. I did not know. But one thing I do know. He is the Messiah, indeed! And He doesn't belong just to the Jews. He is my Messiah, too. And Rachel, He is yours!"

Epher stood up and reached for Rachel who, with

his help, managed to get to her feet. With arms tightly clasped about one another, Epher kissed her passionately again and again. Then, softly, he whispered in her ear, "Oh, my sweet Rachel, look what God has done!"

The happy Arab offered his sweetheart the most elaborate wedding his vast wealth could provide. But Rachel wanted everything to be done as simply as possible and they were married in a civil ceremony at the edge of the Sea at Tyre.

And Rachel named her little boy *Joshua*.